DANIEL

LIVES OF INTEGRITY
WORDS OF PROPHECY

BETH MOORE

LifeWay Press®
Nashville, Tennesee

Published by LifeWay Press®
©2006 • Beth Moore
Third printing October 2006

ISBN 1-4158-2588-2

This book is the text for course CG-1191 in the subject area Bible Study
in the Christian Growth Study Plan.

Dewey Decimal Classification Number: 224.5

Subject Headings: DANIEL, PROPHET \ BIBLE--PROPHECIES \ CHRISTIAN LIFE

To order additional copies of this resource, WRITE to LifeWay Church Resources Customer Service; One LifeWay Plaza; Nashville, TN 37234-0013; e-mail orderentry@lifeway.com; FAX (615) 251-5933; PHONE (800) 458-2772; ORDER ONLINE at www.lifeway.com; or VISIT the LifeWay Christian Store serving you.

Printed in the United States of America

Leadership and Adult Publishing; LifeWay Church Resources
One LifeWay Plaza; Nashville, TN 37234-0175

CONTENTS

ABOUT THE AUTHOR

Beth Moore has written best-selling Bible studies on the tabernacle, David, Paul, and Jesus. Her books *Breaking Free, Praying God's Word,* and *When Godly People Do Ungodly Things* have all focused on the battle Satan is waging against Christians. *Believing God* and *Living Beyond Yourself* have focused on how Christians can live triumphantly in today's world. Beth has a passion for Christ, a passion for Bible study, and a passion to see Christians living the lives Christ intended.

Beth is an active member of First Baptist Church of Houston, Texas. The wife of Keith and mother of two young adult daughters, Beth serves a worldwide audience through Living Proof Ministry. Her conference ministry, writing, and videos reach millions of people every year.

INTRODUCTION TO THE STUDY OF DANIEL

Recently I got a new Bible. As I took it out of the box, I had a sweet moment with God. I ran my fingers across the gold edges of the pages, held it close, and pondered what experiences await me in the years I'll spend with it. In six years walking with God through the pages of my last Bible, I buried my mother, sent my baby off to college, fell crazy in love with a bird dog, married off my daddy, chased a thousand deadlines, married off my firstborn, stood next to countless caskets, stood by my man through a difficult business transition, drove my baby home from college … and those are just the high points. I'm sure your calendar has chronicled the same kinds of ups and downs. God talked me through every one of them while I held onto my Bible for dear life.

As I clutched the new Bible, I reeled with the certainty that just as many ups and downs surely await. I swallowed a rush of fear remembering God apportions grace for every need. I didn't expect Daniel to become one of the most effective antidotes I've ever taken for fear. It shows God in control, absolutely sovereign, never shaken, and nothing can detour His plan for the ages. I have loved the book since the early days of my Bible doctrine classes, but I couldn't have imagined I would write a study on it. Then that familiar fire began to blaze in my soul. God sparks a flame in me toward a certain theme or book in Scripture and fans it until I can no longer resist it. That's what happened with Daniel. It went from a sudden interest in my quiet time to an absolute holy obsession.

This one took me over, Sweet One. I have never studied harder. At times I thought my brain would crack. This Bible study stretched me, but when it was finished, I knew I'd never had a bigger blast. Oh, how I pray you'll commit to let God take you places you've never been. You will not regret it! I believe this journey will rock your world and thrill your senses. When you turn the last page, you will know things about history and prophecy that you might never have anticipated. I make you two promises based on the authority of the Word of God: you will neither waste your time nor become bored. Each Bible study has been a ride in one way or another. If *The Patriarchs* was a camel ride, this one, Dear One, is a rocket ride—*with the windows open*.

God has determined to achieve something very specific in us. Let's cooperate to the fullest. The homework assignments will enhance your journey. You'll have five assignments per week. You'll find five Principal Questions listed at the beginning of each week. Each comes from one of the five lessons during the week and deals with facts from the lesson. They will be identified in the week with a 🦁. Your small group will likely discuss the Principal Questions when you meet each week. In addition you will find Personal Discussion segments identified with a shopping bag symbol.

Know in advance that our structure for the homework is different in this study. In most of my studies the written work prepares you for the video sessions. *Daniel* is *session driven*. Each session will introduce material we study in greater depth through the week. Therefore, the video sessions are absolutely critical to the journey. Studying the member book without the taped sessions will leave gaps that will dramatically reduce the experience. I purposely chose to teach some of the more challenging material face-to-face in the video sessions. Do everything you can to participate in the weekly lectures.

I am filled with anticipation over what God wants to say to us over the next 11 weeks. Join me in asking the Ancient of Days to reveal Himself and His Son powerfully, majestically, and personally. Continually ask God to grant you "the Spirit of wisdom and revelation, so that you may know him better" (Eph. 1:17). I am honored to be your servant. You can do this study, Dear One! You are going to have a blast! Enough! Let's get to it!

DEDICATION

To my beloved nephews, Ben and Joe Meadows,

Continue to stand firm even when you're surrounded by those bowing down to the things of this world.

I'm so proud of the young men you've become. May God make you Daniels in your generation as you refuse to blend in.

I love you,

Aunt Beth

CHOICES TO MAKE

1

1

SESSION ONE
CHOICES TO MAKE

What can we count on to be relevant to us?

1. We also have an enemy who wants to _return us_ to places God called

   us to _leave_ .

"Babylonia" is literally the land of Shinar. Why is this fact significant?
See Genesis 11:1-4,8-9; 12:1; 11:31. _Abram left Ur (Babylon) and when_
they were taken captive (Judah) they were taken
back to Babylon (Ur)

Chaldeans mean Babylonians (margin note)

2. God has also been _Sovereign_ in our _Captivities_

3. We are also from the _seed_ of the _Kingship_ (Dan. 1:3).

4. We are _surrounded_ by a _Babylon_ of our own.

   "'I am, and there is none besides me'" (Isa. 47:8,10). _(This is the message of_
   the world)

   a. Nothing is more _dangerous_ than _friendly_

   Captivity . _(We must not become friendly w/the_
   enemy

   b. _Captivity_ never remains _friendly_ .

5. We, too, will lose our _identity_ and _integrity_

   without _resolve_ .

   • What was it about the food?

   • The word *zeroa* means "that which grows from _sown seed_

- The term would include not only vegetables but __*fruits* grains__ and __*bread*__ that is made from grain."[1]

- In her commentary on Daniel, scholar Joyce Baldwin says that by Eastern standards to share a meal was to __*commit*__ oneself to __*friendship*__ Sharing a meal was of __*covenant*__ significance.[2]

6. God desires to give us __*knowledge*__ and __*understanding*__ of various kinds (v. 17).

DANIEL

On this day, __1-16-07__,

I, __Sandy Winter__, commit to

__learn__!

---

1. Stephen R. Miller, *The New American Commentary: Daniel,* vol. 18 (Nashville: Broadman & Holman, 1994), 69.
2. Joyce G. Baldwin, *Daniel* (Madison, WI: Inter-Varsity Press, 1978), 83.

Father grant me the Spirit of wisdom & revelation so that I may know You better

Greetings, Dear One! I'm thrilled to meet you on this page! Since you're reading this, you must be seriously considering participating in the daily homework assignments. If you do, your journey with God will be greatly enhanced. I love taking part in a corporate outpouring of God's Spirit, but nothing replaces time spent One-on-one with Him. He will speak to you alone in ways you rarely experience in a group.

Now, let's make sure we start the journey on the right foot. I hope you've read the formal introduction to the study on page 6. In it I shared the uniqueness of our approach in this particular series. Understanding that our study is session driven rather than homework driven will be critical to the learning process we have ahead. Our five homework assignments each week will widen the lens and help us grasp a broader understanding of the chapter we considered in the session. Most of the information in the daily assignments will be new, but we will also underscore some concepts and facts mentioned in the sessions.

The weekly homework assignments assume you have viewed the session. At many points in week 1 of your homework, we will reference session 1 with familiarity. If you missed it, you can still do most of your homework, but you will have to navigate some information gaps. If you miss a video session, make it up as quickly as you can so you won't be confused when I reference it. We have many wonderful discoveries to make, and I don't want you to miss a single one. I'm praying for you, Beloved! I'm so honored you're along for the ride. Give particular attention to the following questions this week.

THIS WEEK'S PRINCIPAL QUESTIONS

DAY 1 What are some parallels between ancient Babylon and the western culture that seek to hold us captive?

DAY 2 What specific prophecy of Isaiah did Daniel witness in fulfillment?

DAY 3 What kinds of Israelites did the king order Ashpenaz to bring to Babylon?

DAY 4 Which four young men are singled out in Daniel 1:6-7?

DAY 5 What was the chief of Nebuchadnezzar's court instructed to teach the Hebrew youths?

DAY ONE NOT JUST A TALE OF TWO KINGS

Today's Treasure: *In the third year of the reign of Jehoiakim king of Judah, Nebuchadnezzar king of Babylon came to Jerusalem and besieged it. Daniel 1:1*

Drive within the suburbs of modern Baghdad and you'll find the scattered ruins of one of antiquity's most famous cities. Her name is Babylon. Through the paintbrush of Scripture, we'll see her rise from the dust, robe herself in riches, and paint her face like a woman of the night. Make no mistake: she aims to seduce. Posing as the beautiful life, she morphs into the current image of what every worldly man and woman wants to be—deserves to be. She is popular. She is desirable. She is intoxicating. And did I say she is religious? Ah, yes. She believes in so much of everything that one would be hard-pressed to tell if she believes in anything. To worship self is to worship her. To worship her is to worship her king. She is dressed for success, but underneath her gaud, she is a lifeless mannequin. A fake. A poser. Her prop is the devil himself.

At one time her outer garment was 56 miles of impenetrable walls framing "some two-hundred square miles"[1] of state-of-the-art dwellings, teeming entertainment centers, thriving businesses, at least three palaces, and extravagant temples to numerous gods. Towering above the wall was a 650-foot glimmering enamel ziggurat eerily reminiscent of the tower of Babel. It was "crowned with a shrine containing a massive table of solid gold, and an ornate bed on which, each night, some woman slept to await the pleasure of the god."[2] Over time Babylon's fortress walls finally crumbled, but they could no longer contain her anyway. Somewhere along the way, she ceased to be only a place. She became a mentality. A deadly one.

Few could resist Babylon's charms. Few had a firm enough hold on reality not to fall for her pretense. Daniel holds his place in Scripture because he was one of the few. Our primary goal during part 1 of our series is to join him as individuals who can live in an extravagant, excessive culture without being poisoned by it. We're going to develop alarms for Babylon's charms.

Welcome to the study of the Book of Daniel, Beloved. I'm so glad you've joined me for day 1 of our journey. With a fair amount of confidence, I think I can assure you it will be exhilarating. The wind of the Holy Spirit blows so hard through some of these Scriptures, you may have to re-fix your hair. The material we have ahead will prove thrilling and, at times, very challenging. When you turn the last page, however, I believe God will grant you an exceeding sense of accomplishment in Him because you were willing to do the work. Since our series is session driven, hopefully you participated in session 1 before beginning your homework.

WE'RE GOING TO DEVELOP ALARMS FOR BABYLON'S CHARMS.

If so, at the conclusion of the session, what commitment did you and I make?

That I commit to learn.

We committed to be willing to learn new information, even when it teeters more toward the historical than the personal. Growing in the knowledge of God's Word differs from growing in the knowledge of other academics. You see, we're not seeking human wisdom but "words taught by the Spirit, expressing spiritual truths in spiritual words" (1 Cor. 2:13). Since something much deeper than the attainment of knowledge is at stake here, prayer will be a vital part of the process. Please begin your time today and every day of the study with prayer, asking God deliberately and thoughtfully to grant you depth of *wisdom* and *understanding* (see Dan. 1:20). When you've completed this vital assignment of prayer, initial here: _SLW_

Let's get off the starting block of our journey through the Book of Daniel by becoming adept at finding it. The major and minor prophets can be challenging to navigate. Hopefully, our Bible study groups are not only serving seasoned students of God's Word. Let's make sure we're also reaching out to seekers and babes in Christ who may not know the first thing about finding an Old Testament book of the Bible. Let's start right where they are, or perhaps right where *you* are. The Book of Psalms is regarded by many as a center point in our Bibles. Its position and length make it hard to miss. Therefore, I'd like you to turn to the Psalms and start flipping forward from book to book until you get to Daniel.

In the space below, please write down the names of all nine books starting with the Psalms and ending with Daniel.

Psalms	Proverbs	Ecclesiastes
Song of Songs	Isaiah	Jeremiah
Lamentations	Ezekiel	Daniel

I encourage you to start memorizing these in order this week.

Now, read Daniel 1:1-2. Name the two characters introduced in these opening statements and identify who they are.

Jehoiakim : King of Judah

Nebuchadnezzar: King of Babylon

In the third year of the reign of Jehoiakim king of Judah, Nebuchadnezzar king of Babylon came to Jerusalem and besieged it. And the Lord delivered Jehoiakim king of Judah into his hand, along with some of the articles from the temple of God. These he carried off to the temple of his god in Babylonia and put in the treasure house of his god.

📖 **DANIEL 1:1-2**

Look at your map on the inside back cover. It diagrams the locations and reaches of the world powers mentioned prophetically in the Book of Daniel. For now, concentrate on the Babylonian Empire and the area we often term the Holy Land. Please note the locations of Jerusalem (between the Jordan River and the Mediterranean Sea) and Babylon (starred by the Euphrates River). The space between the two lands constituted nine hundred miles.[3] Imagine the terror of being ripped from your home as a teenager and being taken mile after mile from the only place you've called home. Imagine being Daniel, craning your neck, trying to hold onto one last glimpse of Jerusalem, the city on the hill, and wondering if you'll ever see it again. *He didn't.*

What do you think were some of the first thoughts he might have had as the caravan of captives pulled away from the city?

That he might be killed & that he would never see his home (Jerusalem) again.

A Hebrew could hardly have imagined anything worse. As you continue studying your map, concentrate for a moment on the land God had given to the Israelites. It blanketed both sides of the Jordan River and stretched far north and somewhat south of Jerusalem. Your map shows the reach of the Babylonian Empire in the color green.

No greater tragedy could have befallen the people of God than to lose possession of their God-given land. He had warned them numerous times that if they turned to the idols of the surrounding peoples, He would allow them—even appoint them (see 1:2!)—to be taken captive. God is faithful to keep His Word even when it's a warning. The twelve tribes of Israel tore north from south following King Solomon's death in 922 B.C. The Northern Kingdom retained the name *Israel* while the Southern Kingdom, made up mostly of the tribes of Judah and Benjamin (and later, apparently Simeon), took on the name *Judah*. Daniel was born during the closing days of the Kingdom of Judah.

The Book of Daniel opens in the summer of 605 B.C. at the height of Babylon's fame and fortune. In session 1 we adopted an approach to enhance the personal applications we'll make along our way through the chapters of Daniel. We discovered that the literal city of Babylon in Daniel's account offers almost endless parallels to a figurative Babylon surrounding us; therefore, we determined to relate to Daniel at times by applying Babylon symbolically rather than literally. In the weeks ahead, Babylon will represent certain cultural influences and mentalities that permeate the prosperous West. Please don't misunderstand. I have no intention of tagging our nation a "Babylon." Anyone who travels internationally as much as I do realizes the spiritual blessings and opportunities we have on American soil. As dismal as the political climate may seem at times, we still have many God-seeking leaders in areas of government. Keep in mind we are not attacking our nation. We want to address our excessive, self-centered culture.

List some of the parallels we discussed between Babylon and the western culture that seek to hold us captive. You may review your listening guide, but you'll probably need little more than a glance at Daniel 1:3-4.

Young people w/o defects, handsome intelligent (the same things people are judged by today)

In session 1 we learned what we would call the "Babylon Motto" based on Isaiah 47. Turn there in your Bible. If your translation includes chapter headings, you'll quickly notice that this one concerns Babylon. Both verses 8 and 10 include the statement we're identifying as the Babylon Motto.

Read verses 8 and 10 of Isaiah 47 and fill in the blank according to verse 10.

"You have trusted in your wickedness and have said, 'No one sees me.' Your wisdom and knowledge mislead you when you say to yourself,

"*I am, and there is none beside me.*"

There you have it. Memorize the verse and you'll know in a nutshell what Babylon represents.

13

Share one of the most outrageous examples of the Babylon Motto mentality you've personally encountered.

I have seen people ignored because they are disfigured or handicapped.

The illustrious head of the Babylon "self" was none other than Nebuchadnezzar, her most famous king. "Nebuchadnezzar was the greatest ruler of the Neo-Babylonian period and one of the most competent monarchs of ancient times. He brought Babylon to the zenith of its economic affluence and political power."[4] Picture the city where he was enthroned: "Through the center of the town ran the palm-fringed Euphrates, busy with commerce and spanned by a handsome bridge. Practically all the better buildings were of brick, for stone was rare in Mesopotamia; but the bricks were often faced with enameled tiles of brilliant blue, yellow or white, adorned with animal and other figures in glazed relief, which remain to this day supreme in their kind. Nearly all the bricks so far recovered from the site of Babylon bear the proud inscription; 'I am Nebuchadrezzar, King of Babylon.'"[5] (Many mentions of Nebuchadnezzar in extra-biblical literature ended his name with "rezzar" instead of "nezzar.")

Handsome young Daniel encountered Babylon when the cup of her inviting intoxication was foaming and overflowing. She didn't just offer him a sip. In time, she offered him the world. As we emphasized in session 1, nothing is more dangerous than friendly captivity. Over and over we'll discover that Daniel resisted her poisonous charms on purpose. So must we.

NOTHING IS MORE DANGEROUS THAN FRIENDLY CAPTIVITY.

DAY TWO TIES BETWEEN PAST AND PRESENT

Today's Treasure: *The Lord delivered Jehoiakim king of Judah into his hand, along with some of the articles from the temple of God. Daniel 1:2*

The Book of Daniel is unique in a number of ways that we will highlight as we explore it. One of its distinctive qualities is its original penmanship in both Hebrew and Aramaic.[6] The beginning and the ending portions are in Hebrew (Daniel 1:1–2:4 and 8:1–12:13) while a central portion constituting a little over half of the book is in Aramaic (2:4–7:28). The most logical explanation is that "the employment of the two languages was a deliberate device on Daniel's part."[7]

Fill in the following two-word blank according to 2 Timothy 3:16.

All Scripture is *God* - *breathed* ...

So, we might say that God, the originator of all human language simply exercised some bilingual breathing. While He alone knows why, the Hebrew sections probably related more readily to the Jewish people while the Aramaic sections included information additionally relevant to the Gentile world. Edward J. Young explains the possibility like this: "All in all, the solution which seems to be most free from difficulty is that Aramaic, being the language of the world is used in those portions of the book which outline the future history of the worldly empires and their relation to the people of God, and Hebrew is used in those portions which interpret for the Hebrews the meaning of the visions of the world empires."[8] Please keep this in mind because we will revisit the concept as the transitions occur.

Today's lesson will once again spotlight the opening verses of Daniel. Remember to pray for wisdom and understanding.

Read Daniel 1:1-2. According to what we've just learned, in which language were these verses originally written? Circle one.

Hebrew   Aramaic

If our proposed theory is correct, the opening two verses joined the rest of the first chapter in relating more readily to the Jews than both the Jews and Gentiles. Verses 1 and 2 describe a critical and tragic period of Jewish history and offer ample application to people of God today.

What did Nebuchadnezzar do with the articles taken from the temple of God?

He carried them off to the temple of his god in Babylonia & put them in the treasure house of his god.

Picture some of the sacred articles of the earthly "house" of God displayed in a pagan temple. Imagine the faces of the Jewish people as they helplessly watched the crude manhandling of holy vessels. Please hear this next statement with volume: Tragically, their own disrespect and misuse of the holy structure had unknowingly opened the doors of the temple to the enemy in the years preceding the siege. Since the reign of Solomon, a smattering of faithful kings served in intervals among many unfaithful rulers. One of God's most serious charges against His people was the abuse of His temple. Jeremiah described the condition of God's people just before Judah was taken captive by Babylon. "Both prophet and priest are godless; even in my temple I find their wickedness" (Jer. 23:11). We are rightly shocked when we learn that terribly inappropriate activities took place within the walls of sacred or revered institutions.

Last year I had the privilege of visiting the White House and touring the Oval Office again. Of course, a gold cord was draped across the doorway so that we could view the room only from the hall. As my eyes scanned the regal room and settled on the stately desk, I was awestruck by the importance of what takes place within those walls. Then I remembered some of the allegations that have been issued in history against several individuals for misconduct in that very room. If you are familiar with

"'Both prophet and priest are godless; even in my temple I find their wickedness,' declares the LORD."

📖 JEREMIAH 23:11

my testimony, I think you know I'm not naïve. I have heinous sin in my past, but I would have been scared to death to exercise my sinfulness in certain places.

Someone might retort, "A sin is a sin no matter where it takes place." Indeed it is. But when leaders who know better flaunt sin in sacred places of divine trust, guilt heaps upon guilt. I stood in the hall outside the Oval Office, considered the trust Americans place in our heads of State, and thought, "How could anyone have so little respect?" OK. Switch the scene from the White House to the holy temple in Jerusalem that had first been sanctified and filled by the very glory of God. Imagine the offense that ascended before His throne as His own priests and prophets at the very least misled, deceived, and used the people for selfish gain.

In Jeremiah 6:13-15 the prophet was addressing the sins of Israel's own priests and prophets. How did Jeremiah describe them (v. 15)?

They have no shame of their loathsome conduct. They do not even know how to blush.

LET'S NOT GET USED TO DECAYING MORALS AND STANDARDS.

Beloved, as you and I learn how to have integrity in such an enticing Babylon-world, let's never grow so accustomed to the decaying morals and standards of our culture that we "do not even know how to blush." Things are happening around us that ought to make us blush. Things are broadcast from our television sets that ought to turn our faces crimson. Let's not get used to it. Let's allow it to have a godly affect on us. Trust me when I tell you embarrassment can be a huge motivator for change— I know from dealing with the embarrassment of my own sins.

Jeremiah, Ezekiel, and Habakkuk were Daniel's contemporaries and faithful exceptions. I suppose God never spoke more intensely through His prophets than during the times surrounding the siege of Jerusalem. Jeremiah preached in Jerusalem at the very time Daniel lived within its walls; and, in all likelihood, he heard the prophet's proclamations with his own ears.

If indeed he heard Jeremiah preach warning and coming judgment, what kind of impact do you think the sight of fulfilled prophecy had on Daniel?

He knew God was true to His word and Daniel wanted to be sure he was living a life pleasing to the Lord

Now, wind back the clock one hundred years when a certain king literally opened the doors of the palace, temple, and storehouses of Judah to the Babylonians. Read Isaiah 39:1-8. Who was Merodach-Baladan's father (v. 1)?

Baladan ___King___ of ___Babylon___.

 Set these events beside Daniel 1:1-2. What specific prophecy of Isaiah did Daniel witness in fulfillment? (See Isa. 39:5-6.)

That a time will come when everything in your palace and all that your fathers has stored up until this day will be carried off to Babylon.

What made Hezekiah's reaction in Isaiah 39:8 stunningly selfish?

All he was concerned with was that there will peace and security in his lifetime

Beloved, as we parallel Daniel's Babylon to our own, let's underscore again one of the most vital concepts of our series: the horrific snare of *friendly captivity*. Notice the prince of Babylon won Hezekiah's favor by appearing sympathetic to his illness. Hezekiah then dropped his guard and showed every treasure in Judah. The existence of the priceless articles of Judah was rehearsed in the ears of Babylonian rulers for the next one hundred years. The sin and rebellion of God's people ultimately left them defenseless. God's arm was not too short to save, but their iniquities had separated them from their Defender. (See Isa. 59:1-2.) The powerful King Nebuchadnezzar received the invitation written by their weakness and RSVP'd by looting them.

If you're like me, you have also allowed some of your untreated weaknesses to engrave an invitation to the enemy. Satan recognizes the treasures God has given us more than we do. He knows we are the royal heirs of the kingdom treasury of God. The more we play with Satan's "world," the more the consummate prince of Babylon will try to take. He comes to steal, kill, and destroy (John 10:10). Satan may bide his time until the opportune moment, but make no mistake—he will RSVP with an acceptance. We'll be the ones left with the regret.

If you're willing to share and you'll take care to be appropriate, describe one way you believe Satan tried to act like a friend and sympathize with you in your trouble only to later betray you.

_____

_____

Embarrassing, isn't it? Oh, but what motivation to never let it happen again.

DAY THREE THE POWER OF TRAINING

Today's Treasure: *Young men without any physical defect, handsome, showing aptitude for every kind of learning, well informed, quick to understand, and qualified to serve in the king's palace. He was to teach them the language and literature of the Babylonians. Daniel 1:4*

Today you'll be happy to know we'll at least get further than the first two verses! By the way, have I told you recently how thankful I am for the privilege to study God's Word with you? Getting to love and seek Him by your side is one of the greatest joys in life to me. Malachi 3:16 says, "Then those who feared the LORD talked with each other, and the LORD listened and heard. A scroll of remembrance was written in his presence concerning those who feared the LORD and honored his name." Oh, how I pray that you and I will keep heaven writing!

🦁 Read Daniel 1:3-7. We'll consider different angles of the same text today and tomorrow. Based on verse 4, describe the kinds of Israelites the king ordered Ashpenaz to bring to Babylon according to the following categories:

Family background:	Age and appearance:	Intellectual capacities:
from Royal family	*young men*	*Showing aptitude for every kind of learning*
from Nobility	*handsome men*	*well informed quick to understand*

How long were they to be trained before entering the king's service?
Check one:

☐ 6 months   ☐ 1 year   ☒ 3 years   ☐ 5 years

Many scholars believe the Hebrew youths taken captive by the Babylonians were probably around 15 years old. Assuming this is a sound estimation, the youths were intensely indoctrinated in the Babylonian "language and literature" from then until they were 18 or so. We'll grasp their undertaking more accurately by understanding the word "literature" in verse 4 to encompass anything in written form, including history, religious beliefs, and all manner of cultural propaganda.

I'm not sure the power of a great teacher can be overestimated. I decided my major and minor areas of study in college based on the subjects of my favorite high school teachers. The obvious problem is that not all great teachers teach great truth. Imagine the power a persuasive teacher of dangerous subjects could wield. In the hands of Babylon's best, the sudden exposure of pagan "enlightenment" upon the brilliant, young minds of Daniel and the others could have been utterly blinding.

"The Babylonian sages … were the guardians of the sacred traditional lore developed and preserved in Mesopotamia over centuries, covering natural history, astronomy, mathematics, medicine, myth, and chronicle. Much of this learning had a practical purpose, being designed to be applied to life by means of astrology, oneirology, hepatoscopy and the study of other organs, rites of purification, sacrifice, incantation, exorcism, and other forms of divination and magic."[9] *Oneiromancy* means "divination by means of dreams,"[10] and *hepatoscopy* is "divination by inspecting the liver of animals."[11] Just think what their labs would have been like. And we thought dissecting frogs was bad.

Now, imagine yourself being 15 to 18 years old again. Picture the hair. The blemishes. The styles. The challenges. The temptations. Hard ages in retrospect, weren't they? The years from 15 to 18 bring out the adjective "big." Big on excitement. Big on insecurity. And bigger still on drama.

In a couple of sentences, give a general description of what you were like at this point in your life.

I was unsecure, and verbally abused by my mom

Now, think in terms of 15 to 18-year-old *boys*. Like me, you may have the joy of observing a few from a fairly close vantage point. Others of you have a bird's-eye view because you're raising one … or two … or, may God have mercy on you, three. I wanted to raise a man-child so badly. Thankfully, God has allowed me to share in the lives of three fine nephews who fall into this exact age category. (Where do they put all that food? The dirty-clothes hamper is apparently the only thing they stuff more than their stomachs.) Girls this age are as bombarded with challenges as boys and can fall just as easily. Our present task, however, is to try to get into the minds, so to speak, of the boys in our text.

In your opinion, how easily influenced are boys of this age?

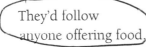

(They'd follow anyone offering food.)   They might follow for a while if it's enough fun.   Their minds are made up and can't be swayed.

Based on our synopsis, picture the culture that surrounded the Hebrew boys in Babylon. What kinds of things do you imagine boys that age would have found impressive in such a rich, indulgent environment?

food, wine, their residence - they were treated like nobility

I was raised in a small Arkansas town with very few entertainment amenities. The closest skating rink was in Malvern—a half hour away, and the closest bowling alley was too far to bother. We did have a movie theater, but my father, Major Dad, was the manager. How much fun can you have with friends *and* your dad? Anyway, I usually had to stay after the movie ended to help sweep up the popcorn. Most of the time, I just stuck to riding my banana-seat bike. *Then we moved to Houston.* Neon lights. Billboards. "Adult" entertainment businesses I didn't even know existed. On the lighter side, skating rinks and bowling alleys dotted every suburb. Malls, superstores, colleges, and junior colleges peppered multilane freeways without a single Piggly Wiggly in sight. For you noninitiates, Piggly Wiggly was the original grocery store chain. Total culture shock. My senses were so overstimulated that I hardly knew where to begin. I felt like my bird dog Beanie did when a whole box of Meaty Bones fell on the kitchen floor.

What about you? Describe your most extreme experience of culture shock.

I realized how blessed I was when I took a bus ride in Jamaica

Expand the balloon of sensory overload until it nearly pops, and you'll have some idea of what Daniel and the others faced. Jerusalem was a thriving city teeming with people, but even at its worst, comparatively speaking, the teens would have led a sheltered existence within its walls. Their transition would have been tantamount to moving from a stickball field into a video game convention only to be relentlessly indoctrinated by experts on exactly how to win.

Whether or not we are conscious of it, you and I are daily being indoctrinated and "trained" by our culture. The field trip is constant. Look back at Daniel 1:4 and recall the categories we assigned to each area in the beginning of our lesson. Hopefully by now you recognize the descriptions in this verse as our most concentrated opportunity to draw parallels to the cultural "Babylon" surrounding us. Let's be vulnerable before God.

Check which of these cultural premiums presents the biggest personal challenge or bothers you the most *and tell why*. Put another way, in what areas has our culture most successfully "trained" or indoctrinated *you*?

- ☐ must be young
- ☒ appearance is everything
- ☐ smarter is better
- ☐ social status matters
- ☐ other _____

Why? *Because when appearance is paramount - the average person is overlooked & people miss meeting some delightful people*

The high premiums our culture places upon age, appearance, and intelligence are obvious. Since all the young men were of royal or noble background, they could relate to our emphasis on economic and social status. In the coming weeks, we will perform some honest appraisals of our levels of integrity in this vastly enticing world. An accurate appraisal will demand straightforward questions and candid answers. Trust that I am asking myself the same ones I place before you.

Read 1 Timothy 4:7-8. List everything these verses tell you about training.
Physical training is of some value but Godliness has value. You all things for both the present life & the life to come

Beloved, you need not hang your head. Training yourself in godliness is *exactly* what you're doing this very moment. The Word of God is the textbook. Its application to the hot pavement of your life is the practicum. God wants us to recognize the critical priority of deliberate training in godliness. We won't be successful without it. Not one moment you spend in Bible study will ever be wasted. It is our hope of resisting the deep indoctrination of worldliness. Help us, Lord. We are weak in our natural selves (Rom. 6:19).

Tutor us, Rabboni, and teach us to win.

DAY FOUR RENAMING AND RESISTING

Today's Treasure: *The chief official gave them new names: to Daniel, the name Belteshazzar; to Hananiah, Shadrach; to Mishael, Meshach; and to Azariah, Abednego. Daniel 1:7*

My young adult daughters bring me indescribable joy. Hangeth thou in there, ye mothers of preschoolers! Ye weary wardens of teenagers! Ye washers of PE uniforms! Groweth not weary in well doing! The harvest cometh! The days seem to pass slowly, but the years fly like the wind. I enjoy so many things about my daughters—but nothing more than sharing our individual walks with Jesus. Their ages, different roles in life, and polar-opposite personalities add all sorts of angles and perspectives to the journey.

This morning I called my firstborn and could tell she was having a rough Monday morning. Like many of us working girls, she was trying to get her home in order after a busy weekend and still make it to her desk on time. There's nothing like trying to be Domestic Goddess and Employee of the Week at the same time, is there, Sister? I told her that one of the most powerful mood changers God had ever taught me was to open up my mouth and say, "I choose joy. I may not feel it, but God has appropriated it and I *choose* it." About an hour later, I received the following e-mail from her. I am so grateful for two humble daughters who will risk people knowing they're imperfect in order to minister. See if you can relate with this:

"I'm choosing joy. … The Lord has refreshed my spirit and given me a new perspective. What a minute cross I have to bear on any given day. I had to repent of being a spineless clot of grievances. Honestly, I would be an absolute MESS without the Lord! I only need Him more and more every day!"

"A spineless clot of grievances." I laughed my head off. We heard the expression somewhere along the way, and the reminder hit me with humor and conviction. Can't we all relate? Actually, that child has been about the furthest thing from a mess, but I love that she recognizes that she is a wreck without Jesus—so is her mother. Our present pursuit is developing integrity in an enticing world. If we'll let Him, God will shrink our clot of grievances in the process. Our text for today consists of a celebratory two verses. We're moving right along, aren't we? I love this pace! This is the pace we get to adopt when the book we're studying is only 12 chapters long.

OUR PRESENT PURSUIT IS DEVELOPING INTEGRITY IN AN ENTICING WORLD.

🦁 Please read Daniel 1:6-7. Write each of the young men's names below and, in the blanks to each side, what they were renamed:

" *Daniel* _____ renamed " *Belteshazzar*
" *God is my judge* " " *Bel will protect* "

" *Hananiah* _____ renamed " *Shadrach*
" *Yah has been gracious* " " *Inspired of Aku* "

" *Mishael* _____ renamed *Meshach*
' *who is what God is* " " *Belonging to Aku* "

Azariah _____ renamed *Abednego*
" *Yah has helped* " " *Servant of Nego* "

Each of the four young men singled out in these passages will become important to us in our study, so practice saying their names aloud. We'll learn a number of ancient names in our series. If we don't learn to pronounce them and picture the people they represent as actual flesh and blood, we'll remain distant from the story line. We'll also be far less likely to relate their challenges to our own.

The name Daniel means, "God is my judge." Hananiah means, "Yah has been gracious." Mishael means, "Who is what God is?" Finally, Azariah means, "Yah has helped."[12] We retain far more information if we record it with our own pens; therefore, go back and write each of these meanings directly under the corresponding names above.

Considering "Yah" is a contraction for "Yahweh," what did each of the four names have in common?

They were all committed to the Lord

Now, let's focus on the Babylonian names they were assigned. Hopefully you noted that each of the Hebrew names included a reference to their God. Their Babylonian names rose in stark contrast to the original because each contained some reference to a false god. "Daniel becomes Belteshazzar, ('Bel will protect'), Hananiah becomes Shadrach ('inspired of Aku'), Mishael becomes Meshach ('belonging to Aku'), and Azariah becomes Abednego ('servant of Nego')."[13] Bel, Nego, and Aku were false gods of the Babylonians. Renaming the young men accordingly was a deliberate attempt to echo constant contradictions of the truth regarding their God.

Assigning new names was a common court practice in the ancient world. Its blatant intention was to change the entire identity of the bearer until the life matched the title. The new name marked new ownership and was meant to hail a new destiny.[14] Actually, God originated the concept. We see the practice of renaming in Scripture as early as Genesis when He changed Abram's name to Abraham. The world system with the enemy at its helm could not resist offering its own counterfeits to serve its own idols. I can't help wondering if this could be the root of much of the name-brand hype. The obvious difference is that God and the world have opposite agendas represented in their name giving. God's agenda is always based on truth while the world's agenda—captained by Satan—is replete with deception.

Go back to your previous exercise and write each of the meanings under the corresponding Babylonian name. Meditate for a moment on the differences. How do you think Nebuchadnezzar intended to shape their destinies through these names?

That they would worship these false gods and therefore become involved in evil doings

GOD'S AGENDA IS ALWAYS BASED ON TRUTH.

In our culture, a name's sound or sentimental value is a far bigger priority than its meaning. In contrast, little was more important to the Hebrew people than a name precisely because of what it meant. Not coincidentally, "Shem," the name of the son of Noah given to his descendants, the Semites, "is, in fact, the common Hebrew word for 'name.' "[15] God purposely chose a people (the Hebrews) from among the Semites to make a name or "shem" for Himself. Imagine, then, the unspeakable offense of being a "shem" or "name" bearer of God called by an idolatrous name.

Recently I had the privilege of leading a three-day conference for college-age women. At one point, my fellow speakers and I wanted to spend a few minutes speaking the truth of God's Word over them concerning their identities in Christ. In order to clear the way, I asked any of them who felt hindered by hurtful, destructive things said over them or names they'd been called to write those haunting statements on a piece of paper and lay it on the altar. To our surprise, the aisles were congested until the altar that wrapped all the way around the platform was completely covered in stacks of paper.

Beloved, has the world (or worse yet, a loved one) ever tried to give you a bad name or a bad identity? ☒ Yes ☐ No If so, what?

I was teased being called Sandwich & Sandywitch

Did you fall for it? Elaborate somewhat.

I think it caused some insecurity in me but never caused me to lose sight of the truth.

Are you still falling for it? If so, how?

Sometimes I'm afraid to ask someone a favor because they might refuse

23

Important!

Daniel, Hananiah, Mishael, and Azariah will prove to us by example that the world can call us what it wants, but it cannot change who we are. You, Beloved, are *God's*. How do we resist the world's titanic pressure? The same way Daniel did. We *resolve*.

DAY FIVE RESOLVE

Today's Treasure: *Daniel resolved not to defile himself with the royal food and wine, and he asked the chief official for permission not to defile himself this way. Daniel 1:8*

Day 4 concluded with a word intended to become very significant to us in our study. The concluding question prompting the word was this: How do we resist the world's titanic pressure?

Glance at the final sentence in yesterday's lesson and fill in the following:

We resolve.

Today you and I are completing our first week of study together. You are off to a great start, and I'm so proud of you. Before we meet for session 2, let's meditate on a few things we've learned and considered together. In our first session we talked about developing and strengthening our own resolve.

Please refresh your memory of the context of the word "resolved" (v. 8) by reading Daniel 1:8-21. How intentional was Daniel in demonstrating his resolve? Describe the evidence. He asked the chief official to test them for 10 days giving them only vegetables & water instead of the royal food. Then Daniel told him to compare their appearance w/ those eating royal food. And after 10 days Daniel & his friends looked healthier & better nourished.

Daniel resolved not to defile his body w/ royal food & wine

Glance over your notes from session 1. Recall our discussion over Daniel's resolve and how it demanded something from him daily. Bone-deep resolve doesn't develop by going to church every Sunday morning or going to Bible study every Tuesday night. Important opportunities like these encourage us in our resolve, but they aren't enough to create and sustain it. Daniel's brand of resolve involved something he was challenged to practice every single day. In fact, you might say he ate it for breakfast, lunch, and dinner. Don't think for a moment he wasn't tested and tempted by the sights and scents of succulent foods. Had his decision been easy, it wouldn't have demanded *resolve*.

EXCELLENT!

I don't know any other way to say this, and goodness knows I learned it the hard way: godliness is never accidental. Neither is victory coincidental. Both stem from up-front, daily resolve.

C-O-N-S-I-S-T-E-N-C-Y

The lifeblood of integrity is becoming the same person no matter where we are—no matter who's around. When we become people of integrity, everything we are on the inside is obvious from the outside. The Latin word for "integrity" literally means "entire." The essence of the term is wholeness and completeness. Integrity is "the quality or state of being complete or undivided."[16] You can see, therefore, how much integrity depends on consistency. Integrity not only calls us to live inside-out, it keeps the outside from coming in. Consistency in our walk and in our talk becomes a transportable cloak of protection around us, going anywhere we go. Life becomes so much simpler when there aren't so many costume changes.

INTEGRITY DEPENDS ON CONSISTENCY.

Do you understand what I mean? If so, say it in your own words from your own experience. *It is a permanent life change. Our walk has to agree with God's word 100% of the time*

Someone might read this part of our lesson and ask, "Do I have to be perfect to be consistent?" How would you contrast the difference between perfection and the kind of consistency that breeds integrity? *If we strive to be perfect all the time, even though we will miss the mark at times, we will be women of integrity because we are running the race God's way*

No, we will not reach perfection in this lifetime on planet Earth, but we can certainly reach consistency. Indeed we must, or the enemy will nearly burn us alive. Never forget what a good shot he is. Satan never wastes a fiery dart by aiming at a spot covered by armor. The bull's-eye is located dead center in our inconsistency. That's where the enemy plans to bring us down.

As we meditate on the lives of these four young Hebrew transplants, I can't help thinking of their parents. Imagine their terror as Babylonian soldiers ripped their sons from their arms and transported them nine hundred miles from home. Surely they were tormented by the fear that their sons would be killed. Then again, if they lived, how long would they resist the draw of such a notoriously carnal land? I wonder if a solitary parent slept through the night again. They may have gone to their graves without seeing the tenacity of their children to press forward against the furious current that called them by a new name and bid them drown.

God's heart was not unmoved. He kindled their choices, empowered their victories, and moved them to the front of their class. The Scripture tells us that "to these four young men God gave knowledge and understanding of all kinds of literature and learning" (Dan. 1:17).

Look back at Daniel 1:4. What was the chief of Nebuchadnezzar's court instructed to teach the Hebrew youths?

He was to teach them the language and literature of the Babylonians. They were to be trained for three years & then enter the King's service

While Babylon did everything it could to indoctrinate their minds and steal their souls, God granted the young men His own knowledge and understanding in every matter. In other words, whatever Babylon taught them, God interpreted to them. They learned the language, literature, and customs all right, but only so God could use them in the midst of it. They read the language of their culture with the lens of God. Thereby, they became culturally relevant without becoming spiritually irrelevant. Against all odds, they retained a God-centered worldview so that ultimately the world could view their God. Amazing.

You and I, our children, and our children's children can do the same no matter how stunningly carnal this world becomes. If we resolve. Beloved, do you want to be a Daniel? Do you want to resist the tidal wave of temptation to blend in? Do you want to live a life of integrity? We will do it on purpose, or we will not do it at all. The enticing voice of the world calls us from billboard to magazine stand, from television to Internet. God's warning to Cain has never seemed more corporate: "Sin is crouching at your door; it desires to have you" (Gen. 4:7). Tenacious obedience, Dear One! We will stand firm amid the current of our culture no other way. God will be glorified and blessing will come. Now or later. Here or there.

Enter the true King's service, Dear Daniel.

A lost world needs to view your God.

WE WILL LIVE LIVES OF INTEGRITY ON PURPOSE, OR WE WILL NOT DO IT AT ALL.

1. Will Durant, *Our Oriental Heritage* (New York: MJF Books, 1935), 224.
2. Ibid., 224.
3. Stephen R. Miller, *Daniel*, vol. 18, *The New American Commentary* (Nashville: Broadman & Holman, 2001), 67.
4. Ibid., 44.
5. Durant, 224.
6. Miller, 30.
7. Ibid., 47.
8. Edward J. Young, *Geneva Series of Commentaries: A Commentary on Daniel* (Carlisle, PA: The Banner of Truth Trust, 1972), 22.
9. John E. Goldingay, *Daniel*, vol. 30, *Word Biblical Commentary* (Nashville: Thomas Nelson Publishers, 1989), 16.
10. Frederick C. Mish, ed., *Merriam Webster's Collegiate Dictionary*, 10th ed. (Springfield, MA: Merriam-Webster, Incorporated, 2002), 810.
11. "Hepatoscopy," *Hyperdictionary* [online], [cited 10 January 2005]. Available from the Internet: *www.hyperdictionary.com*.
12. Goldingay, 17.
13. Spiros Zodhiates, TH.D., gen. ed., *Hebrew-Greek Key Word Study Bible, New International Version*, (Chattanooga, TN: AMG Publishers, 1996), 1022.
14. Goldingay, 17.
15. David W. Baker and T. Desmond Alexander, *Dictionary of the Old Testament Pentateuch* (Chicago: InterVarsity Press, 2003), 753.
16. Mish, 608.

SESSION TWO
A DREAM AND A KINGDOM

The second chapter of Daniel involves Nebuchadnezzar's disturbing dream. The length of the chapter necessitates our considerations of the interpretation alone, but your daily assignments this week take you through the entire chapter, segment by segment. Please see Daniel 2:12-13,24-35, then concentrate on Daniel 2:36-45.

1. Compare verses 36 and 45. Nebuchadnezzar's dream was _true_ and involved _future events_

2. "Nebuchadnezzar's dream covered the prophetic _panorama_ of _Gentile_ history" from his reign until the forthcoming reign of _Israel's Messiah_.[1]

In Luke 21:24 Christ refers to this time period as "_the times of the Gentiles_"

3. In the centuries that followed, _history_ recorded the _fulfillment_ of each prophecy.

(The toes may be the one exception and may represent a political system yet to come.)

Each portion of the statue represents a _world empire_ (see v. 21).

Consider the historical fulfillments:

materials diminishing in value but get stronger

- The head made of _gold_ (vv. 32,37-38)

  Famous ruler: _Nebuchadnezzar_

  Historical fulfillment: _Babylonian empire_, 626-539 B.C.

- The chest and arms made of _silver_ (Dan. 2:39)

  Historical fulfillment: _Medo-Persian Empire_, 539-331 B.C.

  Famous ruler: _Cyrus the Great_ (See Isa. 44:24,28; 45:1-4)

- The belly and thighs made of __bronze__ (vv. 32,39)

  Historical fulfillment: __the Grecian Empire__, 331–63 B.C.

  Famous ruler: __Alexander the Great__

- The legs made of __iron__ (vv. 33,40-43) *(iron breaks everything)*

  Historical fulfillment: __the Roman Empire__, 63 B.C.-A.D. 476

  Famous rulers: Octavian (entitled Augustus), Tiberius, Nero

- The feet made of __iron__ and __baked clay__ (vv. 33,41-43)

  Possible interpretations: The two feet may represent the outgrowth of the divided

  Roman Empire. As stated earlier, the toes on the feet may very well represent a

  political system yet to come. Ten horns foretell a __ten-kingdom__

  (or ten-nation) confederacy that will operate jointly at the time of Christ's return

  (Dan. 7:7,24; Rev. 13:1; 17:12).

4. Compare Daniel 2:34-35 to 2:44-45. The rock represents the kingdom of Messiah,

   the Lord Jesus Christ. This kingdom will fill the __whole earth__

Explore the symbolism in Joshua 8:30-31 and Psalm 118:22-24 (quoted in 1 Pet. 2:4-8).[2]

1. John F. Walvoord and Roy B. Zuck, *The Bible Knowledge Commentary*, Old Testament (Wheaton, IL: Victor Books, 1985), 1334.
2. The story "The Stone the Builders Rejected" comes from James Montgomery Boice, *Daniel: An Expositional Commentary,* (Grand Rapids, MI: Baker Books, 1989), 37-40.

You've made your way to week 2! Bible study is beginning to show all over your face, and I'll tell you how I know. Recently I stood to the side of a platform and tried to absorb the sight of women filling the room as my worship leader led us. They looked completely different than the group of ladies who'd occupied the sanctuary the day before. Their faces seemed lit by holy fire, and their expressions testified to joy. I could not help but think how desperate we are for time away with God to heal from the harshness of this world and to gain the courage to soften up again.

Without stealing away time with God, we won't just grow carnal. We'll grow cold and callous. Whether or not you realize it, these frequent times with God become a healing agent against the world's harsh winds and a healthy defense to still allow you to feel. Ecclesiastes 8:1 says, "Wisdom brightens a man's face and changes its hard appearance." Your mind is renewed and your face grows brighter every day with the reflection of God's glory. I'd say it this way: you're looking mighty pretty.

This is a great time for one last reminder concerning the order we've established for our 12-session, 11-week series. Remember, each week of study follows up the previous session. Because the session-driven approach seemed more comprehensive for the Daniel series, the homework is dependent to a degree on the sessions. If you were unable to participate in session 2, you can still do and apply your homework. Day 5 will be a challenge, however. It reflects heavily upon the previous session. By all means, press ahead and do your homework, but try to make up the session material if at all possible. I want you to get the very most out of our series. Both components—sessions and homework—working in tandem will invite Scripture to leap most vividly from the page and into your life experience.

THIS WEEK'S PRINCIPAL QUESTIONS

DAY 1 How does the dream impact King Nebuchadnezzar (Dan. 2:1-12)?

DAY 2 How does Daniel's approach to Arioch show tact?

DAY 3 When did the revelation come (Dan. 2:19)?

DAY 4 How was God's sovereignty and providence expressed in Daniel 2:20-23?

DAY 5 In what ways did Daniel carefully credit God with the dream's revelation?

DAY ONE A ROYALLY TROUBLED MIND

Today's Treasure: *In the second year of his reign, Nebuchadnezzar had dreams; his mind was troubled and he could not sleep. Daniel 2:1*

Today we begin our second week of study in our series on the Book of Daniel. I'm already hooked and I hope you are, too. My heart nearly leapt out of my chest as I did research for session 2 and week 2. I pray for God to astonish you as well with the wonders of His Word. I'm crazy about you, Sister, and I am delighted that we get to study the Bible together. Let's do everything we can to get the most benefit out of our journey.

Begin your lesson today with a prayer for supernatural wisdom and understanding. Initial here after you've prayed, then proceed: _____

This exercise helps us develop a critical discipline. Heaven alone can testify what insight we will gain as a direct result of this prayer. In Matthew 13:11-12 Christ told His disciples, "The knowledge of the secrets of the kingdom of heaven has been given to you, but not [to the masses]. Whoever has will be given more, and he will have an abundance." A disciple is simply a person willing to learn. An intentional pupil. I have a ninety-one-year-old mentor who is still an intentional pupil in the classroom of Christ. That's what I want to be. I want to know the secret things of God. Don't you? You and I began our series with a commitment to learn. Let's stay intentional. The more we learn, the more God will reveal. We begin with prayer because nothing else stimulates our receptors like it.

This week we will focus on the second chapter of Daniel which consists of 49 verses, necessitating a faster pace than we took last week. If you participated in session 2, you'll recall that we centered specifically on Nebuchadnezzar's dream statue. We will now have the opportunity to rewind all the way to the beginning of the chapter and capture our context.

A DISCIPLE IS WILLING TO LEARN—AN INTENTIONAL PUPIL.

List evidences of the dream's impact on King Nebuchadnezzar (Dan. 2:1-12).

His mind was troubled and he could not sleep

Last week a precious woman approached me at the end of our Sunday School lesson. Appearing very shaken, she described a dream she'd had just before awakening that morning. I understood her alarm as she recounted the dream-scene of her adult son's suicide. She asked if I thought it was prophetic. I quickly confessed to her that I was afraid her question was out of my league. I also tried to reassure her that I've had thousands of dreams, and not one of them turned out to be a prophetic message from God. Although I confess I've made the request, God simply hasn't spoken to me through dreams. I have a feeling God thinks I'm safest just sticking with the written Word. At the same time, you can imagine that I told her to go check on her son. Thankfully, thus far the dream has proved nothing more.

Reflect again on our text. What do you think caused Nebuchadnezzar to feel this wasn't an ordinary nightmare? *Because his mind was so troubled over the dream*

God made sure Nebuchadnezzar knew his was no run-of-the-mill dream. Verse 1 says Nebuchadnezzar's "mind was troubled." This phrase could also be translated, "his spirit was struck."[1] *The New American Commentary* shares J. Slotki's research on the verb: "The root [*pa 'am*] means 'to strike' as with a hammer on an anvil or as a bell. It probably is connected with the rapid beat of the heart due to extreme agitation."[2] Slotki's translation puts a pulse to Nebuchadnezzar's dream. It struck his spirit like a hammer, awakening him with a jolt that left his heart pounding. I hate that kind of dream. Don't you?

Can you remember your last spirit-striking dream? If so, what was it about?

> I can't remember exactly. I think that a noise woke me up & I thought someone was in the house

How were you able to calm down?

> I prayed that the Lord would protect me and it was just a nightmare

Calm escaped Nebuchadnezzar. The text says he couldn't sleep, but a more literal rendering might read, "his sleep was done [or finished] upon him."[3] We know what that's like. Every now and then we awaken so startled or troubled about something that we know sleep is done for the night. Nebuchadnezzar's cultural conditioning deepened his concern. The belief was prevalent among ancient Babylonians that the gods sent messages through dreams.

God knew exactly where to get Nebuchadnezzar's attention. Had a prophet come and delivered him the exact message, he probably wouldn't have attached any supernatural angle to it. He believed dreams were given by the gods, however. He'd soon find out that this dream was given by *the God*.

What kinds of people were summoned to interpret the dream (v. 2)?

> Magicians enchanters, sorcerers & astrologers

Note "the astrologers answered the king in Aramaic" (v. 4). What unique feature about the Book of Daniel did we learn at the very beginning of week 1, day 2? (By all means, glance back if necessary.)

> That the beginning & ending of Daniel was written in Hebrew & the middle in Aramaic

The phrase "the astrologers answered the king in Aramaic" signals the switch from Hebrew to Aramaic. The original text does not resume the Hebrew language until Daniel 7. Do you also remember the theory proposed for the switch? Assuming its accuracy, the portion of Daniel 2 in Aramaic is not only pertinent to the children of Israel but to the Gentile world as well.

If you participated in session 2, just how pertinent did the dream turn out to be for the Gentile world? Briefly explain. You are welcome to glance back at your session guide. *It turned out to cover the panorama of Gentile history from the reign until the forthcoming reign of Israel's Messiah*

Fill in the blank according to verse 5: "This is what I have firmly decided:

If you do not tell me *what my dream was* and interpret it, I will have you cut into pieces" (emphasis mine).

Carefully consider Nebuchadnezzar's demand. He wanted his servants to recite the actual content of the dream before they interpreted it. Either Nebuchadnezzar demanded proof of their supernatural ability by requiring the content, or he had forgotten some of the dream. Both explanations are viable. Have you ever awakened terribly troubled by a dream, but you couldn't remember what it was? Have you tried and tried to rewind it on the tape of your memory like I have?

Among the evidences of the dream's impact, note Nebuchadnezzar's threat against his servants if they did not interpret it. As grotesque as it is, dismembering enemies was a very common practice in the ancient Orient.[4] The "magicians, enchanters, sorcerers and astrologers" knew to take the threat seriously, but they were powerless to save themselves. They always have been.

Look at God's words spoken through the prophet Isaiah a century earlier in Isaiah 47:12-15. The context shows the words were directed to Babylon.

How do Isaiah's words apply to Nebuchadnezzar's predicament in Daniel 2?

There is not one that can save you

The king was so enraged that he ordered the execution of all Babylon's wise men. Try to picture their faces as reality hit. They'd held positions of great prestige and honor in Nebuchadnezzar's kingdom, but they were utterly expendable. They'd enjoyed superiority among the masses, but they had no security. You and I are people of a kingdom. In fact, ours is a kingdom of millions, yet not one of us is expendable "Indeed, the very hairs on your head are all numbered" (Luke 12:7). Ah, yes. He even knows how many of them have highlights.

Beloved, God knows your details. Say it aloud: God knows my details. "Don't be afraid" (Luke 12:7). You are invaluable to your King.

OURS IS A KINGDOM OF MILLIONS, YET NOT ONE OF US IS EXPENDABLE.

Meditate on the astrologers' final words in verse 11, and fill in the blank: "What the king asks is too difficult. No one can reveal it to the king except

the gods, and they *do not live among men*."

If they'd only known our God! The God of both the Old Testament and the New!

Look up each of the following Scriptures as your benediction, and briefly describe how our God differs from the false gods of heathen nations. Celebrate Him while you're at it.

Exodus 25:8 *Our God dwells among us*

John 1:14 *Jesus came wrapped in flesh & dwelt among us*

Our God will dwell with us until we dwell with Him.

DAY TWO URGENT TACT, URGENT PRAYER

Today's Treasure: *He urged them to plead for mercy from the God of heaven concerning this mystery, so that he and his friends might not be executed with the rest of the wise men of Babylon. Daniel 2:18*

Our lesson concluded with the wise men of Babylon facing the ax. Can you imagine the fear and insecurity the news bred among the people? To paraphrase Dr. Martin Luther King Jr., injustice to some threatens the justice of all. If the wise men of Babylon were dispensable, who wasn't?

Daniel and his three fellow Hebrews, though early in their tenure, were already counted among the wise men of Babylon. The timing of their promotion couldn't have been worse. To be a wise man at that time was to be a dead man.

Thankfully, these four men were wise enough to serve the only God who could deliver them.

Pray for insight, then read Daniel 2:13-18. Who was Arioch?

The commander of the King's guards

The root of the original word *tabbah,* translated "guard," means "to slay."[5] In other words, the king's guards in this context were his executioners. Arioch was the commander. Not a pretty job, but in Nebuchadnezzar's kingdom, somebody invariably had to do it. After all, Arioch, too, was dispensable. The text tells us that when young Daniel came face-to-face with the head executioner, he actually had the wherewithal to open his mouth and speak.

How does verse 14 describe Daniel's approach to Arioch?

He spoke to him w/ wisdom & tact

🦁 How does Daniel's approach to Arioch show tact?

Humility ~ Confidence in the Lord

The root of the Aramaic word translated "tact" in this segment means "to taste, to form an opinion of something based on its flavor."[6] Daniel's approach to the captain of Babylon's executioners could have rolled his head to the tune of a machete in a split second (pardon the pun). He mustered the astonishing courage to ask a difficult question that could have been treated as an open criticism of the king, "Why did the king issue such a harsh decree?" Instead, Daniel's tact kept his words from tasting bad on the tongue of the executioner.

Tact. We could all use an extra dose ... but no one more than Christians. Not because we're worse than everyone else but because so much is at stake! I've been told by waiters that people coming into restaurants for Sunday lunch after church are some of the rudest and worst tipping customers they have. Why in the world would we risk the reputation of Christ that way?

Hopefully the shoe of tactlessness doesn't fit you. And if it doesn't fit, don't wear it. At the same time, let's be aware that a number of Christians may have earned all of us a bad reputation. The shoe sits shiny and ready on the shelf whenever we feel impatient or bothered. If we're going to fight the temptation to put it on, we'll need to recognize that we're never more tempted to be rude than when we think someone deserves it.

CHRISTIANS COULD USE AN EXTRA DOSE OF TACT BECAUSE SO MUCH IS AT STAKE!

Let's be really candid. When was the last time you wanted to respond to someone with rudeness?

To a friend who said something hurtful to me

My last time was only a few days ago when I was begging a specialist for help with an alcoholic loved one. She was so curt and unfeeling that I almost got ugly. I kept silently praying, "Help me, Lord. Help me!" He did, or I would've had a handful of her hair in my tight little grip that day.

A tactful approach doesn't cast a vote of approval. Tact is wisdom, not flattery. Merriam Webster defines it as implying "delicate and considerate perception of what is appropriate."[7] To say that Daniel was in a delicate situation when he encountered Arioch is an understatement. His life was at stake. The lives of the lost and searching who have occasion to observe our lives are also at stake. Leaving a bad taste for Christianity in their mouths is deadly.

Based on the definition "to taste, to form an opinion of something based on its flavor," how does Colossians 4:6 perfectly describe Daniel's tact?

The Lord gave Daniel the words to say as not to anger the Commander

Daniel's tact kept his head on his shoulders for a few more minutes. Those minutes turned out to be critical.

Take a look at verse 18. What were they spent doing?

pleading to the Lord to extend mercy to them

The Aramaic word translated "plead" means "to ask, pray for, look for" and, in this context, to do so with urgency. Interestingly, the word occurs 12 times in Scripture, each time in the book of Daniel.[8]

What does the deliberate repetition of *plead* say to us if we want to become like Daniel? *That we are to bombard the throne of God pleading for His mercy*

Now, picture the prayer meeting between Daniel, Hananiah, Mishael, and Azariah. Take a moment and describe how you imagine it.

I believe they would be on their faces before the Lord

My friend, Kathy Troccoli, has mentioned her personal group of prayer warriors to me many times, but until a few days ago I'd never met them. Somehow I'd pictured them being about her age and looking much like her. Instead, those I had the wonderful privilege of meeting had beautiful heads of gray hair and years of wisdom on Kathy and me. I was nearly covetous until the pictures of my own prayer partners came to my mind.

Beloved, do you have a Hananiah, Mishael, and Azariah with whom to pray at your most urgent moments? If so, who are they? (Of course, you don't have to name exactly three.)

Peggy, Bev & Jeannie

What was the occasion of your most urgent prayer with them? *my daughter's pregnancy – emotional state — my pain*

If you have prayer partners for urgent times, or better yet, for any time, express your gratitude to God for them. If you don't, express to God your great need for them and be open to His candidates. Don't picture them looking just like you or being in your age bracket. Young Mom, God may have a senior adult for you at your church who could be one of the biggest blessings in life to you. Senior adult, God might have a young single who could partner with you in prayer like no one else. Ask God to do the pairing. Someone out there needs *you* for a prayer partner, Dear One. *You* are the answer to someone else's prayer. And your character is looking a bit more like Daniel's every single day.

DAY THREE PRAISE TO THE GOD OF HEAVEN

Today's Treasure: *During the night the mystery was revealed to Daniel in a vision. Then Daniel praised the God of heaven. Daniel 2:19*

Yesterday's study left us hanging at the height of drama. Thankfully, we left Daniel, Hananiah, Mishael, and Azariah in the best possible place—on their knees in prayer. Urgent prayer. Rule for victorious living: when the stakes are high, bow down low.

Please read Daniel 2:19-30. When did the revelation come (v. 19)?

During the night

To whom did it come? *Daniel*

I don't think we'll accurately picture our four protagonists having prayed, put on their jammies, and turned in for the night. The threat of being cut into little pieces is enough to keep the toothpicks in your eyelids. I asked you who received the revelation because I want you to imagine being one of the three who *didn't* receive it. Their place was critical. It was on their knees. At the same time, they had to trust that God had given a clear answer that concerned their very lives to someone else. Trusting someone else's relationship with God to the degree that you'd receive a vital message through him is challenging.

Hananiah, Mishael, and Azariah not only had to trust God; they had to trust Daniel as having heard from Him. Few of our lives have been at stake, but most of us have been in positions where we had to trust God's message to someone else that also concerned us (a spouse, boss, pastor, or trusted friend to name a few).

If you can think of a time when you were in this position, share it.

_____

I remember not long ago when I confessed to God that I didn't know whether I could trust _____ to hear from Him in a matter that greatly affected me. He seemed to respond to my heart, "Can you trust Me with _____?" I knew I could. I bent my knee to God's sovereignty and watched Him work. Do you need to fill in those blanks with an invisible name? If so, do it. On the other hand, you may be the person others must trust to hear from God on a matter.

Consider the pronouns in this portion of Daniel 2:23: "You (God) have made known to *me* what *we* asked of you" (emphasis mine). "We" asked but only one ("me") received the answer and became the earpiece for the rest. You may be the "me" in "we" who is chosen to hear from God on behalf of others. The responsibility would be huge, wouldn't it?

YOU MAY BE CHOSEN TO HEAR FROM GOD ON BEHALF OF OTHERS.

DANIEL

THE ANSWER TO URGENT PRAYER CALLS FOR URGENT PRAISE!

What kind of person would you need to be should God choose you to be the "me" drawn from the "we"? *A person of integrity so that my friends believed me and praising the Lord for His mercy*

Daniel had no doubt he'd heard from God. Recall from session 2 the images he described to the king. They were too intricate, exact, and symbolic to be Daniel's imagination. When the revelation came, Daniel received it and then compulsory praise broke forth from his lips. The answer to urgent prayer calls for urgent praise!

Read Daniel 2:20-23—aloud, if possible. Say the words as if Daniel were borrowing your mouth and the passion of your heart to express them.

I'm only going to challenge you to memorize one set of Scriptures during our study. *This is it.* We have at least eight weeks to accomplish it, and God will enable us as we earnestly ask Him. Any time we pray in God's will, we have what we ask. He wants few things more passionately than His Word abiding in us.

Please write all four verses on several index cards. Take them with you and practice until you have committed the passage to memory.

Take heart, Dear One! We're in this together! I'm not going to ask you to do things I won't do with you. Try memorizing one verse per week. Spend the remaining weeks saying them over and over. Practice them in your small group. Remember, even if you don't memorize the segment word-for-word, your mind will still be renewed and the concepts will abide deeply within you. You win either way. You've just penned perfect praises for answered prayer from a sovereign God. Is anything like the ecstatic joy of answered prayer? John 16:24 suggests that few joys are as complete.

Look up John 16:24 and fill in the blank according to the NIV:

"'Until now you have not asked for anything in my name. Ask and

you will receive, and _your joy will be complete_'

Dear One, nothing is more appropriate than jumping up and down for joy over answered prayer. Sometimes we confuse humility with timidity. When God comes through for us, a timid and tentative thanks is not only out of place; it's anticlimactic. When I give my children something, nothing makes me happier than to see them react. I can't imagine many things blessing the heart of God more than enthusiastic thanks. Instead, often by the time the answer comes, our focus has shifted to the next desire, and we take tragically little time for rejoicing.

If we became intentional about noting every single answer to prayer, we'd be astonished by God's attentive faithfulness. Beloved, He answers you affirmatively so much more than you probably realize. Memorizing this segment will give us the opportunity to practice taking note of specific answers and responding with praise because we're going to personalize it by leaving it open-ended. In other words, when we say our Scriptures to God, we will leave room for our own conclusions like this:

"I thank and praise You, O God of my fathers: You have given me

_____. You have made known to me what we asked

of You. You have_____

_____."

As we memorize our segment of Scripture, you and I are going to start looking for opportunities to personalize the ending. If we are to develop Daniel-like character, let's try practicing some Daniel-like approaches. In our next lesson, we'll turn our attentions back to the praises we've written and take a closer look at this approach. Daniel-like prayer warriors are Daniel-like worshipers. Pray on, Dear Sister. Answers will come, and your joy will be complete.

DAY FOUR FROM "HE" TO "YOU"

Today's Treasure: *He changes times and seasons; he sets up kings and deposes them. He gives wisdom to the wise and knowledge to the discerning. Daniel 2:21*

If you're like me and you don't have a solo singing voice, don't you wish you did? Doesn't everybody who can't sing wish they could? I'm of the mind-set that if people can sing, they ought not be able to do anything else. Otherwise, it's just not fair. Take some of my fellow women's Bible study writers, for instance. Mary Kassian, Jennifer Rothschild, and Priscilla Shirer can each sing … *and* teach. I'm galled by it. They can polish off a lesson and then finish it off with a tune. Doesn't that just beat all?

Recently I spoke at a *Women of Faith* conference and all three speakers preceding me ended their talks with a song. I'd had it and said so. Then again, maybe God was doing a new thing, and I just hadn't taken the time to receive it. When I got home, I sat down at the piano, threw open my old, trusty *Broadman Hymnal* and hacked out a few hymns. My passable playing hadn't improved, and I never could find the right key to showcase my voice. Maybe my piano is out of tune.

Singer I'm not. But, psalter? Ah, now that's a different story. Every believer in Christ is called to extol the greatness of God and voice the manifold evidences of His faithfulness. Translation? We were meant to make some joyful noise. If I turn up my David Crowder CDs loud enough, no one but God can hear me anyway. And He likes it. He likes it from you, too, Beloved.

providence

God has a plan and purpose for His world. Providence is not a principle of orderliness or reason; rather, providence is the will of the Creator who is actively involved in moving His creation to a goal. History is not a cyclical process of endless repetition; history is being moved toward the predetermined end.

GOD'S PROVIDENCE IS INTENTIONAL AND PURPOSEFUL.

As promised, we will return to the praises of Daniel and continue to make them our own. His compulsory praise burst forth with God's greatness, almost as if Daniel couldn't stop himself. A man's praise of his God ought not be overanalyzed; however, I'd like us to analyze Daniel's knowledge of his God expressed by his praises. He knew some things about God that we'd be changed by knowing. Before we look them over, let's meditate on a few terms that will be helpful throughout our 11 weeks. The highest theme of the Book of Daniel is undoubtedly the sovereignty of God. We've touched on it before, but we won't grasp this study fully without pouncing on it like kids on a trampoline.

God's sovereignty means that He has supremacy over all things and does whatever He desires with whomever or whatever He pleases. To miss God's sovereignty in the Book of Daniel is to miss the point. Theologically speaking, the providence of God is similar in concept. *Harper's Bible Dictionary* explains, "This God has a plan and purpose for his world. Providence is not a principle of orderliness or reason; rather, providence is the will of the Creator who is actively involved in moving his creation to a goal. History is not a cyclical process of endless repetition; history is being moved toward the predetermined end."[9]

Which parts of Harper's definition of "providence" mean the most to you?

Providence is the will of the Creator who is actively involved in moving His creation to a goal

A thesaurus might use words such as *fate, chance,* and *luck* as synonyms for "providence" but those words find no room in the divine definition. <u>God's providence is intentional and purposeful. God's sovereignty and providence mean that He does what He pleases to accomplish His goals; and, thankfully, He is pleased to involve us in His process.</u> After all, His entire point in creating us was to involve us in His life.

Now, return to Daniel's proclamations of praise in 2:20-23. Note specific ways these verses express God's sovereignty and providence. *wisdom & power are His —*

One of the most easily recognizable proclamations of God's sovereignty in this segment is stated in verse 21: "He sets up kings and deposes them." God's Word is eternal. Unaffected by time. Scripture was inspired to be as fresh each passing day as it was the first. We might say God's breath is always fresh. We established from the beginning that we are surrounded by a Babylonian-type culture. Furthermore, we share a planet with nations and peoples in utter turmoil.

How does the sovereignty of God ascribed in these four verses (20-23) speak to you concerning any current *world* events? *He puts people in office & He removes them. He knows exactly what's going on everywhere. He is in control. Praise You Jesus!*

Our God is the same yesterday, today, and forever. He is no less in charge when the world seems in chaos. He also just as readily gives wisdom to those who seek it today. Don't be thrown by the statement that God "gives wisdom to the wise" lest we think a person has to be wise to ever get wiser. Thank goodness, even the most foolish can become wise. Godly wisdom is ours for the asking (Jas. 1:5). Daniel's point is that God continues to give wisdom to those who have a track record of receiving it. Christ drew a similar concept in a Scripture I quoted on day 1 of week 2.

What do you see in common between Matthew 13:12-13 and Daniel 2:21?

That God gives to those who receive yet & apply it — then He gives more. But those who have little may lose it

If God says something to us, Beloved, we want to hear it and respond to it. If God shows something to us, we want to see it and walk in it. Crudely put, we've got to use it or lose it. After all, "whoever has will be given more" (Matt. 13:12).

Now, let's highlight another rich aspect of Daniel's praise. Get your note cards with the Scriptures from the assignment on day 3. Draw a circle around every reference to God as "He" or "Him." Now draw a heart around every reference to God as "you" (or capitalized "You") and every one of Daniel's personal references using the word "me" in chapter 2:20-23.

What does the obvious shift from third-person references (God as "He") to second-person ("You") and first-person ("me") references mean to you?

David, the psalmist and the man after God's own heart, sometimes expressed the same approach. He switched back and forth between references *about* God and references *to* God. For example, in Psalm 18 David began with words directed specifically to God ("I love you, O Lord, my strength"), then he talked *about* Him ("The Lord is my rock … He is my shield …") for the next 23 verses. From verse 25 through the end of the psalm at verse 50, David switched back and forth. He seemed almost unable to keep talking *about* God without talking *to* God.

The point? Daniel's psalm extols the sovereign God as intimately watchful over the nations but also over the life of His child. It shows God equipping us with a kind of wisdom and power otherwise impossible.

GOD IS SOVEREIGN AND WATCHFUL OVER HIS CHILD AS WELL AS THE NATIONS.

I asked you a moment ago how the four verses speak to you regarding current *world* events. In light of Daniel's shift in the psalm from the international scene to the personal scene, how do the four verses speak to you regarding current *personal* events?

That God is sovereign & being omnipresent, He knows what is best for my daughter, Lisa and me and He is watching over & watching out for us

41

Reread Harper's definition of "providence" on page 40. How do God's sovereignty and providence help you reframe your current circumstances or challenges? Be specific.

_____

How does God's willingness to give supernatural wisdom and power help you reframe your current circumstances or challenges even further?

Helps remove the fear (Satan's attack on me)

In conclusion, read the four verses again as written below, but this time in order to personalize it, apply the open-ended approach we talked about at the conclusion of yesterday's lesson. Reflect on a recent answer to prayer or a specific direction you sought and received from the Lord. Fill in the blanks in verse 23 as they apply to something God has done in your own life. Turn this segment into your own authentic praise rather than a recitation.

"Praise be to the name of God for ever and ever;
    wisdom and power are his. He changes times and seasons;
    he sets up kings and deposes them.
He gives wisdom to the wise and knowledge to the discerning.
He reveals deep and hidden things;
    he knows what lies in darkness,
    and light dwells with Him.
I thank and praise You, O God of my fathers:
    You have given me _____,
you have made known to me what we asked of you,
    you have _____." (Dan. 2:20-23).
"The LORD has done great things for us,
    and we are filled with joy" (Ps. 126:3).

DAY FIVE DANIEL'S INTERPRETATION

Today's Treasure: *In the time of those kings, the God of heaven will set up a kingdom that will never be destroyed, nor will it be left to another people. Daniel 2:44*

You've done a great job this week, Dear One. I hope you're growing more and more fascinated by the material. God is honored by the way you've loved Him this week with your mind as well as your heart. I absolutely love the challenge, and I hope you do, too. Know that I'm praying for you throughout this series and that I'm cheering you on to the finish line. We've arrived at the lesson I warned you about in this week's introduction. Most of today's lesson reflects heavily on the portion of Daniel 2 that we studied in session 2. Some of your answers will require your notes from session 2 or a very good commentary with a similar interpretation. If you have your session notes, get ready to use them. If you don't, you will still be able to accomplish at least half of the lesson, so please press on. Ask God for supernatural wisdom and understanding, then get started.

Read Daniel 2:27-30. Review Daniel's response to the king when asked if he (Daniel) could describe and interpret his (the king's) dream. In what ways did Daniel carefully credit God with the revelation? *No wise man, enchanter, magician or diviner can explain to the king the mystery but there is a God in heaven who reveals mysteries. vs 30 As for me, this mystery that has been revealed to me not because I have greater wisdom than other living men but so you may know the interpretation & understand what went through your mind.*

Now, review Daniel's interpretation in 2:31-45. Read the Scriptures first, then glance back over your notes from session 2. I'm a visual learner, so I am vastly helped any time I can use a diagram or see a graphic. Today we're going to take the material we learned in session 2 and diagram it on a graphic design representing the statue in Nebuchadnezzar's dream.

Please complete each of the following on the diagram on page 44.

1. On the left side of the statue, label the metals or materials beside the corresponding sections of the body.
2. Recall what the statue represents and title the page with it. (You don't have to say it word for word. Conveying the general idea is sufficient.)
3. According to your notes from session 2, label the empires symbolized by the various parts/materials of the body on the right side of the statue.
4. Reread Daniel 2:44-45, compare your notes from session 2, and label the rock in the upper left-hand corner.
5. What will happen to the rock according to the prophecy in verse 35? (Write your answer in this space.) *When the rock strikes the statue it becomes a huge mountain & fills the earth*

6. In this space, note the ways Nebuchadnezzar responded in verses 46-49. *1) He fell prostrate before Daniel & paid honor to him 2) Ordered an offering & incense be paid to Daniel 3) Admitted to Daniel that his God was the God of Gods 4) Placed Daniel in a high position & gave him many gifts. He was over all the wise men & his command made administrator over the province of Babylon*

7. Nebuchadnezzar did not have the personal relationship with God that you and I possess. If he responded in worship, how much more shall we? As we conclude, in light of God's glorious, sovereign plan, how will you respond to Him in worship today? Write a brief prayer in the margin. Be prepared to share a portion of your prayer with your small group.

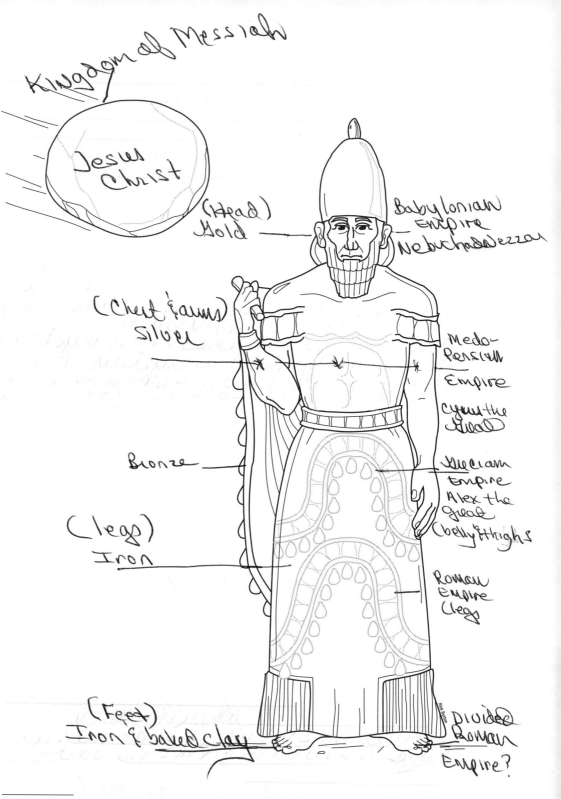

Kingdom of Messiah

Jesus Christ

(Head) Gold

Babylonian Empire Nebuchadnezzar

(Chest & arms) Silver

Medo-Persian Empire

Cyrus the Great

Bronze

Grecian Empire Alex the great (belly & thighs

(legs) Iron

Roman Empire (legs

(Feet) Iron & baked clay

Divided Roman Empire?

1. Stephen R. Miller, *Daniel*, vol. 18 in *The New American Commentary* (Nashville: Broadman & Holman, 2001), 77.

2. Ibid.

3. Ibid.

4. Ibid., 81.

5. Ibid., 84.

6. Spiros Zodhiates, ThD., gen. ed., *Lexical Aids to the Old Testament, Hebrew-Greek Key Word Study Bible, New International Version* (Chattanooga, TN: AMG Publishers), #10302, 1564.

7. Frederick C. Mish, ed., *Merriam Webster's Collegiate Dictionary,* 10th Edition (Springfield, MA: Merriam-Webster, Inc., 2002), 1196.

8. Zodhiates, *Lexical Aids,* #10114, 1563.

9. P. J. Achtemeier, *Harper's Bible Dictionary* (San Francisco: Harper & Row, 1985), 832.

NO SMELL OF FIRE

3

SESSION THREE
NO SMELL OF FIRE

In today's session we're going to gather around the mouth of a fiery furnace and view seven concepts in its light. The third chapter of Daniel is too rich with application to exhaust its fire in one session. Your daily assignments this week will offer much further opportunity to draw parallel concepts to your personal life.

1. Read Daniel 3:1-7.

   The _inspiration_ for building an _image_ doesn't come from the Holy Spirit (Dan. 2:36-40).[1]

2. Read Daniel 3:8-12.

   Glance back at Daniel 2:48-49. The conspicuous absence of our resident " _strong One_ " is a divine set-up to _step-up_ .

3. Read Daniel 3:13-18.

   Consider three different scenarios when people of God face a fiery trial:

   Scenario A: We can be _delivered_ _from_ the fire.

   Dividend? Our faith is _built_ .

   Scenario B: We can be _delivered_ _through_ the fire.

   Dividend? Our faith is _refined_ .

   Scenario C: We can be _delivered_ _by_ the fire _into His arms_ .

   Dividend? Our faith is _perfected_ .

VIEWER GUIDE

4. Read Daniel 3:19-27.

The original language translated "son of the gods" (NIV) means "son of ___deity___."

The definition of *theophany*: a visible ___manifestation___ of ___God___.

[margin note: 4 in the fire – 3 + God]

When the appearance is anthropomorphic, it may very likely be a preincarnate appearance of Christ.

An additional dividend of deliverance in the fire:

Their ___ropes___ alone were ___flammable___ (v. 25).[2]

[margin note: Every time we go thru the fire – there are four of us in the fire – the Trinity + me]

5. Note the final description in verse 27.

Full deliverance means no longer ___smelling___ like ___smoke___.

*[margin note: We can't be lightweight! We can make it thru some fires *]*

6. Read Daniel 3:28-30.

The way to avoid getting ___burned___ is to ___bathe___ in God's presence.
(trust)
(reside)

7. The last mention of their ___names___ was in the context of God's ___fame___.

*[handwritten note: * If we make it thru the culture w/o being defiled – We aren't lightweight !!!]*

1. According to the Septuagint (a Greek version of the Hebrew Old Testament), the image was built in the eighteenth year of Nebuchadnezzar's reign; therefore, sixteen years had passed since Daniel's interpretation of the king's dream.
2. Beth mentions these commentaries: *Daniel, Ezra, Nehemiah: A New English Translation* by Rabbi A. J. Rosenberg (New York: The Judaica Press, 2000) and *Daniel: A New Translation with a Commentary Anthologized from Talmudic, Midrashic and Rabbinic Sources* (Brooklyn: Mesorah Publications, Ltd., 2002).

WEEK THREE
NO SMELL OF FIRE

DAY 1
Taller When Others Bow

DAY 2
Another Side of
Self-Absorption

DAY 3
The Apple of His Eye

DAY 4
The Heart of Loyalty

DAY 5
If He Does Not

I'm so proud of you for making your way to week 3! You're practicing Daniel-like consistency. Integrity doesn't develop apart from consistent resolve. Your resolve is showing; and, far more importantly, your Savior is showing. After writing 11 Bible studies, I've learned that the third week is highly significant. By this time you know what to expect and you're serious about your commitment. I'm serious about mine as well, Dear One. I have the sweetest assurance in my soul that God is pleased with our quest and has great purpose in all He wants to teach us.

The Book of Daniel is storehouse to so many treasures that we could study it a dozen times without unearthing them all. Thankfully, the slower pace we're getting to take allows us to discover a number of them. My prayer is for the pursuit of God and His Word to become, in Steven Curtis Chapman's words, your "magnificent obsession." Never forget how much He loves you and how zealously He pursues your company. And, no wonder. You seem pretty wonderful to me.

THIS WEEK'S PRINCIPAL QUESTIONS

DAY 1 How did Christ's teachings fly in the face of Babylon's self-absorbed, ego-stroked, overindulgent mind-set?

DAY 2 What does James 3:13-16 say about selfish ambition?

DAY 3 What does Galatians 5:15 warn will happen if two people don't cease "biting and devouring each other"?

DAY 4 Based on your own understanding, how would you define *loyalty*?

DAY 5 How did John Hus or Hugh Latimer and Nicholas Ridley exhibit loyalty?

DAY ONE TALLER WHEN OTHERS BOW

Today's Treasure: *He then summoned the satraps, prefects, governors, advisers, treasurers, judges, magistrates and all the other provincial officials to come to the dedication of the image he had set up. Daniel 3:2*

God is magnificently using a friend in her early sixties to minister to women in the eastern part of our nation. She has a faithful and successful husband who has adored her for no less than 40 years. My friend is not only beautiful in spirit, but she is also beautiful to the eye. What some would call a total package, you might say she has everything a person could want. Surely she'd never be intimidated by anyone.

A few days ago she described a gathering she and her husband attended on the west coast. Many of the women were so outrageously gorgeous with such perfectly—albeit artificially—sculpted faces and bodies that she departed the gathering feeling "frumpy and old." My heart ached and not just for her. For all of us. For the woman who asked me why I'd never had my nose fixed. After all, I was almost "there." Where is *there*? And my heart aches for myself; for, though I can talk a big talk, I've only made a small walk toward unshakable security. In one way or another, any woman in our media-driven, imperfection-defying culture has an invitation to insecurity.

I snickered to myself the other day when someone walked me to my car and saw the tape series, "Overcoming Insecurity" on the floorboard. No, I wasn't listening to it with someone else in mind. If she couldn't imagine my needing to listen to that kind of subject, she didn't know me very well! In my natural personality, I am fraught with fears and insecurities. They are, however, the subject of consistent dialogue between God and me. As much as I've prayed to be completely free of them, God appoints some as thorns in my flesh to ensure intimacy, dependency, and humility.

As we continue our session-driven approach, our daily assignments will broaden the look we took at Daniel chapter 3 in the session. Note the image mentioned in Today's Treasure. After reading the account of the 90-foot golden image Nebuchadnezzar set up, we launched session 3 with this point: *The inspiration for building an image doesn't come from the Spirit.* We drew the parallel by pointing out that, for us, image building is any way we intentionally make ourselves seem different—and usually more—than we really are. Image building is the attempt to make impressions that are bigger than we are. Image building may begin with what is true but enhances that truth until it is a lie. For instance, if we've gotten mileage for being "real," we can become a fake at being real.

IMAGE BUILDING IS THE ATTEMPT TO MAKE IMPRESSIONS THAT ARE BIGGER THAN WE ARE.

Share another example of how something true can be enhanced until it's a lie.

So we might ask if "putting our best foot forward" is just another way of image building? The answer depends on whether the foot is still our own. Look like ours? Smell like ours? Then it's probably ours. If not, it's an image. We don't want to confuse image building with an honest attempt to look or do our best, but I won't kid you. A fine line separates the two. Sometimes only the height of sensitivity to the Holy Spirit can signal when we've crossed the line. After all, we are so thoroughly indoctrinated in image building that I'm not sure we easily recognize the difference between excelling and self-selling. Can you think of anything our culture teaches more thoroughly than image building? I can't, particularly as a woman.

Offer a few examples of how our culture teaches women to build an image.

Be a great mom, a great wife, have a great career, keep a perfect house, be thin, be the perfect hostess etc. Dress to the nines, drive new cars

Unfortunately, we girls can't blame all our image building on the guys.

In what ways have you noticed we women constantly sizing one another up?

1. Where do you work? Where do you live, What do you Kids do in school - are they on the honor role? Where did you buy that dress?

I (lovingly) dare you to start catching yourself image building. I fear we are our own worst enemy in our struggle with insecurity. We start the day feeling OK but then see a woman who brings out our size-up—and there we go again, hanging ourselves on our tape measures. You know, we may not see our culture change, but you and I can. It begins with recognizing image building when it rears its golden head.

Let's go back to the beginning of Daniel 3 and take a closer look at the Scriptures we read in our session, this time from a different perspective. Remember to begin every lesson with prayer for deeper knowledge and understanding as we study this fascinating book. After you've prayed, please read Daniel 3:1-7. Our thoughts on this segment of Scripture will span our assignments for both days 1 and 2.

List the seven offices summoned by King Nebuchadnezzar in verse 2.

- satraps   - prefects   - governors   - advisers
- treasurers   - judges   - Magistrates

In all likelihood, the government officials are listed in order of importance. The *satraps* ruled over the larger divisions of the Babylonian Empire just under the King. The *prefects* held high-ranking offices just under the satraps, answering to their direct authority. The *governors* administrated the smaller regions. The *advisers* provided counsel while the *treasurers* and *judges* provided services not unlike those in our local governments. The *magistrates* were similar to our policemen. The KJV draws a familiar picture of the office by translating the word "sheriffs."[1]

As you can see, the gathering was strictly VIP. For those with a public image, you might say. We see no mention of the average Babylonian citizen gathered that day on the plain of Dura.

Recently, Keith and I received a beautiful engraved invitation to a grand White House-sponsored gathering in Washington, D.C. We could hardly believe our eyes. We couldn't imagine how our names could have shown up on such an invitation list. Melissa looked over my shoulder and said, "You have to go! This may be a once in a lifetime opportunity!" I was already planning what dress I'd wear when an equally beautiful card fell out of the envelope. It explained that we had received a commemorative invitation and not one that provided actual entrance into the gathering. Translation? We were invited … but not really. We laughed our heads off. In 30 seconds our 90-foot self-images crumbled in a puff of smoke. To think how close Jethro and Ellie May came to loading up the truck and heading to D.C.!

Nebuchadnezzar's invitation list was solely for the important. If you have a Babylonian mentality, important people bowing down to you is the height of self-importance. We've learned from the beginning to view Babylon as more than a place. Babylon represents a philosophy. A mentality. We're looking at it somewhat symbolically. In session 1, we learned the Babylon motto. I hope you're learning it by heart, but you're welcome to refresh your memory by glancing at Isaiah 47:8,10, a chapter specifically addressed to the "daughters of Babylon."

Write Babylon's motto as quoted in both verse 8 and verse 10:

"I am and there is none beside me."

Isaiah 47 eerily specifies the "daughters of Babylon" as if her mentality is best symbolized by feminine wiles. Indeed, Babylon could be compared in the early chapters of Daniel as a woman trying to lure four young Hebrew men away from their convictions. She seductively tried to woo them into unfaithfulness through ego strokes and overindulgence. You and I have committed that we don't want to be modern equivalents to daughters of Babylon, falling for her lie then helping to perpetuate it. We're opening our eyes to her continual indoctrination and the inevitability of her influence unless we're doing something deliberate to offset it.

YOU AND I DO NOT WANT TO BE MODERN DAUGHTERS OF BABYLON.

Look up each of the following Scriptures and describe how Christ's teachings fly in the face of Babylon's self-absorbed, ego-stroked, overindulgent mind-set.

Mark 10:42-45

Whoever wants to become great among you must be your servant & whoever wants to be first must be slave of all

Luke 9:24-25

Whoever wants to save his life will lose it & whoever loses it for Christ will save it

We are called to be servants not celebrities

Much of the world shares Nebuchadnezzar's point of view: the greatest in the kingdom is the one who can make servants of all. Daniel 3:1-7 lifts a monument to the Babylon mentality. The nine story image Nebuchadnezzar built in Dura might as well have had a brightly colored banner over it proclaiming, "I am, and there is none besides me!" Having the people bow down to the image was tantamount to having them bow down to him. Babylonian thinkers need others to bow in order to feel tall. Nebuchadnezzar didn't bother bending the knees of ordinary people. Babylonian-size egos need bigger strokes than that. They need the strokes of VIPs.

Dear One, I'm a part of this culture just like you are. I'm having my eyes opened to the permeating influence of our Babylonian culture, too. Please don't think for a moment that any point or question I offer you arises from an attitude of condemnation or, God forbid, superiority. I esteem you highly, and I'm pondering the same questions right beside you. Nebuchadnezzar's display heralds some loud questions: do we feel more important when surrounded by those we deem important? Do we feel more important when someone important notices us? Do we like to be seen with those who seem important? Are we name-makers? Or name-droppers? Even the most timid yes to any of these questions nods its head to Babylonian indoctrination.

The need for identity and a sense of significance is as human as our DNA. We begin this search in pursuit of ourselves only to arrive sorely disappointed. Cavernously empty. The honest sojourner cannot stop there no matter how high he's climbed or what position he's attained. If he does, he will forfeit his soul. In search of truth, he is driven beyond himself until all he finds is God. And in bowing down, he is lifted up.

What clue does 1 Peter 5:6 offer to our quest for significance?

When we humble ourselves, God lifts us up in due time

This passage would have turned an ancient Babylonian inside out. I don't doubt you are presently facing a challenge that the world would advise you to approach in an entirely different way.

How would you apply 1 Peter 5:6 to your specific situation?

When someone has said something unfair to me I need to humble myself forgiving them treating them w/ loving kindness

The mirrors of Babylon lie. Only in the reflecting pool of the poured-out life can man finally see who he is.

DAY TWO ANOTHER SIDE OF SELF-ABSORPTION

Today's Treasure: *So the satraps, prefects, governors, advisers, treasurers, judges, magistrates and all the other provincial officials assembled for the dedication of the image that King Nebuchadnezzar had set up, and they stood before it. Daniel 3:3*

Today we'll continue our look at the Babylonian mentality hiding in the shadows of Nebuchadnezzar's nine-story idol. Let's take another look at the crowd gathered in Daniel 3:1-7, but this time let's add a new angle.

To prepare, please reread Daniel 3:1-7.

Hopefully, the familiar Scripture segment sparked recollections of yesterday's lesson. What point from the lesson spoke most personally to you and why?

Even the most timid yes nods its head to Babylonian indoctrination

Do I feel more important when someone important notices me? Am I a name dropper? If there is even a hint of this

The goal of yesterday's lesson was to expose the Babylonian lust for superiority: his willingness to look taller by making those around him seem smaller. Today we're going to kneel on the other side of the plain of Dura and also consider the "humbler" side of self-absorption: an unrelenting struggle with inferiority. Nursing inferiority can be just as self-consuming as seeking superiority. We talked about image building. Bowing down to a poor self-image can be equally unhealthy.

I have battled poor self-esteem much of my life just like many of you. Because of past failures and the ample ammunition I've given my accuser, I sometimes have a hard time differentiating between full-scale failure and a simple misjudgment or mistake. Anything that stirs up that old feeling of failure—no matter how little the infractions compare—can send me on an instantaneous plummet from shaky self-esteem to full throttle self-loathing.

I'll never forget the first time God exposed my periodic bouts of self-loathing as just another form of self-absorption. I was shocked, having thought all along that it was a sign of humility. Nothing like priding yourself in hating yourself. Beloved, let's let this one sink in deeply: constantly thinking little of ourselves is still thinking constantly of ourselves. We can build a poor self-image with our preoccupation until it becomes 90 feet tall.

The Babylonian motto is still legible under an inferior light. "I am, and there is none besides me" can show up in our thoughts as:

"I am ugly, and there is none as ugly as me."
"I am stupid, and there is none as stupid as me."
"I am a fool, and there is no bigger fool than me."
"I am untalented, and there is none as untalented as me."
"I am unlucky, and there is none as unlucky as me."
"I am scatterbrained, and there is none as scatterbrained as me."
"I am pitiful, and there is none as pitiful as me."

Add a few of your own that you've either observed or experienced:

I can't do anything right

CONSTANTLY THINKING LITTLE OF OURSELVES IS STILL THINKING CONSTANTLY OF OURSELVES

A prevailing sense of inferiority is just another form of self-absorption. Buying the press of someone else's superiority balloons the lie. Recently I was upgraded to first class on a flight back to Houston thanks to frequent flyer miles. Our plane departed late; and as we began our initial descent, the flight attendant said over the intercom system, "Many of our passengers have connecting flights in Houston, and a few minutes will be the difference between their making it to their plane or not. We are requesting that you remain seated if Houston is your final destination and allow our connecting passengers to get off the plane first. We appreciate your cooperation."

As soon as the door opened, every single person in the large first-class cabin jumped into the aisle, making him or herself first in line to get off the plane. That they were all connecting was unlikely. In their obvious estimation, the request didn't apply to them. They'd bought the press: they thought they really were first class. It nauseated me. I nearly steamed as I watched all the connectors in the coach cabin have to wait on those who thought they outclassed them. What a total lack of class.

Describe a time when you felt lower class than someone else. Please don't use names if someone would be dishonored.

When I was in elementary school & my grandmother remade skirts for me purchased at the church rummage sale

53

We don't want to be Nebuchadnezzars who feel taller when others bow down to us, but we also don't want to be the satraps, prefects, and other governmental officials who bowed down to a man's superiority. "Kiss-ups" can be as nauseating as "stuck-ups." Shadrach, Meshach, and Abednego bowed to God alone. No man or idol was worthy of worship. Those God placed in authority over them were worthy of respect, but they were not worthy of their worship. The kind of bowing pictured in the third chapter of Daniel was worship, not a demonstration of respect. Shadrach, Meshach, and Abednego were caught in neither the superiority nor inferiority of Babylonian thinking. With their hands, they'd serve anyone. With their knees, however, they'd bow to no one but God.

> Glance back at the list of officials named in Daniel 3:2-3. According to our previous lesson, how were these officials most likely listed?
> ☐ alphabetically (in Aramaic of course)
> ☒ in order of importance
> ☐ by physical stature

Our culture is obsessed with lists. We seem to have top-10 lists for everything under the sun. Do we constantly feel listed by our culture in order of importance? Overlooked? Underestimated? Do we fight the continual pressure to make those lists? If we don't make one, do we look for another? Once we make it on a list, do we begin to obsess about how to make it up the list? Every determined ascent on the list toward number one is another brick on the tower of Babel. Babel's head coach cheers us on, "Make a name for yourself! Make a name for yourself!"

Do you remember the approach the serpent took when he tempted Eve to eat the forbidden fruit? In essence he asked, "Why worship God when you could be one yourself?" (See Gen. 3:5.) Rest assured, Satan wrote all Babylonian doctrine. If he cannot get people to worship him outright, he'll convince people to worship themselves. Anything to insult the Great I Am.

"Eve, do what you want! You are, and there is none besides you!"

Yesterday we talked about the God-planted need in every human to have significance. Don't get the idea that God is most glorified when we are most nullified. One of the most beautiful summations of our life purpose in God's Word is in John 15:8,16.

What do these two verses say about God's desire for us?

We are to bear much fruit so God is glorified

We are meant to bear much fruit so God can be glorified—not us. God's refusal to share glory with us is for our good. Name a few reasons why.

I don't think we could handle it. It would go to our head. And pretty soon we would be part of the Babylonian doctrine

WE ARE MEANT TO BEAR MUCH FRUIT SO GOD CAN BE GLORIFIED.

Let's face it. Humans can't take it. We weren't wired to be worshiped. The magazine covers at grocery store checkouts are all the evidence you need to suggest the utter abnormality of media idols' lives. Nebuchadnezzar would have known their pain. He was on the top—the most powerful man alive on planet Earth at the time. Yet he was also among the least secure. We think we want to be on top, whether socially, professionally, athletically, or ministerially. Yet nothing breeds more insecurity. Kings like Nebuchadnezzar constantly demanded displays of loyalty because their positions were never secure. They lived in constant fear of insurrection.

No, you and I don't occupy thrones, but we may find ourselves at desks or in positions that bring out a surprising territorialism in us. Can you relate to what I'm describing? If so, how?

_____

_____

Our culturally indoctrinated brains need a fresh washing by the Word. Let's read James 3:13-16. List everything this segment says about selfish ambition.

Selfish ambition is earthly unspiritual and of the devil. Where you have selfish ambition you will find disorder & every evil practice

The world says, "Seek position!" The Word says, "Seek God!" If in our humble pursuit of God we find ourselves with a fleeting moment's position, it's a platform for God's glory. A sovereign trust. Matthew 6:33 tells us that if we give our entire lives to the pursuit of God, everything else of value will find us. We'll have a head-on collision with calling, a sense of purpose, satisfaction. You've been chosen, Dear One, by the God of all creation for a life worth living. And you feel inferior?

> *"Who is wise and understanding among you? Let him show it by his good life, by deeds done in the humility that comes from wisdom. But if you harbor bitter envy and selfish ambition in your hearts, do not boast about it or deny the truth. Such 'wisdom' does not come down from heaven but is earthly, unspiritual, of the devil. For where you have envy and selfish ambition, there you find disorder and every evil practice."*
>
> **JAMES 3:13**

DAY THREE THE APPLE OF HIS EYE

Today's Treasure: *But there are some Jews whom you have set over the affairs of the province of Babylon—Shadrach, Meshach, and Abednego—who pay no attention to you, O king. Daniel 3:12*

Today we move slightly forward in our broader look at the third chapter of Daniel. After prayer please pick up your reading with Daniel 3:8-12. Picture the scene vividly. Place yourself in the room as the astrologers come before King Nebuchadnezzar and denounce the Jews. Consider verse 12 most carefully.

55

Describe how you imagine the sound of their tone.

Indignation - offended that they would disobey their beloved King

What do you believe was their motive?

Jealousy

The word "denounced" in verse 8 means "ate the pieces of."[2] The translation provides a disturbing visual, doesn't it? In effect, the astrologers were trying to kill the three with their words. We have a New Testament verse that draws a similar picture.

What does Galatians 5:15 warn will happen if people don't cease "biting and devouring each other"?

They will be destroyed by each other

Years ago we had to give our beloved dachshund, Coney, to an elderly couple because she bit small children. When she bit the first child, Keith warned me that a second bite would mean she had to go. Needless to say, she bit again. We cried, but Keith stood firm. He explained that once a dog saw how quickly someone would retreat with a bite, it could rapidly form a habit we couldn't count on breaking. I am convinced that "biting and devouring" in relationships is also rapidly habit forming, particularly if, like Coney, the biter gets the desired reaction.

What kind of reactions might biters and devourers (with words) be seeking?

Attn; importance, popularity, especially in Job Market "I'm a better and more loyal worker than him."

Keith and I used to bite and devour each other with words during heated conflicts. In fact, I'm sure each of us still has a scar or two from an old bite. By that I mean something said that hurt badly enough not to be forgotten.

 Do you have scars from word-bites? ☒ yes ☐ no

If so, what have you done about them?
☒ grown bitter   ☐ ended the relationship   ☒ forgiven them
☐ accepted them   ☒ bitten back   ☐ other _____

Back then, Keith could win a fight with his temper while I could win a fight with my words. Needless to say, neither was a win. At least one of us was always left emotionally bloody. I vividly recall him saying to me, "You may say it better, but that doesn't make you right." I was convicted to the core. Somewhere along the way Keith and I no longer got any satisfaction out of hurting each other. Today if one of us thinks we've hurt the other's feelings, we're sick at heart until we're forgiven.

I asked you earlier what you've done with the scars left from word-bites. Keith and I had to talk some of them out many years after the actual bite. Often the other had no idea the words still echoed. I have scars from other word-bites I'm not in a position to talk out with the biter. Those require the healing balm of Christ alone. You may feel silly talking to Him about something said years ago, but keep in mind that He knows you well enough to be fully aware it's still an issue.

Unlike the scene in Daniel 3, biting and devouring is probably most common within family walls. Why might this be true? *Because people all secure that the family won't stop loving them whereas if you did it outside of the family you might lose a job & certainly would lose some friends.*

Among other reasons, word-bites are probably most common within families because we think relatives will love us enough to keep putting up with them. Biting and devouring one another is an unhealthy and miserable way to live. We don't need to just keep putting up with it. We need to be healed.

To heal permanently, however, we have to break old habits and make new ones. I was impressed recently by a mom who came to the end of her rope with some biting and devouring in her home. She announced to her family that they were about to form new habits of communication. She explained that, of course, they'd still disagree, but they could find less destructive ways to do it. They discussed as a family what a few of those less destructive ways would be and drew up a set of game rules. A few days ago, she told me they were on day 18 of practicing new forms of communication. How wise for her to treat verbal biting like the addiction it is!

Does her example speak to you personally in any way? If so, how?

Just to be careful how I say things (how I word things)

Daniel 3:8 and Galatians 5:15 both draw pictures of biting words, but please note an important difference. Galatians 5:15 portrays people biting each other. In Daniel 3:8, the biting was strictly one-sided. Shadrach, Meshach, and Abednego had no idea they were being eaten alive. Even when they were made aware several verses later, they still didn't bite back. We have a term for one-sided biting. It's called *backbiting*. That's something sons and daughters of Babylon do. You and I want no part of it. Backbiting is just as habit-forming as back-and-forth biting.

If we're people who enjoy talking about others behind their backs, yet we're realizing how unpleasing it is to God, how could we apply our sister's example in the previous paragraph for breaking a backbiting habit?

Talk to the Lord about it instead of others

The astrologers weren't just biting any backs. They were very intentional about the backs they chose.

FORMING AND PRACTICING NEW AND HEALTHY HABITS IS A WISE WAY TO TREAT VERBAL BITING.

Daniel 3:8 specifies that they "came forward and denounced the _Jews_."

Daniel 3:12 reeks with attitude: "There are ___Some Jews___ whom *you have set* over the affairs of the province of Babylon" (emphasis mine).

Don't miss their blatant charge of the king's poor judgment. They knew if they could convince him that the Jews had made a fool of him, he'd react violently. Several of my commentaries point out the strong probability of anti-Semitism in this scene. *The New American Commentary* says, "These astrologers expressed great hostility toward 'the Jews.' Although personal jealousy was likely the primary motive for the astrologers' animosity, anti-Semitism may have been involved."[3] Shadrach, Meshach, and Abednego were not just men who had somehow raised the ire of the astrologers. They were Jews. Their accusers intentionally made nationality an issue. One of my Jewish commentaries reads, "the fine distinction between the single Jew and the whole Jewish People has always eluded anti-Semites."[4]

How is this statement true of all prejudice?

_____

Satan authors all anti-Semitism. He has been driven through the ages by two motivations. First he knew the Messiah would come through God's chosen nation, so he tried everything possible to destroy them. The second reason explains why the attack continued after Christ's coming: Satan hates God and since he cannot touch Him personally, he tries to hurt Him by hurting those He loves. Recently I watched a PBS special on Auschwitz. I was stunned and sickened all over again by man's capacity for evil. One of the scholars spoke of the inability to bring any kind of peace or conclusion to it because it portrayed such hopelessness. Though I shared the horror, I stopped short of hopelessness. Death is not the last word. A sovereign, powerful God sits upon His throne, and nothing misses His gaze. He will right all wrongs. I do not know how, but I know Who.

As you conclude today's lesson, please read Zechariah 2:7-9.

GOD IS ON HIS THRONE, AND HE WILL RIGHT ALL WRONGS.

"The Lord Himself (i.e., as the Angel of the Lord or as the Messiah) speaks in verses 8-9, though some interpreters refer parts of this statement to Zechariah's explanation of his prophetic call."[5] A point of interest for us is the reference to the "Daughter of Babylon" in this segment. Of course, God's defense stands against any foe.

Applying the figure of speech used in Zechariah 2:8, whoever touched Shadrach, Meshach, and Abednego, people of His chosen nation, also touched ___the apple of God's eye___

Think of the apple of an eye as the pupil. How quickly would you notice something touching the pupil of your eye?

Immediately

✳ Dear One, if you have received Christ, you are the spiritual seed of Abraham. (See ✳ Gal. 3:29.) Nothing touches you without touching His eye. Nothing bites you without Him feeling it. He sees. He knows. He acts. And, best of all, He heals.

DAY FOUR THE HEART OF LOYALTY

Today's Treasure: *Shadrach, Meshach and Abednego replied to the king, "O Nebuchadnezzar, we do not need to defend ourselves before you in this matter." Daniel 3:16*

Greetings, Apple of God's Eye. I hope you're feeling cherished and fought for today. Your God is for you, Dear One. Your battle is the Lord's. I'm looking forward to our study today. We'll move to the next segment in our chapter and take a look at the verses we discussed in video session 3 from an additional angle.

Read Daniel 3:13-23. Glance back at your notes from the session and record a new insight you received specifically pertaining to this segment of Scripture.

_____

_____

Look at the response of Shadrach, Meshach, and Abednego in verse 16. Paraphrase their words to the King: _We don't have to defend ourselves to You, we stand before an audience of One—the true God!_

The three young men didn't step aside for an emergency meeting to try to get on the same emotional page and then present a formal statement. We also don't get the feeling from the text that they prepared their defense prior to being dragged before the king. For people with true conviction, certain decisions have already been made. "We do not need to defend ourselves before you in this matter." No amount of discussion would change one simple fact: they would not bow. No matter what.

Like me, you probably respected them even more for their conviction when you realized the bonfire was so close, you could have seen the flames in the reflection of their eyes. Imagine being on a mission trip witnessing personally to the lost in a country where evangelism is treated as a criminal offense. Upon incarceration you are told that if you don't renounce Christ, you'll be tortured. How much harder would maintaining your convictions be if they took you to the actual torture chamber to make the threat?

Recently I squirmed all over the couch next to Keith while he watched the movie *Braveheart* for the umpteenth time. A man-flick if I've ever seen one. And, no, I don't like R-rated movies, but Keith has overruled me on a few war films. He loves them. Go figure. I always cover my eyes and plug my ears with my fingers during the part where William Wallace, the undisputed leader of the Scottish resistance (played by Mel Gibson), is tortured for neither renouncing his stand nor begging for mercy.

The preceding scene where he is praying alone in his cell is one of the most moving parts of the film. He knows he is about to be tortured, knows the pain will be nearly unendurable, and openly admits his fear to God. To me, his willingness to give himself to it is more impressive precisely because he is afraid. History's heroes are neither superhuman nor fearless. Shadrach, Meshach, and Abednego were bravehearts long before William Wallace painted his face blue. They had to yell "no!" to powerful King Nebuchadnezzar over the roar of the nearby crackling fire.

While preparing for a Sunday School lesson a while back, I stumbled across the meaning of a word that stirred me and caused me to think. It describes the three young men in Daniel 3 perfectly. Before you read the Scripture segment, grasp the context: King David is nearing his life's end. As his final act of public worship, he has requested and received offerings for the construction of the temple. The segment you'll read is part of David's prayer for his son, Solomon, heir to the throne, and for the Israelites who would serve under his reign.

Now, please read 1 Chronicles 29:17-19.

As you know by now, integrity is the theme of part 1 of our study. The NIV renders the actual word integrity in verse 17, but all of the translations convey the idea.

List everything you learn about integrity from 1 Chronicles 29:17.

Our hearts are tested to prove our integrity

I relish the appearance of the word "integrity" in 1 Chronicles 29:17, but the word that caught my attention in preparation for my class is in the next verse.

Fill in the blank according to 1 Chronicles 29:18.
"O Lord, God of our fathers Abraham, Isaac and Israel, keep this desire in the

hearts of your people forever, and keep their hearts _*loyal*_ to you."

 Based on your own understanding, how would you define *loyalty*?

_____

_____

Your definition may correspond with a part of the definition of the original Hebrew word. Give it close consideration: "to be firm, be established, be steadfast, be faithful, be sure, be reliable, be fixed, be certain; to be ready, be prepared; to be determined … Signifies initial preparation or formation, actual preparation for a future event."[6]

Now circle any part of the definition that provides fresh insight to you.

Godly loyalty meant many of the things I imagined, but the part of the definition that spoke fresh truth to me was the element of preparation: "be prepared." Think about this for a long moment: *loyal* is not something we suddenly are at the flash-moment of testing. It's something we already were that surfaces in the test. Stay with me here. Loyalty, therefore, means that when a sudden temptation poses a character question, if we have true conviction in that area, we do not have to consider how we'll answer it. Loyalty means the question has already been answered. We simply act upon it.

You and I don't claim to be Christian supermodels, but surely we have some questions we've answered in advance. For instance, I don't have to wonder what I'd do if placed in the position to die in order for one of my children to live. No discussion. No need to pray about it. It's done. No matter how painful the death, the question is already answered. For those of us who are parents, my example was probably too easy.

What other question have you answered before circumstance poses it?

Dabble in the occult, sexual relationship outside of marriage, steal something

At times like these I so wish I were in the same small group with you. I'd love to know what you just wrote. Let's stay on this same line of thinking with another prodding consideration. Absolutely no condemnation or super-spiritualization is meant by the question I'm about to ask. We are in this Bible study by the thousands, and each of us comes from a different background, pace, length, and depth of relationship with God. You may be just beginning to get to know Him, and deep bonds of loyalty haven't had time to grow. The reason I'm posing the following question is to invite you into Shadrach, Meshach, and Abednego's position.

Here goes: *Have you predetermined your loyalty to Christ?* In other words, have you already answered the question in your own heart and mind about whether anything could make you turn away from Him? Could any circumstance (such as an unhealed disease, unanswered prayer, loss of a loved one, an incarceration in a country where Christianity is illegal, or other situations) make you renounce your faith in Christ?

Important to ponder-e

I'm not going to give you a space to write the answer because this question is meant for your own private meditation. The question is posed not only to invite our firm resolve in Christ but also to consider that until we resolve certain things, Satan will threaten us unmercifully.

In the margin describe several ways the Evil One could take advantage of us if we haven't resolved the issue of our loyalty to God.

convince us that God doesn't love us - "If He were a loving God He wouldn't allow this to happen.

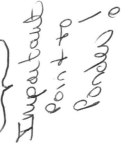

LOYAL IS SOMETHING WE ALREADY WERE THAT SURFACES IN THE TEST.

61

SATAN
MOST OFTEN
TEMPTS US IN
OUR AREAS
OF LEAST
RESISTANCE.

The enemy did everything possible to tempt me to quit ministry. He knew I felt unworthy of it anyway, so I was easy prey. For a certain long season, he taunted and harassed me unrelentingly until I almost couldn't take it anymore. One day I overheard my own words to Keith almost as if they were coming from a stranger. "I don't think I want to do this anymore." Then it hit me. I don't usually talk straight to the Devil, but as soon as I regained some strength, I yelled, "You might as well stop it! I will never, ever, ever quit! You'll have to kill me, and then I'll just be home with Jesus. So, go ahead!" He's since tried to get to me in other areas where I didn't have equal resolve, but he doesn't often tempt me on this one any more. My mind was made up. Since then I've tried to follow suit in other areas.

Can you think of a way the enemy continues to threaten you personally because he is not yet convinced of your resolve? ☒ yes ☐ no
health, daughter

I'm sure the Enemy thought Carrie McDonnall was too young at 26 to have the steadfast loyalty to Christ that serving Him would require after her precious husband, David, was killed. The spray of automatic weapon fire descending on their vehicle that day in Iraq not only killed David but three other missionaries dearly loved by their families also lost their lives. Carrie alone survived—and not without devastating injuries. I just left her delightful company a few days ago where we shared a podium, ministering to a gathering of people.

I wonder how the enemy felt when Carrie walked across that stage, sharing her unwavering resolve and love for Christ to a cheering standing ovation. Caught in the snare he set for her, I hope. Through the power of the Holy Spirit, she infused every listener with the courage to persevere and to remain faithful to God, come what may. Satan underestimated Carrie's spiritual maturity. Obviously, some questions were already answered the day she received her call to Iraq. That's the loyalty of Shadrach, Meshach, and Abednego. Lord, make it ours.

DAY FIVE IF HE DOES NOT

Today's Treasure: *But even if he does not, we want you to know, O king, that we will not serve your gods or worship the image of gold you have set up. Daniel 3:18*

Our third week of study has flown by! I am thoroughly engrossed in the Book of Daniel. I hope you are, too. It gets even more exciting, but let's not get ahead of ourselves. We still need to wrap up week 3. Let's read the remainder of our chapter.

In your opinion, what is most amazing about the event in Daniel 3:24-30?

① Four men walking around in furnace (Jesus) We have a group of 4 in everyone - the Father Son & Holy Spirit ② There was no smell of smoke

What a fabulous account! It possesses every element of the greatest novella: the heartless, egomaniacal dictator; the scheming, manipulative coworkers; and a band of young men separated from their leader, leaving the reader to wonder, "Will they stand up to the test without him?" Yep, the third chapter of Daniel is a nail-biter down to the quick. Loyalty prevails, but who can survive that fire? Wait just a moment! What's that I see? Didn't we throw three men in the fire? Why do I see four?

Not only is Jesus the second Adam (1 Cor. 15:45), He's the fourth Man in the fire! Shadrach, Meshach, and Abednego are retrieved; and the egomaniacal king praises their God! Beloved, it just doesn't get any better than that. That's what you call a great ending. But what do you call an ending that seems anything but great? In session 3, we considered three different scenarios when people of God face a fiery trial. We need to reiterate these scenarios until we know them by heart.

If you participated in the session, please glance back at your notes and record each scenario and its dividend in the space that follows. If you were not able to participate, you'll find the scenarios and dividends listed on page 66. Writing these scenarios with your own pen will help you retain them.

Scenario A: _We are delivered from the fire_

Dividend: _Our faith is built_

Scenario B: _We can be delivered thru the fire._

Dividend: _Our faith is refined_

Scenario C: _We can be delivered from the fire unto His arms_ DEATH/LIFE!

Dividend: _Our faith is perfected_

Briefly describe a time you experienced either "Scenario A" or "Scenario B."

My faith is refined as I've struggled w/ health problems

That we're alive to take this Bible study tells me we haven't yet experienced "Scenario C." That's what our lesson is about today. From an earthly perspective, "Scenario C" is the path of most resistance. Let's explore further the question we posed in session 3: What if we're not delivered _from_ the fire like others have testified, nor delivered _through_ the fire like Shadrach, Meshach, and Abednego? What if we die in the fire? Where is the Fourth Man _then_?

What person of faith have you known who seemed to die in the "fire,"

whether from disease or sudden tragedy? _My brother - struck by lightning_

Did you, like most, question why? _No_

Have you ever been able to come up with an answer that was satisfying, at least to you? ☑ yes ☐ no If so, what was it?

God sees the whole picture & I don't but because I trust His love I trust him

In 1401 John Hus was ordained into the priesthood. He taught at Charles University in what is now the Czech Republic. Each week he preached to a packed house of roughly three thousand people at the Bethlehem Chapel in Prague. A follower of John Wycliffe, Hus was a vocal proponent of each person's inalienable right to read the Bible in his own language. He stood for the absolute authority of the Bible in the church and openly denounced immorality and extravagance in the lives of clergy. He was confined to a cell next to a sewer system and told to recant. Hus refused unless someone could prove him wrong through Scripture. He stated to the council, "I would not, for a chapel full of gold, recede from the truth."[7]

The furious council formally condemned Hus and turned him over to the civil authorities. "The executioners undressed Hus and tied his hands behind his back with ropes, and his neck with a chain to a stake around which wood and straw had been piled up so that it covered him to the neck. Still at the last moment, the imperial marshal, Von Pappenheim in the presence of the Count Palatine, asked him to save his life by a recantation, but Hus declined with the words _'God is my witness that I have never taught that of which I have been accused by false witnesses. In the truth of the Gospel which I have written, taught, and preached I will die to-day with gladness.'_ There upon the fire was kindled with John Wycliffe's own manuscripts used as kindling for the fire. With uplifted voice Hus sang, _'Christ, thou Son of the living God, have mercy upon me.'_ His ashes were gathered and cast into the nearby Rhine River."[8]

John Hus gladly died … but not a glad death. Are you familiar with the saying "we'll cook his goose"? The phrase was originally a reference to Hus, whose last name means "goose" in his native Czech.[9] Where was the Fourth Man in the fire?

In 1553 Queen Mary ascended the throne of England. Her name would go down in history as "Bloody Mary." "At least two hundred people were put to death for their religious convictions during her reign."[10] No few of them with great cruelty.

Last year I had the privilege of walking the streets of Oxford, England, where Bishops Hugh Latimer and Nicholas Ridley were taken in 1555 "to be examined by the Lord's Commissioner in Oxford's Divinity School."[11] The examination turned into a trial. Their crimes? Vocal insistence on a more biblical Christianity. They were examined over and over, "shamefully baited, teased, and tortured by every kind of unfair and unreasonable dealing." Still, "they gallantly fought a good fight to the end, and never gave way for a moment to their adversaries."[12]

On October 16, 1555, "they were brought separately to the place of execution, which was at the end of Broad Street, Oxford, close to Balliol College. Ridley arrived on the ground first, and seeing Latimer come afterwards, ran to him and kissed him, saying, 'Be of good, heart, brother; for God will either assuage the fury of the flames, or else strengthen us to abide it.' They then prayed earnestly, and talked with one another, though no one could hear what they said."[13]

Which of our scenarios did Ridley seem to describe to Latimer? ☐ A ☐ B ☒ C

As the ropes were harnessed around him, Ridley prayed, "Heavenly Father, I give unto Thee most hearty thanks that Thou hast called me to be a professor of Thee, even unto death. I beseech Thee, Lord God, have mercy on this realm of England, and deliver it from all her enemies."[14]

"Ridley's brother had brought some gunpowder for the men to place around their necks so death could come more quickly, but Ridley still suffered greatly. With a loud voice Ridley cried, 'Into thy hands, O Lord, I commend my spirit,' but the wood was green and burned only Ridley's lower parts without touching his upper body. He was heard to repeatedly call out, 'Lord have mercy upon me! I cannot burn … Let the fire come unto me, I cannot burn.' One of the bystanders finally brought the flames to the top of the pyre to hasten Ridley's death."[15]

Before Latimer died, he was heard encouraging Ridley, "Be of good comfort, Mr. Ridley, and play the man! We shall this day light such a candle by God's grace, in England, as I trust never shall be put out."[16]

Where was the Fourth Man in the fire? Before we try to answer that very difficult question, recall the definition of loyalty we expounded on in day 4. Describe loyalty in your own words:

> Knowing what you believe (are convicted of) & standing by that belief (or that person, especially the Lord)

🦁 How did these men exhibit loyalty?

John Hus: He stood for absolute authority of the bible in the church & openly denounced immorality & extravagance in the lives of clergy. He would not recant, & he was burned to death

Hugh Latimer and Nicholas Ridley: Vocal insistence on a more biblical Christianity. They fought to the end never giving in to their adversaries

Was God loyal to them? And if so, where was the Fourth Man in the fire? Right there with them, Beloved. Each man was flanked by the power and presence of God the Father, Son, and Holy Spirit. In heavenly mathematics, the sum total of those in the fire is always four: one believer plus a holy Trinity. Hus, Latimer, and Ridley were delivered, Dear One, straight from the fire into the heavenly kingdom of the Living God (2 Tim. 4:18). Reflect again on our definition of *loyalty*; and let's see if God, too, exhibits this kind of loyalty. In other words, has He already decided in advance of the question or circumstance to remain with us?

THE FOURTH MAN IS WITH US EVEN IN THE FLAMES.

Romans 8:38-39 answers the question beautifully. How do these two verses describe the predetermined loyalty of God?

Nothing will ever be able to separate us from the love of Christ.

GOD'S ULTIMATE GOAL IS FOR US TO ABIDE WITH HIM.

God always abides with us, but we are wise to remember that His ultimate goal is for us to abide with Him. *Literally.* Christ's own plea? "Father, I want those you have given me to be with me where I am" (John 17:24). At some point, Beloved, you and I are going home. He alone knows how. Sometimes God delivers us from the fire. Other times He delivers us through the fire. Still other times He delivers us by the fire into His arms.

What motivates the difference? Somehow and in some way, Beloved, glory is at stake. The last words of John Hus prophesied the coming of a firestorm of faith within one century that could not be quenched. His words proved true. Latimer and Ridley also died for causes that could not be extinguished. Our God is able to deliver us, Beloved. Every time! And how often He does! If ever He does not and the flames of death or tragedy consume us, it is to light a fire somewhere and in some heart that can never be extinguished. Trust Him to the death. Trust Him through the death. In the blink of an eye, we'll understand.

THREE SCENARIOS WHEN WE FACE TRIALS

Scenario A: We can be delivered from the fire. Dividend? Our faith is built.

Scenario B: We can be delivered through the fire. Dividend? Our faith is refined.

Scenario C: We can be delivered by the fire into His arms. Dividend? Our faith is perfected.

1. Stephen R. Miller, *Daniel,* vol. 18 of *The New American Commentary* (Nashville: Broadman & Holman, 2001), 111.
2. Ibid., 116.
3. Ibid.
4. Rabbi Hersh Goldwurm, *Daniel* (New York: Mesorah Publications, Ltd., 1998), 118.
5. John F. Walvoord and Roy B. Zuck, eds., *The Bible Knowledge Commentary of the Old Testament* (Wheaton, Ill. : SP Publications, Inc., 1985), 1553.
6. Spiros Zodhiates, ThD., gen. ed., *Lexical Aids to the Old Testament, Hebrew-Greek Key Word Study Bible, New International Version* (Chattanooga, TN: AMG Publishers), #3922, 1522-23.
7. "John Hus: Faithful Unto Death," *Christian History Institute* [online], [cited 21 January 2005]. Available from Internet: *http://chi.gospelcom.net/GLIMPSEF/Glimpses/glmps014.shtml.*
8. "English Bible History: John Hus," [online], [cited 21 January 2005]. Available from Internet: *www.greatsite.com.*
9. "John Hus: Faithful Unto Death."
10. "Ridley and Latimer at the Stake," *Christian History Institute* [online], [cited 21 January 2005]. Available from Internet: *www.chi.gospelcom.net.*
11. Ibid.
12. J.C. Ryle, "Why Were Our Reformers Burned?" from *Five English Reformers,* [online], [cited 21 January 2005]. Available from Internet: *www.williamtyndale.com.*
13. Ibid.
14. "Ridley and Latimer at the Stake."
15. Ibid.
16. Ibid.

FAREWELL
LESSONS
FROM
NEBUCHAD-
NEZZAR

4

4

SESSION FOUR
FAREWELL LESSONS FROM NEBUCHADNEZZAR

Today we proceed to one of the most astonishing chapters in the Book of Daniel. The lesson God has for us today is one we want to learn in the classroom and not on a field trip. Let's be particularly attentive, praising God for a perfect example of 1 Corinthians 10:6:

"Now these things occurred as examples to keep us from setting our hearts on evil things as they did."

Read the following segments of Daniel: *4:4-5,9-19,22,24-31.*

PART ONE: THE SET UP

Nebuchadnezzar's example waves two warning signs that we're being corrupted by our "Babylons."

1. We _lose touch_ with the _poor_ . Note the KJV translation:

"by _showing mercy_ to the _poor_ ."

Compare verses 4 and 27. The Aramaic word translated "showing mercy" (KJV) or "being kind" (NIV) corresponds to the Hebrew transliteration by the same spelling (*chanan*).

The Hebrew word means "to be favorable, be kind, be gracious; to pity, have mercy;

to bestow; to _complain_ ; to make _lovely_ "[1] (Isa. 58:10-11).

2. We lose touch with our own _poverty of spirit_ . (Matt. 5:3) See verse 30.

The "I" is emphatic in the Aramaic, meaning it would well translate, "I, _myself_ ."

Bottom line: The way _down_ is _up_ .

VIEWER GUIDE

PART TWO: THE FALL DOWN

1. God knows _where_ and when to _draw the line_. In *Daniel: God's Pattern for the Future,* author Charles R. Swindoll writes, "God's patience is geared toward our _repentance_ "[2] (see also Rom. 2:4; 2 Pet. 3:9). His patience, however, does _set limits_.

   Read Daniel 4:31-33. Various diagnoses have been offered through the years for Nebuchadnezzar's temporary condition. The two most common are lycanthropy and boanthropy.

   Please note: This is not a lesson about _____. This is a lesson about _____ _____. The theme of our lesson is stated succinctly in verse 37.

2. God's patience _set limits_ Thankfully, so does His _discipline._ (See v. 23.)

Conclude with Daniel 4:34-37.

Bottom line: The way _up_ is _down_

1. Warren Baker, Lexical Aids of *The Complete Word Study Old Testament* (Chattanooga, TN: AMG Publishers, 1994), #2604, #2603, 2316.
2. Charles Swindoll, *Daniel: God's Pattern for the Future* (Plano, TX: Insight for Living, 1996), 52.

DANIEL

WEEK FOUR
FAREWELL LESSONS FROM NEBUCHADNEZZAR

DAY 1
My Pleasure to Tell

DAY 2
The Lap of Luxury

DAY 3
Stubborn Minds

DAY 4
Stripped Leaves and Scattered Fruit

DAY 5
Break Off

Our fourth session introduced us to the final chapter involving King Nebuchadnezzar, Babylon's most powerful ruler. Many scholars approximate the timing of Daniel 4 at about 30 years following the episode in the fiery furnace. If the estimation is accurate, Daniel was about 50 years old and the king significantly older at this point in the saga. If you participated in session 4, you probably agree that the final lesson written on the chalkboard of Nebuchadnezzar's life was the most important.

What title would you give to this episode?

_____

God is called the "Most High" or the "Most High God" in the Book of Daniel first in the fourth chapter where it then echoes five more times. By the end of the week, we'll not wonder why. Please watch for each of the six occurrences throughout this week of study. As you come to each one, record the verse and any contextual insight into the name in the space below. I've included the first one as an example:

v. 2 *"The Most High God"* - *performs miraculous signs and wonders*

VS 17 " " " " - is sovereign over the kingdoms of men

VS 24 The Most High - _____

VS 25 " " " - _____

VS 32 " " " - _____

VS 34 " " " - _____

_____ - _____

THIS WEEK'S PRINCIPAL QUESTIONS

DAY 1 How did Nebuchadnezzar feel about sharing what God had done for him?

DAY 2 How does our culture define *contented* and *prosperous*?

DAY 3 How can you tell King Nebuchadnezzar still didn't get the picture (Dan. 4:8)?

DAY 4 Why was King Nebuchadnezzar so incomparable in his day (Dan. 2:37-38)?

DAY 5 What did Daniel advise King Nebuchadnezzar to do in verse 27?

DAY ONE MY PLEASURE TO TELL

Today's Treasure: *It is my pleasure to tell you about the miraculous signs and wonders that the Most High God has performed for me. Daniel 4:2*

Our very wise God knows how the human mind He created learns best. He instructs us in both Testaments not just through laws and commands but through the examples of human lives that hold mirrors to our own. A fitful child sitting in the worship service beside his mom might flip through her Bible to amuse himself, only to be disappointed over the lack of pictures. An adult seasoned in the Word realizes that Scripture is full of pictures: masterpiece portraits, as a matter of fact, of real, live flesh and blood people who encountered the Living God, whether they meant to or not. Ever the Teacher, God doesn't just tell. He shows.

Daniel 4 draws an unforgettable image of what can happen to a human—no matter how powerful, no matter the state of his relationship with God—when he allows his heart to swell with pride. Frankly, it sends shivers up my spine. As I shared with you in session 4, I've tasted just enough of this lesson to know that I never want another bite. I don't even want to smell the scent of it cooking. I'll take as many refresher courses as God's Word teaches. Anything to keep from taking another field trip through my own experience! How about you? Then let's learn our lessons well this week.

Let's begin by reading Daniel 4:1-3. These words of acclamation followed a hard lesson learned. Nebuchadnezzar shares the lesson in verses 4-37, but verse 1 describes his audience. To whom was his testimony addressed?

To the peoples, nations, and men of every language who lived in all the world
"THE Whole World"

No one rich or poor, powerful or oppressed, healthy or infirm, enslaved or free, male or female, old or young, from east or west, of color or not, is exempt from the temptation to dangerous pride. "To the peoples … who live in all the world." Pride is not a circumstance. It's a state of mind. It's an equal opportunity agent of Satan—his absolute specialty. We can become as proud of our self-discipline, sacrificial giving, and self-denial as of our worldly successes and goods. A good friend in ministry told me something that I've always remembered. Embarrassed, I admitted to her that I had never participated in a 40-day fast of juice and water like so many others had. She said, "Beth, I'm sure there are many exceptions to what I'm about to say, but I've rarely seen anybody emerge from a 40-day fast who wasn't sooner or later proud of it. Isn't the enemy sly?" she said. "He will try to take the very thing meant to instill humility and twist it into pride." Ouch!

Please don't misunderstand. God has ordained that some breakthroughs have such satanic opposition, they only come by prayer coupled with fasting. The point is not that we cast the disciplines aside so that we can be humbled by our consistent

NO ONE IS EXEMPT FROM THE DANGEROUS TEMPTATION OF PRIDE.

defeat. God forbid! The point is recognizing that different things inflate pride in different people. Satan sets the bait according to the bite. Worldly Christians are snared by things like power, money, appearance, and position. Any one of these could find its way into ministry as easily as secular business. In more "spiritual" people, Satan will use spiritual bait like smugness over spiritual disciplines. A wife who studies Scripture in-depth must be very careful that she doesn't develop a superiority complex over a husband who doesn't. Likewise, a woman who, through Christ, has broken free from an area of bondage must guard herself from haughtiness and pride toward those still in process.

Offer your own example of a sly way the enemy can tempt a "spiritual" believer to pride. *Teaching a Bible Study, Speaking at a retreat, etc.*

Some egos are swollen over what they do. Other egos are swollen over what they don't. Most of us are tempted by one of the traps more than the other. Whether or not you fall into the pride trap, just between you and God, which is your bigger temptation: what you do (performance) or what you don't (abstinence)? This exercise is to help us recognize where Satan has the most success in us as individuals. You may leave the answer blank, but if you're willing to answer, try to also explain why one is the bigger snare for you.

My bigger temptation to pride is: ☒ performance ☐ abstinence

because *I guess I like the positive feedback as I didn't receive it as a child.*

Nebuchadnezzar's proclamation came from the vantage point of hindsight. In other words, he issued his testimony to "the peoples … in all the world" after his sanity was restored. Somewhat tongue in cheek, I'd like to suggest that the best time for a public testimony tends to be after we're thinking straight again. I have heard and unfortunately given some testimonies at times of such naked emotion that the recipients may have been more horrified than edified. At the very least, they were confused by the ramblings of a woman who had not yet dealt with the situation enough to get her own clarity from God. Let alone make sense of it to an audience.

Have you ever given a testimony that was perhaps a bit premature? ☐ yes ☒ no

Heard one? ☒ yes ☐ no

We are wise to be particularly careful about sharing testimonies of a sexual nature (whether in the context of past sin or abuse) in groups of both men and women. Author Norman Grubb suggests using "veiled language" in mixed company, calling to my mind the veil that once hung between men and women in synagogues. While no veil hangs between us in our places of worship now, the concept of veiled language creates a memorable image for appropriate times.

If you've heard premature testimonies, you might agree that a platform for testimony is sturdiest when built over a little time spent healing.

🦁 Please note Nebuchadnezzar's wording in verse 2 and fill in the blank:

"It is my ___pleasure___ to tell you about the miraculous signs and wonders that the Most High God has performed for me."

Nebuchadnezzar's newfound humility was already showing. You see, in order to testify to God's greatness and power, he had to show himself foolish. Indeed, beastly. Recently I read Psalm 73:21-22 in *Today's English Version,* and its wording invited me to relate to Nebuchadnezzar. "When my thoughts were bitter and my feelings were hurt, I was as stupid as an animal." I may not have looked as animal-like as Nebuchadnezzar, but I have acted as stupid as an animal over my bitterness and hurt. Do I have any company in this?

We're tempted not to 'fess up, but sometimes others around us need to know there is life after foolishness or failure. For the hearers to think as highly as they ought of God, Nebuchadnezzar risked their thinking lowly of him. Still, he gave the testimony with pleasure. As will be true of others toward us, we're never more impressed with Babylon's king than when he was least impressed with himself.

Are we as willing to take the risk of looking foolish to share a powerful testimony? Let's think this over together. Have we not seen God "high and lifted up" most often when our self-exaltation tumbled down? Our greatest purpose in life is to glorify God: to make Him famous in our lands. Isaiah 26:8 says it perfectly: "Your name and renown are the desire of our hearts." A testimony is a powerful way to make God famous in our sphere of influence. In order to do their jobs, our testimonies must be carefully filtered of subtle and sometimes accidental self-glorifications. You may have heard a testimony that left you wondering whether God or the giver was exalted. I would be horrified if someone thought that of me after I shared my testimony. Wouldn't you?

OUR GREATEST PURPOSE IN LIFE IS TO GLORIFY GOD.

Food for thought: Do you think a testimony that ended up glorifying the giver as much or more than God was intended to do such? ☐ yes ☒ no

If your answer is no, how do you think it happens?

We all deal w/ pride & because we live in a world that judges you by your accomplishments, it's easy to get off track

In the introduction to our study, I shared with you that I've just gotten a new Bible. I didn't share with you, however, why I got it. I think it might apply about now. Melissa, a straight shooter if you'll ever meet one, took a look at my Sword one day and said, "Mom! Get a new Bible! Yours looks like you study it a lot!" You see, we can even unintentionally give a lofty impression of ourselves to others with well-worn Bible study tools! We never want a listener or a watcher to wonder who we intended to look big. From heaven's perspective, we never stand taller than when we bow down to lift God up. Only God's tape measure records more inches from the knees to the head than the feet to the head.

At the same time, in our attempt to humble ourselves and willingly look foolish, we can get too graphic and still take the attention away from God. Sharing too much can also have a strong tendency to glorify man rather than God. You see, the essence of giving glory is drawing attention. If our testimonies are so graphic that they steal the attention from the point (God's greatness), they cheat Him of glory, however unintentionally. Keep in mind that Nebuchadnezzar's season of insanity in all likelihood lasted seven years, yet he described it in one paragraph (see v. 33). Some of us, yours truly included, would have written a mini-series! Relatively speaking, Nebuchadnezzar told us just enough to convey the seriousness of his estate, strike the fear of God in us, and magnify the throne of heaven.

Do you get my point? If so, say it in your own words:

_____

T.M.I. Some testimonies simply contain too much information. If a detail will paint a graphic picture in permanent ink in the listener's head, we might need to leave it out. We want one thing permanently painted on the mind of our listener: the greatness of God.

 Beloved, if you have known God for long or, like Nebuchadnezzar, known about God for long, you have a testimony. Somebody needs to hear it. By any chance, is your testimony one that risks your looking foolish? Mine is!

If your answer is yes, describe in generalities how.

_____

_____

Does it make God look big? Wise? Powerful? If so, how?

Yes shows that He is big (sovereign—in total control) wise—gives wisdom to those who ask

If God presented you with the opportunity to share this testimony, whether one-on-one or with a small group, would you be willing to look foolish for God to be magnified and another life edified? ☒ yes ☐ no

IN GOD'S ECONOMY, THE WAY UP IS DOWN.

When you begin to see fruit, Dear One, you will increasingly not only be willing, like Nebuchadnezzar, you will be pleased. In God's economy, the way up is down. When measured from our knees to the tips of our heads, Beloved, we keep getting taller.

DAY TWO THE LAP OF LUXURY

Today's Treasure: *I, Nebuchadnezzar, was at home in my palace, contented and prosperous. Daniel 4:4*

Let's start today's lesson with a couple of personal questions to prepare us for our study. Think about when you were young, perhaps a teenager, when you first began to have serious thoughts about how you wanted your life to turn out.

What kind of goals did you have for life? In other words, what was your idea of personal success?

To have a good job, make a good salary, travel,

Have your life goals or ideas of success changed at all since that time? ☒ yes ☐ no If so, how? *Personal success will be when I died others will say she was a woman who walked w/ God!*

I'm not sure Daniel's Babylon will offer us a more blatant opportunity to compare cultures than the one in this lesson. Today we continue our look at the intriguing fourth chapter of Daniel. Tomorrow we will consider a much longer portion of Scripture, but for now I'd like to draw your attention primarily to one verse that is replete with meaning.

Please complete Daniel 4:4. "I Nebuchadnezzar was *at home in my palace, contented & prosperous.*

Contented and prosperous. Who could ask for anything more? In Babylon, life doesn't get any better than that. Nor does it to most Americans, for that matter. Before we look at the meanings of the Aramaic words translated *contented* and *prosperous,* explain how you think our culture defines each.

Contented: *happy & at peace*

Prosperous: *wealthy*

The intention of the word "contented" in Daniel 4:4 very likely encompasses what you've described. *The New American Commentary* adds further insight: " 'Contented' is a translation of the Aramaic word *seleh,* which means properly 'at ease' or 'at rest,' conveying both contentment and security."[1]

The added dimension of "security" is well worth our further attention. Let's just spread out a blanket and sit down with it for a minute. As women, I'm not sure we yearn for anything more consistently than security. Yes, we have a ferocious need for love, but we find even the most passionate romance almost unbearable if it is riddled with insecurity and uncertainty. Many of us would choose security even over contentment. I can't think of anything I've searched the world to find any more vehemently. I was an insecure child who grew into an insecure adult and made at least a hundred insecure decisions, some of which still cost me.

How about you? Describe the premium you have placed on security through the course of your life and why.

Because I didn't feel secure in my home life when I married, I wanted to feel loved & accepted which would have made me feel secure

Were you more successful in your pursuit of security than I was? Frankly, nothing on earth has eluded me more, and the misguided search has led me to the pit more than once. Nebuchadnezzar thought he'd found security in Babylon. When we intertwine the two concepts of contentment and security wrapped up in the Aramaic word *seleh,* we picture a life that has finally discovered a means of security in which it can contentedly rest.

Recently a dear young woman voiced a concern to me about a friend her age. The friend is living with a man significantly older and who holds little physical attraction for her, but, simply put, he is rich. "He seems like a nice enough guy, but he is nothing like I've ever seen her date. What in the world is she doing?" Looking for security, that's what. If she could count on it to last, we might be tempted to bid her best wishes, but we know better. Oh, the money might last, but the sense of earthly security doesn't. Soon we grow insecure with our present means of security and demand something more … or something different. All this world and its inhabitants can offer us is a false and fleeting sense of security.

How does David's state of mind in Psalm 30:6 remind you of Nebuchadnezzar's in Daniel 4:4? *David felt secure in the Lord. Nebuchadnezzar felt secure in temporal things*

Hebrews 12:26-29 echoes the trouble with dependence on earthly securities. Read these verses and think conceptually. Why does God allow or appoint things in our worlds to "shake" at times? *So that we will recognize what is truly important*

Sometimes we don't recognize true security until all lesser forms prove false. I have a wonderful husband who would give me the world, but he cannot give me security. Neither can more money or more possessions. The human need for security is deeper and wider than anything the oceans of this earth can fill. Until our worlds quake and things start to shatter, we have no idea what lasts.

How does Psalm 62:1-2 beautifully convey the concepts of authentic *seleh*?

The only place we can truly experience contentment + security is when Jesus is the center of our lives. All temporal things can be shaken but nothing can shake the Lord.

Nebuchadnezzar had learned the hard way that he couldn't even trust his own mind. Let's turn our attentions briefly to Nebuchadnezzar's second description. (Fill in the blank.)

"I, Nebuchadnezzar, was at home in my palace,

contented and __*prosperous*__" (Dan. 4:4).

"'Prosperous' renders the Aramaic *ra'enan*, 'flourishing,' and corresponds to the biblical Hebrew *ra'anan*, 'luxuriant,' which is used to describe luxuriant or flourishing trees."[2] We'll discuss the correlation to trees tomorrow, but for now please specifically focus on the word *luxuriant*. Nebuchadnezzar was feeling fat and sassy, napping in the lap of luxury.

Beloved, we've just had a head-on collision with the definition of high life in Babylon: lazing in the lap of luxury. As addictive as cocaine, one little snort of luxury and we decide we were born for it. Princesses at heart. Actually, those of us in Christ are princesses at heart but not in the kingdoms of this world. The kingdom we call home is coming to earth with a smiting Rock not cut by human hands. (See Dan. 2.) Until then, if we're not careful, we can confuse the pursuit of life with the pursuit of luxury. We develop a taste for it quickly; and when it's withheld, we cry foul.

In our own Babylon, some of us are wrapped in such luxury that we think a chemical peel is a fiery trial. Babylon's heads of state stomp their feet and cry, "Give me luxury, or give me death!"

WE ARE PRINCESSES BUT NOT IN THE KINGDOMS OF THIS WORLD.

In relative terms, most of us doing this Bible study are counted among the prosperous on planet Earth. Many of us have tasted luxury at one time or another, even if it was as a visitor on someone else's turf. Describe your own biggest brush with outright luxury.

Taking a cruise where I was waited on & I never had to ask for anything - It was just taken care of

Some of us don't just visit luxury. We live at its address. One way or the other, we Westerners live on what is arguably the most lavish soil in the world. And we have some stuff, don't we? I laughed as I heard my friend Luci Swindoll describe her move into a new home and the insurmountable number of boxes she'd simply labeled "stuff." Most of us can totally relate, but here's the question on the table today: is it just stuff?

On a scale of 1 to 10, how important is our stuff? Could we take it or leave it? Release it without a fit if we had to? Or has it corrupted us? Addicted us? In twenty years of speaking, I've stayed in every kind of lodging from roach motels to citadels. Every now and then I've laughed and thought to myself, "Now, this is living!" But I know better. And so do you.

Beloved, what is real living in your opinion?

Having an intimate relationship w/my Savior, knowing that He is in control and that He loves me more than I can imagine & He has a wonderful plan for my life

Let's conclude our lesson by looking at an ironic blessing Nebuchadnezzar spoke over his audience in verse 1. "May you prosper greatly!" And yet he began the testimony of his cataclysmic descent with the words, "I, Nebuchadnezzar, was at home in my palace, contented and prosperous." God unapologetically desires to prosper His children spiritually (John 15:8), but today's lesson throws the spotlight on the temporal kind.

You and I naturally want the best for our loved ones. We pray for them to excel, to win, to succeed, to prosper, to be kept from difficulty and certainly pain. Yet, if God answered our every prayer for their ease, could they handle it? Would their lives ever mean—as my grandmother would say—more than a hill of beans?

More than anything else, O God, we pray that You would prosper our loved ones with an abundance of You! If they can handle some ease and earthly success in the process, so be it! But whatever You do, O God, insist that they live. Really live. "The thief cometh not, but for to steal, and to kill, and to destroy: [You have] come that [we] might have life, and that [we] might have it more abundantly" (John 10:10, KJV). O Lord, make us courageous enough to pray that no earthly luxury would ever cheat us of true prosperity.

Important!

> **O GOD, WE PRAY THAT YOU WOULD PROSPER OUR LOVED ONES WITH AN ABUNDANCE OF YOU!**

DAY THREE STUBBORN MINDS

Today's Treasure: *Finally, Daniel came into my presence and I told him the dream. (He is called Belteshazzar, after the name of my god, and the spirit of the holy gods is in him.) Daniel 4:8*

If you were able to participate in this week's video session, you will recall references in Daniel 4 to Nebuchadnezzar's second dream. Today we'll perform a quick review and pour some foundation; then we'll start analyzing the dream tomorrow. Remember, over thirty years have passed since King Neb's first prophetic dream recorded in Daniel 2.

Hopefully the first dream is fairly fresh on your mind since it was our subject matter throughout week 2. The slower, steadier pace of this particular study (twelve chapters in eleven weeks) affords us the opportunity to get to know this material like the back of our hands. We want God to infuse these truths into the depths of our inner beings, causing this book of the Bible to make itself at home in us (see John 15:7). This pace offers a wonderful opportunity for a Colossians 3:16 kind of work, inviting "the word of Christ" to "dwell in [us] richly." Rich words! That's the kind of prosperity you and I want to seek.

Repetition and the deliberate practice of recollection are vital if we want God's Word to abide and remain a storehouse of riches in us long after we conclude our study. So, how about a quick pop quiz on the first dream before we further absorb the second? What was that? I didn't quite hear your answer. I'm going to assume you responded with a hearty affirmation, so here goes!

The following questions and exercises will refer to Nebuchadnezzar's first dream recorded in Daniel 2. At first, try your hardest to exercise your mind and not look back at the chapter or your previous notes. Give yourself time to see if the Holy Spirit will jog your memory (see John 14:26). Reading through all of the questions first will provide plenty of hints. After you answer as much as possible from memory, by all means take a guilt-free glance back at Daniel 2 and any of your notes.

What image was in Nebuchadnezzar's first dream?

A large statue

What kinds of metals or materials comprised the image?

Gold silver iron bronze & baked clay & iron

Recall to the best of your ability the parts of the statue's "body" made up of each of those materials: *Head - gold, the chest & arms - silver the belly & thighs - bronze, legs - iron, feet - baked clay & iron*

You may remember that each of the materials from the head to the foot of the statue represented Gentile world empires. Do your best to remember all four of the empires and write them in order in this space.

Head - Babylonian Empire - Nebuchadnezzar
Chest - Medo-persian Empire - Cyrus the Great
Belly & Thighs - Grecian Empire Alexander the Great
Legs - Roman Empire - Augustus, Tiberius, Nero
(Feet - Divided Roman Empire)

Beside the name of each empire in the previous question, write something you recall or associate with each one based on session 2.

Now, most importantly, what is the significance of the rock in the dream?

It represents the kingdom of the Lord Jesus Christ

Very good! See there, you remembered more than you thought you would! You may be annoyed at me right now, but I am devoted to studying God's Word with you and to each of us getting the very most out of our study. And, yes, I'll probably keep annoying you with repetition, and I'll tell you why. Along the way, I've studied some truths in God's Word that are as fresh today as they were when I received them. I could tell you almost verbatim the 10-chapter outline of several Bible studies God has allowed me to write. They abide all the way in my subconscious where my deepest feelings and motivations are stirred and changed. They dislodge lies I've believed since childhood and replace them with truth.

Through this process of mind renewal, I don't just make different decisions for a season. I become entirely different for a lifetime. I'd be willing to bet my brain is "blonder" than yours. If God can cause His Word to dwell richly in me, He can cause His Word to dwell richly in anyone! Ask Him to perform miracles over your mind and to utterly invade your subconscious.

Let's move forward now toward King Nebuchadnezzar's second prophetic dream, stopping short of the description. Please read Daniel 4:4-9.

The king's immediate response to his second dream was similar to that of his first. He summoned his wise men, but they were unable to interpret the dream. This time, however, we see no threat of cutting them into pieces and turning their houses into piles of rubble.

What might have happened to King Nebuchadnezzar as he aged?

It seems as though like many, he has mellowed w/age

Some things about Nebuchadnezzar had obviously changed. For instance, he appears to have mellowed somewhat. Other things were unfortunately much the same.

 Read Daniel 4:8 carefully. Based on his descriptions of Daniel, how can you tell that King Nebuchadnezzar still didn't get the picture?

When he said that Daniel was named after his god & the spirit of the holy gods is in him.

Nebuchadnezzar could not seem to dislodge his polytheistic thinking. You see, the truth that Daniel's God is the one and only God had never taken root in the inmost places of Neb's heart, transforming even his subconscious values and beliefs. In his estimation, he greatly honored the God of Daniel by ascribing Him as higher than all other gods. Daniel must have been frustrated beyond description at times. You may have experienced something similar.

Have you ever felt you'd made tremendous progress with someone regarding his or her understanding of spiritual matters, only to realize at times that he or she still didn't get the picture? ☒ yes ☐ no

If so, what did you end up doing? *I stepped back & got out of God's way. He brought a neighbor who talked to her a couple of times & then He gave me the privilege of being the vessel to Holy Spirit worked thru*

Sometimes God releases us after a season. Other times He calls us to remain a voice of truth in someone's ear long after the last glimmer of effectiveness. Daniel hung in there with King Nebuchadnezzar. If Daniel knew anything at all about his God, he knew He was sovereign. Yes, even over the mind of the king. That much was obvious. Like Daniel, we are also powerless to force spiritual understanding on another person. We can encourage, teach, and urge, but we can't make them "get it."

How can we turn the concept conveyed in Luke 24:45 into a powerful prayer for the person we're urging toward truth? Write a prayer in this space for someone you know without necessarily using his or her name.

_____

_____

_____

_____

_____

_____

Imagine, every time a person gains understanding of scriptural truths, the entire Godhead has been at work. God the Father must ordain it, the Son must open it, and the Holy Spirit must infuse it. The intentional and miraculous work of the Godhead in one individual brain! Now, that's amazing! Weren't we also hardheaded at one time? And look who's studying Scripture! Thank Him for the miracles taking place in you right now, and keep praying those same miracles over the mind of another.

DAY FOUR STRIPPED LEAVES & SCATTERED FRUIT

Today's Treasure: *He called in a loud voice: "Cut down the tree and trim off its branches; strip off its leaves and scatter its fruit." Daniel 4:14*

Yesterday we talked about King Nebuchadnezzar's obvious inability to get the full picture of God's identity. Consequently, his picture of Daniel was also out of focus. People who don't get the picture about God are just as unlikely to get the picture about us. First John 3:1 tells us why: "The reason the world does not know us is that it did not know him." You need look no further for any man's god than where he derives his identity.

Every human being finds his or her identity in something or someone. As believers in Jesus Christ, our entire identity is wrapped up in our God. Praise God it's not wrapped up in this Babylon-type culture that surrounds us. In this furiously, ever-changing society, the picture we were trying to match would already be outdated by the time we felt we could reflect it. We'd have to download a whole new set of images and in the process, implode with self-absorption … not unlike a certain king.

Daniel 4 inks a few images we definitely want to download into our mental files. Without them we can't put the finishing touches on the Bible's portrait of Babylon's most famous king. Today we'll turn attentively to the details of Nebuchadnezzar's dream. Please begin with prayer then carefully read Daniel 4:10-18.

> **AS BELIEVERS IN JESUS CHRIST, OUR ENTIRE IDENTITY IS WRAPPED UP IN GOD.**

The image in King Nebuchadnezzar's first prophetic dream was a statue. What was the image in the second dream (today's segment)?

A tree

Take a look back at the latter half of day 2 where we discussed the meaning of the Aramaic word for "prosperous." We learned that the word "corresponds to the biblical Hebrew *ra'anan,* 'luxuriant' "[3] (see p. 77).

According to the definition, what is the word *luxuriant* used to describe?

luxuriant or flourishing tree

You've likely discovered the most probable cause for the image in Nebuchadnezzar's second dream. By feeling like a luxurious and flourishing self-made tree, the king inscribed an open invitation to God to sharpen up His woodcutting skills. Two images of the same tree appear in verses 10-15. Few of us are artists, but we can all draw stick figures.

In the space below, please draw the tree before and after the "messenger" (v. 13) came down from heaven and called for the transformation. Get as detailed as space allows. (No whining and no skipping allowed! Remember, we retain far more of what we write or draw. Furthermore, I often have the pleasure of running into fellow students, and I joyfully check homework whenever possible.)

BEFORE (vv. 10-12):   **AFTER** (vv. 14-15):

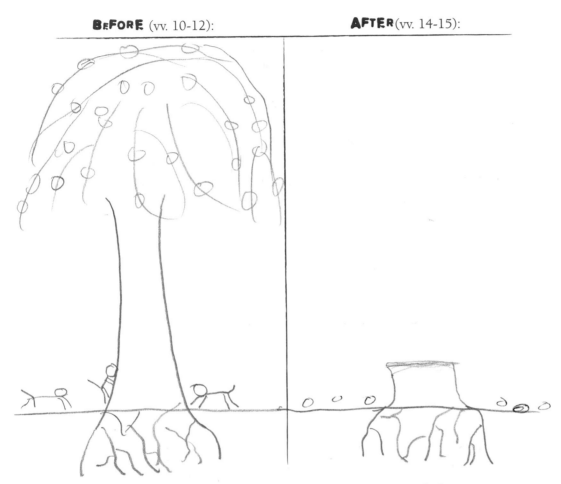

How did the first tree symbolize Nebuchadnezzar's reign in Babylon up to that time?

_____

In our very first daily assignment (week 1, day 1), we learned that Nebuchadnezzar's reign was unparalleled in Babylon, earning him the reputation of one of the most competent rulers of the ancient world. Babylon spiked to the zenith of its political power and affluence during his reign. Astonishingly, the entire empire lasted only 23 years after Nebuchadnezzar's death. It then collapsed like a lung with no air.

According to Daniel 2:37-38 why was King Nebuchadnezzar so incomparable in his day? *Because the God of heaven had given him dominion & power & might & glory And He had placed mankind & the beasts of the field & the birds of the field in his hand. He was the head of gold*

83

Remember, Daniel's words in 2:37-38 were specifically addressed to the king. Somehow Nebuchadnezzar's memory stored the "king of kings" part better than the "God of heaven" part. Funny how spiritual amnesia works. <u>Man has a far greater tendency to remember what someone has done to him than for him</u>. Had the king more clearly recalled God's goodness to him, he might not have had such a humbling experience to indelibly mark his memory.

Yes, Nebuchadnezzar's reign had been like a sheltering, fruit-bearing tree, but God alone seeded it, watered it, raised it, and blessed it. <u>Without God, the kings of the earth are as nothing—including those who never acknowledge His name</u>. Interestingly, God likens men and nations to trees a number of times in Scripture, several of which are in the context of chastisement and being cut back (see Isa. 2:12-13; 10:34; Ezek. 31:3-4).

The towering size of the tree in the dream suggests how long it had flourished. It might also hint at the height from which the branches could fall as the scene alters radically. The NIV reads, "In the visions I saw while lying in my bed, I looked, and there before me was a messenger, a holy one, coming down from heaven" (v. 13).

The original language for "looked" adds more drama. The Aramaic word "expresses great surprise and might be rendered more emphatically, 'look!' "[4] The more literal translation of "messenger" in verse 13 is " 'one who is awake' "[5] One commentator called messengers by this Aramaic term "the Wakeful Ones."[6] This description occurs nowhere in the Bible outside these three appearances in this chapter (vv. 13,17,23), but don't draw the conclusion that other angels sleep. Psalm 121 tells us God never sleeps. He obviously keeps His ambassadors awake and at watch as well. The term is used in Daniel 4 most likely in keeping with the interruption of King Nebuchadnezzar's sleep. In other words, while the king tried to sleep, the "Wakeful One" came to work.

The messenger's command resulted in the tree being stripped of its leaves, trimmed of its branches, and cut to a stump. Conclude your lesson today with a look at verse 15. What kind of limit was set on the harm to the tree?

> That the stump & its roots bound w/ iron
> & bronze remain in the ground, in the
> grass of the field

Hopefully you were able to attend session 4 and recall the point we made concerning the limitation voiced in verse 15. If so, what is its significance?

> God was going to make His
> point but it would only
> be for a set time

Beloved, sometimes a prolonged rebellion and resisted warning can result in a drastic chastisement, but God's desire, particularly toward His beloved child, is neither to destroy nor condemn. It is to re-grow us free of the fruit-rotting parasite of pride. God is not trying to destroy us. He's trying to keep us from destroying ourselves.

GOD'S DESIRE IS TO RE-GROW US FREE OF THE FRUIT-ROTTING PARASITE OF PRIDE.

Important!

DAY FIVE BREAK OFF

Today's Treasure: *Therefore, O king, be pleased to accept my advice: Renounce your sins by doing what is right, and your wickedness by being kind to the oppressed. It may be that then your prosperity will continue. Daniel 4:27*

Let's glance at what God has empowered us to accomplish this week before we tie up the loose ends of week 4. In session 4 we focused on the fulfillment of Nebuchadnezzar's dream recorded in Daniel 4:28-37. Our daily assignments have covered the background leading up to the fulfillment.

- On day 1 we discussed Nebuchadnezzar's willingness to look foolish to magnify God.
- On day 2 we talked about Nebuchadnezzar's false security and his taste for luxury.
- On day 3 we had our pop quiz and then discussed the frustration of dealing with those who—spiritually speaking—just don't get the picture.
- On day 4 we (begrudgingly?) did a little artwork and glanced at the interruption of a good night's rest by a "Wakeful One."

Today we will complete our background check by focusing on Daniel's interpretation of the king's dream. If you didn't participate in session 4, today's conclusion of our daily assignments will leave you hanging. If at all possible, try to make the session up. If you can't, by all means read and meditate on the final verses of Daniel 4 after the conclusion of today's lesson.

Dear One, I am so thankful for the privilege of serving you. I love you and I'm praying for you. Now, pray for yourself and get started!

Please read Daniel 4:19-27. Record each occurrence of the title "Most High" in the space provided on page 70. Remember, we're looking for six occasions. You will also need to glance ahead at verses 32 and 34 for the remaining two.

Which part of the interpretation recorded in verses 20-27 do you imagine was most disturbing to King Nebuchadnezzar?

Let him live like the wild animals until 7 times pass by him — vs 23

Daniel had served under Nebuchadnezzar for over three decades, experiencing favor and exalted position under his rule. Sometimes position brings privilege. Other times position seems to bring nothing but problems. At this point in Daniel's life, he surely thought he had more responsibility than he could handle.

Glance back at Daniel 2:48-49. What had Nebuchadnezzar done for Daniel after he interpreted the first dream? *He made him ruler over the whole province of Babylon & placed him in charge of all its wise men & lavished many gifts on him*

Daniel 4:9 adds "chief of the magicians" to our protagonist's job description. The term didn't mean he pulled rabbits out of hats or quarters out of ears. A chief of magicians was the head of the royal conglomeration of wise men.

The term "magician" reflects the cultic sources many of the wise men sought for supernatural wisdom. Anyone willing to listen knew the source of Daniel's wisdom. God granted supernatural knowledge and insight to His servant and used a pagan king as the visible glove on His invisible prospering hand. At this point in Daniel's tenure, his high position placed him in a difficult position.

According to Daniel 4:19, how did Daniel first react to Nebuchadnezzar's description of the dream?

He was greatly perplexed & his thoughts terrified him

Imagine being in Daniel's position after hearing the content of Nebuchadnezzar's dream. The terminology "greatly perplexed for a time" suggests Daniel was temporarily dumbfounded. Can't we relate?

When did you last hear something that temporarily dumbfounded you?

_____

_____

Then perhaps you can relate to Daniel's reaction. The Aramaic suggests he was "appalled" and "astounded."[7] This may have been one of those times when Daniel didn't feel particularly blessed by his God-given ability to "understand visions and dreams of all kinds" (Dan. 1:17).

As he stood speechless before the king, what kinds of things might have been going through Daniel's mind (v. 19)? *He may have wondered what would happen to him — was the Lord still in his corner*

Though Daniel was appalled, he did not shrink back from his divine appointment. Surely his heart was pounding and the blood was flowing through his veins like hot oil when he climactically pronounced, "You, O king, are that tree!" (v. 22).

Daniel's words are eerily reminiscent of the prophet Nathan's to another king centuries earlier. Not a pagan Nebuchadnezzar, but a king after God's own heart. King David had sinned grievously against God by committing adultery with Bath-sheba and having her husband, Uriah, killed in battle. Furthermore, David refused to own up to his sin for months. God sent the prophet Nathan to David, and he confronted the king by telling him the story of a rich man who took a poor man's only precious possession. Furious, David responded, " 'As surely as the LORD lives, the man who did this deserves to die! He must pay for that lamb four times over, because he did such a thing and had no pity.' Then Nathan said to David, 'You are the man!' " (2 Sam. 12:5-7).

Sometimes we don't recognize ourselves until we judge another and hear the Holy Spirit resound within our hearts, "You are that person!" We can only imagine the look of horror on King Nebuchadnezzar's face as Daniel declared, "O king, you are that tree!" The shift in imagery to the man driven from the masses to live among the animals was even worse.

Like David, Nebuchadnezzar was offered a season of repentance that might have drastically reduced the severity of chastisement. What did Daniel advise the king to do? Check all that apply. (See v. 27.)

☒ care for the oppressed   ☐ turn to the Lord
☒ renounce his sins   ☒ do what is right

In session 4 we discussed God's profound offense at a person's willingness to sit contentedly in luxury without concern for the oppressed. We recognized carelessness toward the needs of the oppressed as a vital sign that we've been corrupted by our Babylons. As we draw this week's study to a close, concentrate on the advice Daniel gave Nebuchadnezzar to "renounce" his sins.

The original word *peruq* is translated accurately by the KJV: "break off thy sins." The idea could be illustrated by breaking off a yoke from around the neck. Daniel was probably telling Nebuchadnezzar to break off his wicked branches before God broke him.

Beloved, I want to share something with you out of compassion and empathy. I have learned the hard way that some things don't need to be moderated. They need to be stopped. Broken off. Ended. You know me well enough to know I'm not talking about marriage, but I am talking about a host of other things.

Some things—substances, activities, relationships—are so toxic to us that moderation won't work. Have you made this discovery for yourself?

☒ yes ☐ no If so, how?

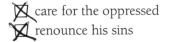

Some things don't need to be cut back. They need to be cut off. If you are someone who desperately needs to hear this point, I wish I could sit across the coffee table, hold your sweet hands, look you straight in the eye with overflowing love, and

SOME THINGS DON'T NEED TO BE CUT BACK. THEY NEED TO BE CUT OFF.

say, "I understand how difficult this is. But you must let it go. Don't just release it. Renounce it. Push it off. You must, or it will eventually destroy you." Get some help! Get some accountability! Get to it, because it's getting to you.

Daniel's advice to Nebuchadnezzar to break off his sins by doing what was right was brilliant replacement "theology." He didn't just tell him to stop doing one thing. He told him to start doing another. Scripture is full of exhortations to not just cease one activity: replace it with another. Isaiah 1:16-17 says, "Stop doing wrong, learn to do right!"

When we cease a habitual activity, to do absolutely nothing in its place is the fastest track back to addiction. Remember, nature abhors a vacuum. We all yearn to be filled. Ephesians 5:18 says, "be filled with the Spirit"! God has a healthy replacement for the old destructive filler. Seek Him and find it! Get godly counsel, get into a support group, but whatever you do, don't just ignore the warning like Nebuchadnezzar did. If my plea is resonating with you, I lovingly implore you as one who has been there:

Break it off before it breaks you.

God loves you so, Dear One. Otherwise, why on earth would He care? "Whom the LORD loves He chastens" (Heb. 12:6, NKJV).

---

1. Stephen R. Miller, *Daniel*, vol. 18 in *The New American Commentary* (Nashville: Broadman & Holman, 2001), 130.
2. Ibid.
3. Ibid.
4. Ibid., 133.
5. Ibid.
6. Ibid., 136.
7. From the *New King James Version*. Copyright © 1979, 1980, 1982, Thomas Nelson, Inc., Publishers.

THE
HANDWRITING
ON THE WALL

5

5

SESSION FIVE
THE HANDWRITING ON THE WALL

(handwritten margin note: Masiyah – (Messiah) Annointing)

The fifth chapter of Daniel unfolds about thirty years after Nebuchadnezzar's sanity was restored. Twenty-three years have passed since Babylon's most famous king's death, and his crown has already fallen into four different hands. Today's lesson centers on events that happened October 12, 539 B.C. under the rule of Belshazzar, Nebuchadnezzar's grandson.

Read Daniel 5:1-6.

1. Belshazzar made the grievous mistake of treating the ___holy___ as ___unholy___.

   Compare Leviticus 8:10-11 and 2 Chronicles 7:16. The Hebrew transliteration for

   "consecrate" is *qadas* meaning "to be clean, ___pronounce___ clean (ceremonially

   or morally); to consecrate to God, ___declare___ as holy, ___treat___ as holy. Signifies

   an act or state in which people or things are set aside and ___reserved___

   ___exclusively___ for God."[1]

2. We, too, are ___holy vessels___ in the ___house___ of the Lord (2 Tim. 2:20-21).

   See Ephesians 1:1,4 and 2 Corinthians 1:21-22. The lexical form of the word

   translated *saints* (Eph. 1:1) and *holy* (Eph. 1:4) is *hagios* meaning "holy, sacred,

   separated from ___ordinary___ or ___common usage___ and

   ___devoted___ to God. Something holy is that which has been brought into

   relationship with God ... and designated by Him as having a ___sacred___

   ___purpose___ or special significance ... ___Marked___ as holy, classified

   as belonging to God ... sacred, hallowed, consecrated."[2]

3. Satan has no greater agenda than attempting to ___desecrate___ what God

___consecrates___

His methods are many, but one of his specialties is reflected in Daniel 5:2-3.

4. God does not overlook Satan's ___mistreatment___ of holy ___vessels___ any

more than He ___overlooked___ Belshazzar's. Read Daniel 5:5-10. See verse 12.

The phrase "solve difficult problems" is literally "___loosening of knots___"[3]

Look ahead to Daniel 5:26-30.

A generalized translation of the handwriting on the wall might be:

Mene: ___I am___

Tekel: ___I know___

Peres: ___I act___

5. Vessels that have been ___treated as unholy___ can be ___treated___

___as holy again___

See 2 Timothy 2:20-21 and Ezra 1:2,7-8; 8:28-29.

1. Spiros Zodhiates, *Hebrew Greek Key Word Study Bible, New International Version, Old Testament Lexical Aids,* (Chattanooga: TN: AMG Publishers, 1996), #7727, 1547.
2. Ibid., *New Testament Lexical Aids, #41,* 1572.
3. Stephen R. Miller, *The New American Commentary: Daniel, vol. 18* (Nashville: Broadman & Holman, 1994), 160.

I hope you participated in session 5 and recall its great significance. Daniel 5 records the means and the end of mighty Babylon. At its conclusion, the kingdom of gold falls to the strong arms of silver: the Medes and the Persians. We have only two remaining weeks in part 1 of our series. Though Babylon and all it has come to represent to us will certainly find mention in part 2, it will no longer be the primary theme. Prophecy will take its place as our major emphasis. We will, therefore, give priority attention this week and next week to the concepts and parallels we can draw from ancient Babylon. I am so proud of you for hanging in there! Your participation and enthusiasm bless me beyond words.

THIS WEEK'S PRINCIPAL QUESTIONS

DAY 1 Who was the new Babylonian ruler introduced in session 5 (Dan. 5:1)?
DAY 2 What parallel can you draw between Belshazzar and Satan
 (2 Tim. 2:20-21,26)?
DAY 3 What does James 1:13-18 tell you about God?
DAY 4 How is Daniel described in Daniel 5:10-17?
DAY 5 What was Belshazzar's defining mistake (Dan. 5:22)?

DAY ONE BELSHAZZAR, FACT OR FICTION?

Today's Treasure: *King Belshazzar gave a great banquet for a thousand of his nobles and drank wine with them. Daniel 5:1*

As we begin our fifth week of study, let's glance over our shoulders and briefly take stock of where we've been. At the conclusion of session 1, many of us signed a statement of commitment together. What was the commitment?

Is it happening, Dear One? Are you learning? Are many of the truths tucked into the pages of Daniel beginning to abide in you? One of our goals has been to develop such a working knowledge of the Book of Daniel that we could readily cite the major theme(s) of any chapter upon its mention. Let's give it a try and see if we're making progress toward our goal.

Without looking at your notes or your Bible, see if you can recall and write the primary subject matter of Daniel 1–4. Give yourself time to reflect, and I believe you'll remember. If absolutely necessary, take a quick glimpse back at the chapters—but hopefully only for a hint.

Daniel 1: _____

Daniel 2: _____

Daniel 3: _____

Daniel 4: _____

Thanks for cooperating with a few pop quizzes along the way. Remember, deliberate recollection is a vital part of retaining information. Great job! Let's get back to date.

🦁 Session 5 introduced a new ruler on the Babylonian scene. What is his name?

(See Daniel 5:1.) ___King Belshazzar___

Please be careful not to confuse his name with Daniel's similar Babylonian name, Bel(te)shazzar. Circle the syllable in Daniel's Babylonian name that distinguishes it from the king in Daniel 5. Ironically, foolish Belshazzar's brief appearance in Scripture offers encouragement for our faith. Today I'll tell you how. Throughout the centuries a number of commentators argued that Belshazzar, Babylon's ruler in the fifth chapter of Daniel, was a fictitious character invented by the book's author. They argued that his name was completely unaccounted for except in the Book of Daniel and works dependent on it, such as the writing of Baruch and Josephus.[1]

Independent historical accounts clocked Nabonidus as the last king of Babylon while Scripture recorded its final ruler as Belshazzar. Who was right?

___Scripture___

Here's a lesson I've learned. When someone comes up with an "error" in God's Word, be very cautious about jumping on the bandwagon with them. The chances are extremely good that their wagon is setting in quicksand. In the past any number of experts have claimed to find flaws in the Bible only to be later proved that Scripture was right and they were wrong. In this case, as others, time surfaced truth.

Behold the words of researchers since the late nineteenth century: "abundant evidence has come to light that demonstrates not only that Belshazzar did live but that he was both the son of and co-regent with Nabonidus."[2] Nabonidus "was absent from Babylon for 10 of his 17 years," indicating why Belshazzar was appointed co-regent and "exercised kingly authority even though Nabonidus actually held the throne."[3]

Why would any king desert his throne for such a long period of time? Nabonidus appeared to have more interest in "restoring and expanding the Babylonian religion" than attending to the endless politics surrounding the throne.[4] His passion for restoring temples and re-igniting the worship of Babylonian gods may have come from his mother, the high priestess of the moon god at Haran.[5] Nabonidus spent much of his absenteeism "conducting archaeological expeditions in Arabia."[6]

This co-regency explains why Belshazzar offered "third highest ruler in the kingdom" to anyone who could interpret the handwriting on the wall (see Dan. 5:7). Nabodinus and Belshazzar occupied places one and two.

SOONER OR LATER, TIME WILL ALWAYS SURFACE TRUTH.

Much controversy has surrounded the Book of Daniel. Critics of its authenticity and historicity loved throwing the enigmatic Belshazzar in the face of those who stood for the truth of the Bible. His appearance in Scripture seemed to many to be a huge historical blunder … until time brought its historical authenticity to light. Sooner or later, time will always surface truth. Beloved, I am utterly convinced that when all is said and done, the secular recordings of history will have to bow down to the preeminence of God's Word.

How does 1 Corinthians 1:18-25 lend support to the previous statement?

God has made foolish the wisdom of the world

Scholars through the centuries who claimed Belshazzar was fictitious counted themselves among the wise and intelligent. God proved them foolish. Belshazzar's name is not the only thing out of the fifth chapter of Daniel to surface. "Archaeologists have excavated a large hall in Babylon 55 feet wide and 165 feet long that had plastered walls. Such a room would have been sufficient to house a gathering" the size of the one described in Daniel 5.[7]

Do you recall from session 5 the description of the wall on which the hand wrote? Fill in the following blank based on Daniel 5:5.

"Suddenly the fingers of a human hand appeared and wrote on the

the plaster of the wall, near the lampstand in the royal palace."

These archaeologists very likely excavated the same plaster walls that God once used for a chalkboard. How like our God to wait patiently to uncover mysteries! Certainly, He has no such obligation. He has given us His Word and called us to walk by faith and not by sight. He is merciful, however, and (dare I say?) good-humored enough to bring various archaeological supports and historical confirmations on a number of select issues to thrill us. God knows His Word stands, so all of man's doubting and debating doesn't disturb Him one iota. In fact, I think He enjoys spilling theological puzzle pieces out on a card table. Over time He arranges one then another in blocks and segments of indescribable beauty. He is a God who undoubtedly loves discovery … maybe because He never got to learn anything. He's simply always known. The Bible beautifully portrays Him as a God of *progressive revelation*. I'll explain.

Second Timothy 3:16 tells us that "all Scripture is God-breathed," but He purposely didn't "exhale" it in one long breath. Rather, like a man inhaling and exhaling over the course of many years, God used time, man, and the unfolding of history to breathe sixty-six books onto parchment over the course of 1,500 years. The Old Testament is incomplete without the New. The New Testament cannot be understood without the Old. A thorough study of the Book of Hebrews requires an understanding of Exodus and Leviticus. The Book of Revelation begs a watchful eye on the Book of Daniel. John 1 can't be appreciated without Genesis 1, and the examples go on and on.

God issued His revelation patiently and progressively. Those of us who believe in the truth of the Word also attest to the sufficiency of Scripture. I'll ask Dr. Wayne Grudem to define what I mean: "The sufficiency of Scripture means that Scripture contained all the words of God he intended his people to have at each stage of redemptive history, and that it now contains all the words of God we need for salvation, for trusting him perfectly, and for obeying him perfectly."[8]

Now, apply the concept to your own personal relationship with God through His Word. Describe what the sufficiency of Scripture means to you.

God's word gives me everything I need!

How does 2 Peter 1:3-4 lend support to Grudem's definition of the sufficiency of Scripture?

_____

To me, the sufficiency of Scripture means that God has given me His Word containing all I absolutely must know and must have. Everything else is gravy. But, you see, I'm an Arkansas girl and I like gravy. The Bible is complete and fully sufficient. My absolute delight! But I dearly love seeing God reveal a mystery or two through historical discoveries. I already believe God's Word is truth, but I celebrate any skeptic baffled enough to possibly believe.

THE BIBLE IS COMPLETE AND FULLY SUFFICIENT.

While the progressive revelation of God's inspired Word is complete, I think He continues to allow and appoint discoveries in support of revelation. We have a perfect example in today's lesson: the discovery in the late nineteenth century of a ruler by the name of Belshazzar who co-reigned with Nabonidus.

The last century has uncovered all sorts of interesting archaeological finds that support and expound upon Scripture. In recent years, news leaked that one of the caves of John the Baptist may have been uncovered. Are these discoveries accidental? Or is God up to something? By now you know I think God is up to something. As the time of His Son's return hastens, I believe God is bringing attention to Himself and His Son in all sorts of ways.

What Scripture-supporting mystery do you personally wish would be discovered?

_____

Who knows? It might. It could happen in your lifetime. God is always stirring up gravy. Until faith becomes sight, however, questions will remain and debates continue. As 2 Peter 3:15-16 says, segments of Scripture are "hard to understand" and plenty of "ignorant and unstable people" will "distort" them "to their own destruction."

Keep in mind, not all ignorant and unstable people appear so. Don't be dissuaded by the scoffs of self-proclaimed scholars, and never forget that arrogance is not a sign of true intelligence.

Inhale a fresh breath of faith today! Take heart and believe! Discoveries like the documents supporting Belshazzar excite my faith and cause me to clap my hands like a child and shout, "Do it again, Lord! Do it again!" Before the clock of earth stops ticking, God may well divulge countless other clues … in His own good time.

Then, one day, we'll know fully—even as we are fully known (see 1 Cor. 13:12). Be encouraged, Dear One. God is not only right. He will *prove* right. Nothing remains hidden except by His hand.

DAY TWO UNHOLY USE OF HOLY VESSELS

Today's Treasure: *So they brought in the gold goblets that had been taken from the temple of God in Jerusalem, and the king and his nobles, his wives and his concubines drank from them. Daniel 5:3*

I enjoyed yesterday's attentions to the historicity of Scripture. I hope you did, too. Recently a coworker told me that one of our Bible study participants in the taping of Daniel said, "Please thank Beth for not thinking we are too dumb to learn all of this." My heart was so tendered, I could have cried. Too dumb? I think every single one of you is brilliant! If I were a bettin' woman (something my grandmother always said), I'd bet I have much more faith in you than you have in yourself.

Do you know why I started writing Bible studies in the first place? Because I had class members much like you who pushed me to no end. They wanted to learn more than I could give them in weekly lectures, so they stayed after me until I wrote homework. I knew I didn't have it in me. I begged God to make me smarter than I was and to give me gifts of biblical insight. I dug deeper and deeper because my class members were so bright they nearly buried me. They wanted to learn more than I knew. What was a girl to do? Study!

Anybody can do it! Yours truly used to think that her spiritual gift was accessorizing an outfit. Now I'd rather read a commentary or peruse a Bible dictionary any day over a *People Magazine*. Melissa and I like to say our love language is Bible software. Amanda's is books. If "Blonder Than She Pays to Be" and her progenies can mine the hidden treasures of Scripture, anybody can!

Every class I've had since the first pushy group has taken up where they left off. It's high time for paybacks. As long as they keep pushing me, I'll keep pushing you. And in the process, we may just learn some Scripture. All of us have a long way to go in the study of God's inexhaustible Word, but aren't we having a blast going some of that distance together? Beloved, revel in the wonder that God can change our minds and make us smarter than we'd be!

Some lessons primarily target the mind. Yesterday's is an example. Other lessons are aimed at the core of the heart. That's the bull's-eye today and tomorrow.

Please reread the portion of Scripture that held our primary attentions in session 5: Daniel 5:1-9. What part of it did God use to speak to you?

_____

I want to recall a very important part of session 5 with you today in case it hit a nerve. Even if it's not the portion that spoke most personally to you, it's the kind of subject that ought not be quickly dropped. Our video sessions together accomplish many wonderful things, but they don't give *you* a format to explore and express your responses. Thankfully, your daily assignments do. In session 5 we talked about the unholy use of holy vessels, and we drew a parallel between Belshazzar and Satan.

🦁 Read 2 Timothy 2:20-21,26 and briefly describe the parallel.

We are His holy vessels and He wants to use us for a holy purpose

If you have received Christ Jesus as your Savior, you are a holy vessel. We learned in our session that Babylon (as a cultural mentality) profanes what is holy. Long ago we established that Satan is the author of all Babylon-like doctrine. Do you feel like Satan has used you in any way—and to any degree—to bring dishonor to the name of Christ? In retrospect, do you see where you cooperated with him in a scheme that probably grieved the heart of Christ? I ask you this question not for the sake of rekindling guilt or self-condemnation. On the contrary, I think many of us could use some deep healing where this subject is concerned.

We don't deal openly enough with the matter of debilitating regret—the kind that could bring tears to many of our eyes even right now. Let's talk this through for a few minutes.

Satan cannot inhabit those of us who are in Christ because we are "sealed for the day of redemption" (see Eph. 4:30), but he can certainly use us for his purposes if he gains our cooperation. Subtlety is his specialty, so we're often unaware at first that we're cooperating. Count me among those who obliged far too many times. Those of us who have used our bodies for unholy purposes of sexual sin can readily recognize the concept, but that's not the only way to mistreat a holy vessel. It's certainly not the only way I mistreated mine. All manner of abuses to the physical body apply, but think even more broadly.

- Have we, the people of God who are called to be builders of home and church, ever been used by the enemy to tear them down?
- Have we been used by the enemy to cause others either to stumble or to have less faith?
- Were we once cynics and scoffers in regard to spiritual things that are now dear to us?
- Do we fear we may have influenced others adversely before we changed and don't know how to make up for it?

THOSE OF US WHO HAVE RECEIVED CHRIST JESUS AS SAVIOR ARE HOLY VESSELS.

• Have we treated someone dishonorably even though we were Christians, and now it's too late to fix it?

Each example represents a way Satan can use a holy vessel to "toast" an unholy cause. Each is a way Satan can use a holy child of God against his or her own Heavenly Father. Please know that I nudge these tender places only out of love and belief that God wants to bring healing. Let's explore the subject through a series of questions calling for written answers. Some of these were raised or intimated in our session, but I want you to have a chance for candid response. We will discuss your answers both today and tomorrow.

First of all, are you able to fully accept the truth that you are a holy vessel? Do you see yourself as holy? ☐ yes ☒ no   Why or why not?

Because I miss the mark so often

If you don't see yourself as holy, are you able to see others in the body of Christ as holy? ☒ yes ☐ no   If so, give a few of their first names:

_____

Why do you more readily see them as holy? _Because we know ourselves so well. We can't read their minds_

If you are willing—however generally—describe a way Satan tried to use you, a holy vessel, for an unholy cause.

_____

On the following scale of 1 to 10, how much has this unholy use affected you through the years? Please be very honest. Circle your answer.

Almost not at all   1   2   3   4   5   6   7   8   9   10   Far too much

What role has regret played in your life?

_____

Let's deal with one kind of inappropriate response to Satan's misuse today and another kind tomorrow. If you recognize that you've been "used" by Satan but you can't say you've suffered any measurable godly sorrow over it, you may not have taken the liberating opportunity to look it in the face and repent of it. Repentance of sin is one of the most wonderful privileges Christ has given us through His cross. Astonishingly, we get up off repentant knees as white as snow (see Ps. 51:7), utterly pure (see 1 John 1:9), and totally restored to fellowship with God (see 1 John 1:6-7). We haven't repented, however, until we've experienced what 2 Corinthians 7:10 calls "godly sorrow." It's the kind that "brings repentance that leads to salvation and leaves no regret."

Sometimes we lack godly sorrow because we still cherish the sin. In other words, we're not sorry we did it. For instance, "I hurt that person and I'm glad. She deserved it." Or, "I'm not sleeping with him anymore, but I'm not sorry I did. I still think about it often and enjoy the thoughts." Beloved, those are examples of cherished sin that blocks repentance. Psalm 66:18-19 says, "If I had cherished sin in my heart, the Lord would not have listened; but God has surely listened and heard my voice in prayer." Unrecognized or cherished sin may still be a hindrance in your walk with God and your progress toward great fruitfulness. Believe me, I've been there and Satan would have stopped at nothing to keep me there. Is he trying to keep you there as well?

If this applies, Dear One, open your eyes to the truth! See the handwriting on the wall! You are a holy vessel Satan may be trying to use for unholy purposes. You are God's holy child, and He wants you prepared for great use. If you can feel the heaviness of conviction in your chest, Beloved, please talk this over with God. Have courage enough to ask Him to give you godly sorrow over any conceivable way you made the enemy's day. I've been there, too.

If this doesn't apply to you but you believe it applies to someone you love, pray for them right now and ask God to open their eyes and grant them godly sorrow that leads to repentance. What greater gift could there be?

DAY THREE HEALTHY SORROW

Today's Treasure: *As they drank the wine, they praised the gods of gold and silver, of bronze, iron, wood and stone. Daniel 5:4*

Today we continue exploring parallels drawn from Belshazzar's misuse of God's holy vessels in Daniel 5:1-9. Glance back at the passages and refresh your memory. Yesterday we saw the first of two inappropriate responses to having allowed our holy vessels to be used for unholy purposes. Simply put, we can think it's no big deal. I hope we're beginning to realize what a big deal it really is and we don't want it to happen again.

We talked about the necessity of godly sorrow that brings true repentance. Those who truly have a heart for God and fully awaken to what Satan has done can have all sorts of adverse reactions, ranging from despair to wrath. Anger can often signal blame. If we don't take personal responsibility for our cooperation, we won't repent because we've shifted all the blame on someone else. Perhaps the other person involved. Perhaps the enemy. Are you ready for this? Perhaps even God. The Book of Daniel is all about the sovereignty of God. We can twist the concept of God's sovereignty until we make Him responsible even for our seasons of sin.

I had an interesting discussion with a woman just a few days ago. After she shared her turmoil with me, I told her I'd pray for her. Imagine my surprise when she said, "Go right ahead. I, myself, am not speaking to God, but you can speak to Him if you want." I soon learned that a recent season of sin and rebellion in her life had resulted in painful consequences. She was furious with God for letting her make the wrong decisions.

List everything James 1:13-18 tells you about God: _He does not change. He is not tempted by evil nor does He tempt others_

_____

"The tempter came to him and said, 'If you are the Son of God, tell these stones to become bread.'"

📖 **MATTHEW 4:3**

What is the enemy called in Matthew 4:3? _____

If Satan is the tempter, how does James 1:13-18 depict us as the cooperator?

_____

The fifth chapter of Daniel taken alone might suggest that Belshazzar and the Babylonians were the only ones to blame for the unholy use of holy vessels. But let's remember that the idolatry of the Israelites and their low regard for the temple and its furnishings opened the door for captivity. God promised vengeance to Babylon for her mistreatment of His people, but His people were not innocent. They had developed a high regard for the Canaanite world that surrounded them, deciding it had more to offer than their God. A high regard for the things of this world always signals a lowering regard for God. The Israelites had ceased regarding the holy as holy. The same thing can happen to us. When we have a low regard for what God has called holy (Himself foremost, followed by what belongs to Him), we open the door for captivity.

 If we are God's children and we regard God as holy but not ourselves as His holy possessions, how is the door still open for captivity?

_____

_____

For much of my life I've had a fairly high regard for God, but I nourished a very low regard for myself. Much of my sin resulted from my unbelief that I was valuable and precious to God, coupled with my unwillingness to treat my own vessel as holy.

Can you relate? Or have you loved someone that, if willing, could relate? Explain how.

_____

The first inappropriate response to the awareness that we've treated holy things as unholy is a lack of repentance. The other extreme is debilitating guilt and an unwillingness to let go of past failure long after repentance. God is looking for the healthy response of godly sorrow that brings repentance, not emotional self-mutilation.

I nearly imploded over relentless, untreated regret. I couldn't understand what 2 Corinthians 7:10 meant by "Godly sorrow brings repentance that leads to salvation and leaves no *regret*" (emphasis mine). I was sorrowful over my sin to the degree that I could hardly pull myself off the floor. I had years earlier turned from the sin and no longer cherished any part of it. I despised it. The trouble was, I also despised myself. Regrets? Oh, my! Did I ever have regrets! If I had godly sorrow, why did I still have regrets? Doesn't 2 Corinthians 7:10 intimate that one cancels out the other? Allow me to share what I realized based on the *Amplified Bible*.

> "For godly grief *and* the pain God is permitted to direct, produce a repentance that leads *and* contributes to salvation *and* deliverance from evil, and it never brings regret; but worldly grief (the hopeless sorrow that is characteristic of the pagan world) is deadly [breeding and ending in death]" (2 Cor. 7:10).

First, the regret to which this verse refers is most pointedly the regret of unrepentance. In other words, if we repent, we won't regret that we *didn't* repent. Nor will we regret the deliverance. Hear the tone in the KJV: "For godly sorrow worketh repentance to salvation not to be repented of: but the sorrow of the world worketh death."

Secondly, I realized that my debilitating regret was characteristic of worldly sorrow, not godly sorrow. Read the Amplified Version of 2 Corinthians 7:10 again. Do you see "worldly grief" defined as "hopeless sorrow"? I grieved and regretted my past with feelings of hopelessness. My deep failures felt like hopeless blights on my track record. My past was behind me and nothing could fix it. At times I felt such despair about my past that I secretly wished I were dead. Not only can worldly sorrow lead to death in spiritual terms, its hopelessness can cause someone to wish death on himself.

IF WE REPENT, WE WON'T REGRET THAT WE DIDN'T REPENT. NOR WILL WE REGRET THE DELIVERANCE.

Have you ever felt "hopeless sorrow"? ☐ yes ☐ no   If so, what kind of future did you picture for yourself?

_____

_____

Beloved, my "hopeless sorrow" totally missed the meaning of the biblical word *redemption*. God redeems something by buying it back through the payment of a ransom. He gave the life of His Son as the ransom to buy us back from the clutches of sin. He has also bought back the rights to our past and all its failures. If we cooperate, He'll turn every single one of those failures into something useful for His kingdom. To me, that's the meaning of "full redemption" in Psalm 130:7.

Put your name in the blank where the word "Israel" was.

"O _____, put your hope in the LORD, for with the LORD is unfailing love and with him is full redemption."

If you've nursed hopeless grief over your past, put your hope in the Lord! He loves you unfailingly! He wants to fully redeem every part of your life until even your failures bring Him glory. Will you let Him?

After the fall of Babylon, Cyrus king of Persia sent the exiles of Judah home with the gold and silver articles Nebuchadnezzar stole from the temple and Belshazzar lifted to his gods. (See Ezra 1.) The holy vessels found their rightful place again. If you haven't already, you must find yours, too. Go home, Holy Child, with all your heart and soul to your faithful God. He doesn't set His goblets on shelves. He puts them to good use.

DAY FOUR AN EXTRAORDINARY SPIRIT

Today's Treasure: *This man Daniel, whom the king called Belteshazzar, was found to have a keen mind and knowledge and understanding. Daniel 5:12*

On day 1 we considered the historicity of Belshazzar, the ruler of Babylon in the fifth chapter of Daniel. On days 2 and 3 we further developed the parallel between the holy vessels Belshazzar treated as unholy and Satan's unholy treatment of us—the holy vessels of God's present "house." Today we'll move significantly forward in our chapter as we learn additional lessons about how to live in Babylon without being corrupted by it.

Read Daniel 5:10-17. Who told Belshazzar about Daniel? _____

 List all the ways she described Daniel:

_____

_____

Daniel 5:2 includes both Belshazzar's wives and concubines in the profane revelry at the king's banquet. In contrast, the "queen" referenced in verse 10 "came into the banquet hall" only after hearing the king and his nobles screaming—as I suggested in our session—like girls. "She must have been a highly prestigious individual to enter the banquet hall uninvited, and when she arrived, she seemed to take charge. For these reasons most commentators since the time of Josephus (first century A.D.)

have identified her as the queen-mother, either the wife of Nebuchadnezzar or the wife of Nabonidus. If the wife of Nebuchadnezzar, she probably was the grandmother of Belshazzar."[9]

Remember not to be confused by the repetitive references in Daniel 5 to Belshazzar as Nebuchadnezzar's "son." Close descendants in the ancient world were often called sons of a noteworthy forefather. Nothing was unusual about calling a grandson a son. Additionally, successors to a throne could be called the predecessor's son. Belshazzar met both qualifications for royal sonship. The queen referenced in verse 10 is more likely Belshazzar's grandmother than his mother because Nebuchadnezzar's wife stood to have far more familiarity with Daniel than the wife of Nabonidus.

The timing of Daniel 5 is significant, so try to grasp the following time line:

- The fifth chapter of Daniel opens about 30 years after the restoration of Nebuchadnezzar's sanity.
- Nebuchadnezzar had been dead for 23 years. He died in 562 B.C. after a 43-year reign.[10] Babylon began an immediate decline.
- Nebuchadnezzar was succeeded by his son Evil-Merodach. "'Evil-Merodach' is an unflattering term (in Hebrew, the first word means 'fool') applied to the Babylonian ruler Amel-Marduk (which means 'Man of Marduk'). Evil-Merodach ruled for only two years. His brother-in-law assassinated him in 560 B.C."[11]
- Neriglissar then ruled for four years from 560 to 556 B.C.[12] (Jer. 39:3,13 refers to him as Nergal-Sharezer.)
- He was succeeded by his young son Labashi-Marduk, who ruled only two months (May and June 556) before he was assassinated and succeeded by Nabonidus.[13]
- Nabonidus reigned for 17 years from 556 to 539 B.C. and appointed Belshazzar as co-regent.
- Belshazzar's banquet and the subsequent events recorded in Daniel 5 took place on October 12, 539 B.C.[14]

Plot these events (using abbreviations or initials) on the following time line. It begins with Nebuchadnezzar's rise to power in 605 B.C. and ends with Belshazzar's banquet. Plot Daniel's exile to Babylon in 605 B.C. as well.

605 B.C. ————————————————————— 539 B.C.

The chaos, betrayals, assassinations, and subsequent changes of leadership help explain why the years brought such rapid transition that Belshazzar did not know Daniel. In Daniel 5, our protagonist is 80 years old. The queen's familiarity suggests why many scholars believe she is Nebuchadnezzar's widow. She would have known

Daniel very well. In all likelihood, Daniel lost his high-ranking position after the death of the great Nebuchadnezzar and over time served Babylon's kings out of close range and in relative obscurity.

Many of the queen's descriptions of Daniel were familiar to us, but we note several this week for the first time. In session 5 we drew our attentions to the queen's claim that Daniel could "solve difficult problems." We learned that a literal rendering of the Aramaic is "'the loosening of knots,' referring to the loosening of knotty things or difficulties."[15] I asked you at the time what knot you wish God would enable you to loosen. What came to your mind?

_____

Have you asked God to help you loosen that knot since our session together?
☐ yes ☐ no

Remember, James 4:2 says that sometimes we have not because we ask not. (Don't force me to say, "We have knot because we ask not.") Whether or not God gives *you* the ability to loosen that knot, He can untangle it effortlessly. Persist in prayer until He does!

Look at another noteworthy description. The queen told Belshazzar that Daniel had "a keen mind." The Aramaic might be translated "an extraordinary spirit."[16]

What do you think she meant?

_____

How does God describe His servant Caleb in Numbers 14:24?

_____

The terms *extraordinary* and *different* imply something similar. In our culture's colloquialism, Caleb and Daniel stuck out like sore thumbs. Neither one of them joined the carnal or unbelieving masses in their responses toward God. They refused to blend in. The magnetic draw of Caleb and Daniel's cultures failed to overtake them. They never assimilated. Neither did they settle into the lowest common denominator of devotion practiced by their closest friends or kin. We get caught in that trap sometimes. We abide in our subgroups by unspoken codes dictating how far we'll go in our devotion to God. Anyone who goes overboard or takes it too seriously is considered eccentric, not extraordinary. For some, the flow of the world can be easier to resist than the flow of Christian mediocrity.

As you've considered becoming Daniel-like in your own Babylon-world, in all honesty, whose opinions or attitudes have you dreaded most (check one):

☐ worldly individuals who might think you've lost your mind
☐ mediocre Christians who might think you've gone too far

SOMETIMES WE HAVE NOT BECAUSE WE ASK NOT.

My respect for Daniel escalates when I consider the fact that he maintained such an extraordinary spirit long after he lost his visible position. We are often more motivated to exercise courage and demonstrate integrity when people are watching us, especially if they seem impressed with us. Even if we're criticized, we might reason that at least we're in the spotlight. For some, the lust for a platform can make criticism quite bearable. Daniel maintained his integrity long after anyone seemed to notice. He remained extraordinary in his ordinary estate. Dear One, you and I determined from the beginning of our present journey that we wanted to be Daniels.

 What does Daniel's example in today's lesson mean to you in your own struggle with Babylon?

_____

_____

You and I want God to be able to look on us amid our overindulged, self-absorbed culture, then glance to His right and say, "She has an extraordinary spirit, doesn't she, Son?" Perhaps Christ will nod His head and, while thinking the thoughts of an anxious bridegroom, lean over and say, "And isn't she beautiful?"

> **DANIEL MAINTAINED AN EXTRAORDINARY SPIRIT LONG AFTER HE LOST HIS VISIBLE POSITION.**

DAY FIVE WEIGHED AND FOUND WANTING

Today's Treasure: *You his son, O Belshazzar, have not humbled yourself, though you knew all this. Daniel 5:22*

Today we will give our final attentions to the fifth chapter of Daniel. You have worked hard this week. God will bless you lavishly in His choice way for your willingness to study His Word and your courage to apply it. You are doing "your best to present yourself to God as one approved, a workman who does not need to be ashamed" and as one who desires to "correctly handle the word of truth" (2 Tim. 2:15). Don't think for a moment that God doesn't notice. The "eyes of the LORD range throughout the earth to strengthen those whose hearts are fully committed to him" (2 Chron. 16:9).

As God looks upon a Babylon-like culture where so many either ignore Him or treat Him with tokenism, He sees your head in His Book and your attempts to apply His precepts and He is *pleased*. God isn't looking for perfection. He's looking for purity of heart: our authentic desire to do His will and give Him glory. I'm honored to be your sister. You make me want to seek Him and love Him more and more.

Read Daniel 5:18-31. What was Belshazzar's defining mistake (v. 22)?

lack of humility

King Nebuchadnezzar's temporary insanity may have been hidden at the time from the masses, but his children and grandchildren were undoubtedly and painfully aware. Any family member who didn't see his madness firsthand most assuredly overheard the sordid details. If Nebuchadnezzar's family was like most of ours, they probably would have preferred to keep the whole ordeal a secret rather than risk people thinking their royal blood could be tainted with insanity. Nebuchadnezzar, however, preferred the public route. With pleasure he testified of his fall to pride and the uncontested greatness and power of God Most High. Unquestionably Belshazzar knew the consequences his grandfather had endured as a direct result of his sinful pride. "You … have not humbled yourself, though you knew all this" (v. 22).

Can you think of any easier route to victory than learning from the mistakes of others? Oh, the pain we'd avoid! Really think about it: why do we tend to be more like Belshazzar, refusing to learn from others' mistakes?

_____

Though our overwhelming tendency may be to learn from our own mistakes, surely most of us have learned a lesson or two secondhand.

 Have you witnessed difficult consequences or severe chastisement in someone else's life that scared you so badly that you determined never to follow suit? Please don't give names, but describe why it had such an enduring effect on you.

_____

_____

IF THE LESSON DIDN'T HURT US PERSONALLY, SOMEHOW IT DOESN'T TEACH US PERSONALLY.

I asked you earlier why we often refuse to learn from others' mistakes. The most likely answer was hidden close to the question. Pain, the very thing we'd avoid by learning from others' mistakes, also tends to be the most effective teacher. If the lesson didn't hurt us personally, somehow it doesn't teach us personally. I read recently that very few people agree to a radical transformation based on pain they've caused others. Most must experience it themselves. Sad, isn't it? Must everything hurt to help? Couldn't healthy fear of consequential pain also have an effect? Let's pray it will! And let's pray likewise for our loved ones.

Pain is unavoidable on planet Earth, but we can greatly impact the kind of pain we suffer. I very often ask God to deliver my family members and me from pain associated with evil or wrongdoing. I submit to the pain of God's refining fire, but I don't want Satan to get another chance to burn me.

How about you? Are you beginning to learn without getting burned?
☐ yes ☐ no   If the answer is yes, give a relatively recent example.

_____

According to Daniel 5:23, what did Belshazzar do instead of humbling himself based on what he knew?

"Instead, you have _____ _____ __ _____ the Lord of heaven." Bad idea.

The idea conveyed in Daniel 5:23 is echoed from the opposite mountain in 1 Peter 5:5. When we continue in pride even when we know better, we "set ourselves up against the Lord of heaven" (Dan. 5:23).

According to 1 Peter 5:5, how does God respond?

_____

"All of you clothe yourselves with humility toward one another, because God resists the proud, but gives grace to the humble."

📖 **1 PETER 5:5 HCSB**

Do you see it? When—through unrelenting pride—we set ourselves up against God, He sets Himself up against us. Based on the authority of the Word and lessons learned the hard way, I promise you we'll lose. The verse doesn't say He *condemns* the proud. Once we belong to Him, nothing can snatch us from His hand because He will never release His grip. Beloved, God can still love us and oppose us. He will not let us prosper indefinitely in our pride. He can't. He is God, the Lord of heaven. He will defend His great Name and spotless reputation.

Read the rich verses of Isaiah 63:7-10. How do they underscore the concepts of Daniel 5:23 and 1 Peter 5:5?

_____

If God would oppose His child for pride and rebellion, we can only imagine what fury He'd unleash against those who openly despise Him and profane His holy possessions. Further in Daniel 5:23, Daniel called out Belshazzar for treating holy vessels as unholy and for inciting others to join him. You can rest assured that God will call your enemy, the devil, to account for every single time he treated you, God's holy child, as unholy.

Let's look at the meaning of the renowned "handwriting on the wall." What four words did God write on the wall of Balshazzar's banquet hall (v. 25)?

_____   _____

_____   _____

GOD WILL CALL THE DEVIL TO ACCOUNT FOR EVERY TIME HE TREATED YOU, GOD'S HOLY CHILD, AS UNHOLY.

"Literally, the translation is 'a mina, a mina, a shekel, and half shekels.' To interpret this cryptic message, Daniel digs down to the lexical roots. *Mene* comes from the verb 'to number, to reckon'; *tekel,* from the verb 'to weigh'; and *upharsin* [or singular, *peres*], from the verb 'to break in two, to divide.'"[17]

How did Daniel apply the handwritten words to Belshazzar (vv. 26-28)?

Mene: _____

Tekel: _____

Peres: _____

The interpretation of *mene* was painfully clear. And just in case Belshazzar missed his finish, God repeated it. Look at Daniel's interpretation of *tekel.* Whether we're frightened or relieved by the prospect, God's Word assures us that the kings of the earth and the heads of state will receive a divine evaluation. *A report card from God.* Belshazzar's grade? "F" for *found* "lacking, deficient in moral worth."[18] "As if [Daniel] had said, 'Thou thinkest thy dignity must be spared, since all men revere thee; thou thinkest thyself worthy of honour; thou art deceived says he, for God judges otherwise; God does not use a common scale, but holds his own, *and there thou art found deficient;* that is, thou art found a man of no consequence, in any way.'"[19]

The final word, *peres* (or *parsin* in some translations), means "divided," but God wrote it as a word play on Belshazzar's board that day. Like ancient Hebrew, Aramaic scripts were written only in consonants. The consonants in *peres* are exactly the same consonants in "Persians."[20] God not only told Belshazzar that the kingdom would be divided. He told him who would accomplish it, all in one word. "That very night Belshazzar, king of the Babylonians, was slain" (Dan. 5:30).

The head of gold is gone. The empire of silver has come.

1. Stephen R. Miller, *Daniel*, vol. 18 in *The New American Commentary* (Nashville: Broadman & Holman, 2001), 147.
2. Ibid.
3. John F. Walvoord and Roy B. Zuck, eds., *The Bible Knowledge Commentary of the Old Testament* (Wheaton, IL: SP Publications, Inc., 1985), 1344.
4. Ibid.
5. Ibid.
6. Spiros Zodhiates, ThD., gen. ed., *Hebrew-Greek Key Word Study Bible, New International Version* (Chattanooga, TN: AMG Publishers, 1996), 1030.
7. Ibid.
8. Wayne Grudem, *Systematic Theology* (Grand Rapids, MI: Zondervan, 1995), 127.
9. Miller, 159.
10. Walvoord and Zuck, 1344.
11. Zodhiates, 461.
12. Walvoord and Zuck, 1344.
13. Ibid.
14. Miller, 151.
15. Ibid., 160.
16. Ibid.
17. Charles R. Swindoll and Bryce Klabunde, *God's Pattern for the Future,* Insight for Living Bible Study Guide, From the Bible teaching of Charles R. Swindoll (Plano, TX: Insight for Living, 1996), 59.
18. Edward J. Young, *Daniel* (Melksham, Wiltshire: Wm. B. Eerdmans Publishing Co., 1949), 127.
19. John Calvin, *Commentaries on the Book of the Prophet Daniel*, vol. 1 (Grand Rapids, MI: Baker Books, 1998), 343-44. Citation is to the Baker edition.
20. Miller, 166.

IN THE
LIONS' DEN

6

SESSION SIX
IN THE LIONS' DEN

In today's session we begin our considerations of Daniel's sixth chapter. Our session and our daily assignments this week will draw part 1 of our series to a close. Very soon we will shift our focus from *Integrity in an Enticing World* to *The Ancient of Days and the End of Times*. Much about the Book of Daniel may have been unfamiliar to you. Today, however, we meet our protagonist in the place we most readily associate with him: the lions' den.

PART ONE

A VIEW OF DANIEL IN PRAYER

Read Daniel 6:10-16. Consider three ways we can react in an emergency:

- We can __panic__. ~ Do the wrong thing

- We can become __paralyzed__ ~ Do nothing

- We can __pray__. Compare Psalm 55:15-18. ~ Do the power thing

  (For the origin of praying "toward Jerusalem," see 1 Kings 8:33-35.)

  Like Daniel, we want to practice a __holy__ __habit__ long enough

  that it becomes the __old__ __pattern__. Also see Philippians 4:6-7.

VIEWER GUIDE

PART TWO

A VIEW OF DANIEL IN THE LIONS' DEN

Read Daniel 6:17-28.

Consider the wonderful side of life in Babylon and the lions' den.

We have opportunities …

- To experience _gloriously intense encounters_ with God. Compare 2 Timothy 4:16-18.

- To emerge from a _terribly hurtful_ situation _unhurt_ (see v. 22).

    The Aramaic word for "hurt" means "to ruin … to hurt, injure."[1]

    See Daniel 2:44 for another very significant translation of the same word.

- To see a worldly _Darius_ become _impressed_ with _our God_

---

1. Spiros Zodhiates, *Hebrew-Greek Key Word Study Bible,* New International Version, Old Testament Lexical Aids, (Chattanooga: AMG Publishers, 1996), #10243, 1564.

WEEK SIX
IN THE LIONS' DEN

Today we begin our final week in part 1 of our series on the fascinating Book of Daniel. Though part 2 will undoubtedly offer reminders of life and survival in Babylonian-type cultures, we are rapidly approaching our final focus on *Integrity in an Enticing World*. You have remained so faithful, Dear One. In our fast-paced, postmodern Babylon, no more precious commodity exists than the resource of time. You have devoted hours to the study of God's Word in the last five weeks. He promises that we will never receive His Word in vain. He sends it replete with divine purpose.

Clearly one of God's intentions is to teach us to fight the good fight against the constant indoctrination of our own surrounding Babylon. He also has personal objectives for each of us that, with our cooperation, will result in a great and God-glorifying harvest. Through the pages of our study, God is busy revealing to us healthy as well as unhealthy branches. He's showing us where He wants to flourish us and where He wants to retire us. I assure you, Beloved, God is getting into my personal business in this Bible study. I am confident He's doing the same with you. Let's allow Him unhindered access, trusting that our God is ever for us. (See Rom. 8:31.)

THIS WEEK'S PRINCIPAL QUESTIONS

DAY 1 What would happen at the completion of the captivity (Jer. 29:10-14)?
DAY 2 Why is Babylon symbolically described as a prostitute?
DAY 3 How does Revelation 18 describe Babylon's excessiveness and wealth?
DAY 4 What is the context of the word "corrupt" in Daniel 6:4?
DAY 5 What does Psalm 137:1-6 describe?

DAY ONE SAME SPOT, DIFFERENT DESPOT

Today's Treasure: *It pleased Darius to appoint 120 satraps to rule throughout the kingdom. Daniel 6:1*

Today's is a history lesson. Stick with it, Sweet One, and don't let your mind wander. Remember, we want to grow past the Babylonian approach to Bible study that says, "If you want my attention, make it about *me!*" All Scripture is *for* us, but refreshingly, all Scripture is not *about* us. That which is for us, however, can have a profound impact on us. Persevere through the beginning of our week, and expect increasing opportunities for personal application as we go.

Week 5 concluded with the toppled head of Babylon, the golden empire, and the rise of the silver-armed empire of the Medes and Persians. As you'll recall, the parts of the dazzling statue in Nebuchadnezzar's dream (see Dan. 2) represented the four Gentile empires stretching from Babylonian supremacy to the empire preceding the everlasting kingdom. In session 2 we looked up the phrase Christ used for this era. Let's refresh our memories.

Fill in the blank according to Luke 21:24:

"Jerusalem will be trampled on by the Gentiles until ___the times___

___of the Gentiles___ are fulfilled."

Now, fill in the blank according to the final words of Daniel's fifth chapter:

"That very night Belshazzar, king of the Babylonians, was slain, and ___Darius___

___the Mede___ took over the kingdom, at the age of sixty-two" (vv. 30-31).

The closing words of Daniel 5 present phase two in the strategic "times of the Gentiles." Though the foolish, irreverent Belshazzar lost his life in the takeover, the shift from Babylonian to Medo-Persian rule was otherwise relatively peaceful. "The city had been under assault by Cyrus. In anticipation of a long siege the city had stored supplies to last for 20 years. The Euphrates River ran through the city from north to south, so the residents had an ample water supply. Belshazzar had a false sense of security, because the Persian army, led by Ugbaru, was outside Babylon's city walls. … The army diverted the water north of the city by digging a canal from the river to a nearby lake.

With the water diverted, its level receded and the soldiers were able to enter the city by going under the sluice gate. Since the walls were unguarded the Persians, once inside the city, were able to conquer it without a fight."[1]

Let's have a quick review to make sure we got it. Based on the preceding paragraph, *how* did the Medo-Persians enter Babylon? _The army diverted the water north of the city by digging a canal from the river to a nearby lake. Because the water was diverted, its level went down & the Persians went under the sluice gate._

Nebuchadnezzar's mighty Babylon not only fell. It fell embarrassingly easily. You see, God shut it and opened it according to His sovereign will—not according to its self-sufficient strength. Under the divine inspiration of the Holy Spirit, Jeremiah delivered powerful and detailed prophecy concerning Judah's captivity in Babylon.

Read Jeremiah 25:11-12. How long did he prophesy the captivity would last?

(Check one.) ☐ 7 years ☒ 70 years ☐ forever

Now read Jeremiah 29:10-14. What would happen at the completion of this period of years? _The Lord has a wonderful plan for them. And when they cry out to Him, He will listen. The Lord will bring them back to the place where they were exiled from_

eschatology
a branch of theology that deals with the final events in history, beliefs concerning death, the end of the world, and the ultimate destiny of mankind

John Walvoord explains Jeremiah's prophecy and the fulfillment of it this way:

> "From the first subjugation of Jerusalem (605 B.C.) until the Jews returned and rebuilt the temple foundation (536) was approximately 70 years. From the destruction of the temple (586) until the temple was rebuilt (515) was also about 70 years. So Jeremiah's prophecy about the 70-year duration of the Babylon Exile was literally fulfilled."[2]

What a fitting consideration on the eve of part 2 in our journey with Daniel! As we prepare to study prophesy and eschatology, we can have confidence that God does what He says. *Every single time.*

Session 6, the final session of part 1, focused on the most familiar story in the Book of Daniel: Daniel in the lions' den. I can still vividly recall the watercolor illustration my childhood Sunday School teacher showed our class. The lion looked so friendly, he may as well have purred and licked Daniel's balding head clean. I didn't quite get the point.

Did God give you any new insight into the well-loved account during the session? If so, please share it. *As we see prophecy fulfilled it just reinforces the fact that the Lord fulfills all his promises (prophecy)*

Our familiarity with this story lets us use Daniel 6 as our "home base" while we broaden our scope far beyond it to bring a cohesive conclusion to *Part 1: Integrity in an Enticing World.*

Please read Daniel 6:1-3. What do these verses entail? (Check one.)

☐ the overthrow of Babylon   ☒ establishment of the new administration
☐ the rise of Cyrus the Great   ☐ the training of Siegfried and Roy

The opening verses of Daniel 6 provide our transition into a new administration. The NIV translation of Daniel 5:31 tells us that "Darius the Mede took over the kingdom." A more literal rendering of the Aramaic is "Darius the Mede *received* the kingdom" (emphasis mine). The wording is significant because the name *Darius* has not surfaced thus far outside the Word of God as the ruler over Babylon in this particular period.

Scripture and secular historical documentations agree: Cyrus the Great was the Medo-Persian king who oversaw the conquest of Babylon and ruled the expansive empire. So, who was Darius? Many scholars throughout the centuries have been unconcerned about the absence of his name on record for several reasons. Babylon was "a comparatively small portion of the vast Medo-Persian Empire."[3] Cyrus the Great could easily have appointed Darius to rule over this segment of the empire.

Look ahead to Daniel 9:1 for a moment and fill in the blank (NIV):

"In the first year of Darius son of Xerxes (a Mede by descent), who

_____was made ruler_____ over the Babylonian kingdom."

The wording could suggest an appointment. Many scholars believe Darius is another name for Ugbaru, the leader of the invasion into Belshazzar's Babylon. Other scholars think Darius may be another name for Cyrus himself. Leaders in the ancient world were often called by several names, so either case is feasible.

Scholar Joyce Baldwin joins the camp that believes Cyrus and Darius were the same person based on a possible and plausible rendering of Daniel 6:28. Look ahead to the verse for a moment. Baldwin explains that "the word *and* here and often in the book ... has the force of 'namely', or 'that is', so being used explicatively. The writer is explaining that the two names belong to the same person."[4] If Baldwin is correct, Daniel 6:28 could read, "So Daniel prospered during the reign of Darius, that is Cyrus the Persian."

We'll keep an open mind throughout the remainder of our study, making room for both possibilities. Wouldn't we get a kick out of Darius' identity surfacing in historical findings in our lifetime, much like Belshazzar's in the late nineteenth century? Just think! If we hear any such thing, we'll actually know what historians are talking about! See? We can rest assured that when we finish our study of Daniel, we won't be able to say, in Melissa's terminology, "I'm dumber now."

As Daniel 6 unfolds, please understand that Daniel, our protagonist, is under new authority but in the same old city. Cyrus the Great had not yet issued the decree to release the exiles. He would do so over the next year. (The decree would come in 538 B.C., after which 50,000 exiles would begin returning to their land and rebuilding the temple.) Daniel, however, was in his early 80s at the time of Babylon's fall to the Medo-Persians. He would serve the one true God in the city of Babylon for the rest of his life. He would see his heaven land long before his earthly homeland lay on the horizon.

Read Daniel 6:4-9.

Do jealousy, selfish ambition, and conspiracy against God's faithful one(s) sound familiar in the Book of Daniel? ☒ yes ☐ no If so, where have you encountered it before?

_____from my mom_____

Daniel missed the fiery furnace, but he won't miss the lions' den. You see, rulers can change dramatically while the surrounding culture remains largely unaltered, at least for a while. The fact that the biblical stage is still set in Babylon invites us to continue our emphasis on the Babylonian mentality all the way to the end of part 1. The Medo-Persians moved into the city, but the Babylonian mentality didn't make haste and move out. Cultures are rarely reflections of a single leader. Let's see for ourselves.

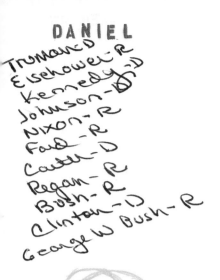

DANIEL

Truman–D
Eisehower–R
Kennedy–D
Johnson–R
Nixon–R
Ford–R
Carter–D
Regan–R
Bush–R
Clinton–D
George W Bush–R

mores [MOHR-ays]
the fixed morally binding
customs of a particular
group; moral attitudes;
habits, manners

In the margin write in historical order the names of the presidents of your country who have served in your lifetime. Beside each name give a brief description of his character or leadership ability as you understand it, however media-biased it may be.

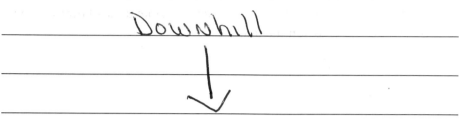 Now, reflect on the cultural changes that have taken place in America in your lifetime. How would you describe them?

_____ Downhill _____

_____ ↓ _____

In your opinion, has American culture and its mores risen and fallen dramatically under the direct influence of each president? Circle: Yes or (No)

Probably Not –but it sure seems like it

From your vantage point, you may have answered the question with a yes, but the steady increase of depravity and godlessness in our nation despite several vocally Christian presidents casts my answer with a no. We can have godly heads of state yet find ourselves nearly engulfed by the waves of godless culture. Let's face it. One lifeguard can't stop a tsunami. Cultures are stronger than individual human leaders because they are dictated by masses and cultivated by time. To evoke lasting cultural change, a strong leader would require an impressive following and an equally impressive block of time.

Cultures are also stronger than human leaders because they are influenced by unseen powers. Invisible principalities. Throughout week 6, we'll learn that the force behind the Babylon mentality is bigger and darker than any king history can name. Still, One sits high above him, enthroned between the cherubim and cloaked in unapproachable light. Babylon's king is running out of time.

DAY TWO MYSTERY BABYLON

Today's Treasure: *With her the kings of the earth committed adultery and the inhabitants of the earth were intoxicated with the wine of her adulteries. Revelation 17:2*

In our previous lesson we discussed the fall of Babylon to the Medes and the Persians and her continued place in the saga of Gentile rulers. From the beginning of our series, we have related characteristics of sixth century B.C. Babylon to the culture surrounding us. We are applying the concepts of Daniel's first six chapters to the postmodern mind-set of the prosperous and pompous West.

Today and tomorrow we fast-forward all the way to the Book of Revelation. There we will gain a much deeper understanding of the Babylonian mentality from an eschatological perspective. I want to warn you in advance that pulling chapters out of context in Revelation is near suicide from an interpretational point of view.

While our approach may incite more questions than answers, I'm willing to take the risk because Revelation's description of Babylon splashes fluorescent color all over the black-and-white images of the Book of Daniel. We will survive our out-of-context approach by keeping one goal jealously before us at all times: gaining insight specifically into the Babylon mentality.

Today we'll search Revelation 17 for portrayals of Babylon. Tomorrow we'll follow suit in Revelation 18. The latter will have particular significance because, like Daniel 5:30-31, it addresses the fall of Babylon. *A future Babylon.*

As we get started, let's nail down our precise goal one more time. What is our solitary goal as we consider Revelation 17 and 18 over the next two days?

To gain a much deeper understanding of the Babylonian Mentality

If you didn't write, "To gain insight specifically into the Babylon mentality," I need to see you after class. Actually, you're really darling, and if you didn't get the picture in your head at first, perhaps you've got it now.

Before we get started with our reading, pray! Then read Revelation 17:1-5. What title was written on "her forehead"? *Mystery - Babylon the Great - The Mother of Prostitutes and of the abominations of the earth*

The word "mystery" already suggests that we would be foolish to become dogmatic about exact interpretations of the details in this passage. Let's resist the urge and stick to our goal.

Before we search the chapter for representations of Babylon, let's lay the foundation by considering several differences between "mystery" Babylon and the one where Daniel resided. Much debate has existed among equally brilliant scholars and theologians concerning the identification of Babylon in the Book of Revelation. Searching the best commentaries available, you'll discover widely varying views.

Two of my commentaries identify Revelation's mysterious Babylon as Rome. Encouraging until you realize one sees it as early New Testament Rome while the other sees it as a future Rome, greatly revived and powerful. In both cases Babylon is symbolic of Rome. Others suggest the Babylon of Revelation will be a future city built in the same vicinity as ancient Babylon and called by the same name. Part of this reasoning comes from the twice-mentioned Euphrates River in the Book of Revelation. You'll recall from our previous lesson that the Euphrates ran through Nebuchadnezzar's Babylon from north to south.

In all three scenarios mentioned thus far, Revelation's Babylon is an actual city, be it past or future. Other scholars believe Babylon is strictly symbolic in the final book of the Bible. What the city represents is most important to us in achieving our present goal. Before we widen our scope on Revelation 17, turn all the way back to the first mention of Babylon.

Who was Nimrod and what was his relationship to Babylon according to Genesis 10:8-12? *He was the son of Cush. He grew up to be a mighty hunter before the Lord; one of the first centers of his kingdom was Babylon*

1st world ruler in scripture is "Nimrod"

You and I have been discussing the "times of the Gentiles" and the empires of various world rulers. You just stumbled onto the first world ruler in Scripture. His name is Nimrod, and the contrast between God-rule and world-rule first manifests in Scripture right here. Nimrod represents the desire of man to rule his own world. Author Mark Hitchcock describes Babylon as the "capital city of the first world ruler."[5]

Meditate on the additional information on Nimrod provided by *The Bible Knowledge Commentary*:

> "Nimrod, who founded Babylon, had a wife known as Semiramis who founded the secret religious rites of the Babylonian mysteries, according to accounts outside the Bible. Semiramis had a son with an alleged miraculous conception who was given the name Tammuz and in effect was a false fulfillment of the promise of the seed of the woman given to Eve. … Tammuz, according to the tradition was killed by a wild animal and then restored to life, a satanic anticipation and counterfeit of Christ's resurrection."[6]

From our New Testament perspective, we know Satan was behind these "secret religious rites." What do you think he was attempting to do? *Convince the people that the messiah had come*

Two critical words surface in the previous quote. Please fill in the following blanks from the quote to discover them:

"A son … who was given the name Tammuz and in effect was a *false* *fulfillment* of the promise of the seed of the woman given to Eve."

Beloved, there you have it. You'd be hard pressed to discover two words more perfectly depicting Satan's goal: providing *false fulfillment*. He will manipulate anything possible—including religion and forms of affection—to provide false fulfillment for our souls. Never think for a moment that Satan is anti-religious. Spiritual beings are driven to seek spiritual things, and we are spiritual beings. Satan's aim is to provide any effective counterfeit or diversion.

Does this make sense to you in light of your own experience? ☒ yes ☐ no

If so, how? _Because he tries to drive a wedge between human relationships by causing me to question if I really can count on anyone_

OK. Where is the bridge between Nimrod's Babylon and Revelation's Babylon? Hitchcock suggests the connection: "Since Babylon was the capital city of the first world ruler and is pictured as Satan's capital city on earth throughout Scripture, it makes sense that in the end times, Satan will once again raise up this city as the capital of the final world ruler."

So, you see, Hitchcock views Revelation's Babylon as Satan's capital city on earth at the end of times. He adds, "With the exception of Jerusalem, no other city is mentioned more than Babylon in the Bible. Scripture refers to Babylon 290 times and presents this city as the epitome of evil and rebellion against God."[7] That the Book of Revelation records the fall of Babylon the Great (Rev. 18) just before unveiling the New Jerusalem (Rev. 21) is no coincidence. The Bible depicts them as being total opposites.

Finally, read all of Revelation 17 and answer the following questions designed to help you grasp the information most pertinent to our goal.

What is Babylon called in verse 1?

the great prostitute

How does verse 2 depict her influence over the earth's inhabitants? _the inhabitants of the earth were intoxicated w/ the wine of her adulteries_

How is she dressed according to verse 4? _She was dressed in purple & scarlet and was glittering with gold, precious stones & pearls_

What is she holding in verse 4? _She held a golden cup in her hand filled w/ abominable things and the filth of her adulteries_

Sound familiar? John penned an eerie echo of Belshazzar's feast and his unholy use of holy vessels.

How is Babylon described in Revelation 17:6? _She was drunk w/ the blood of the saints – the blood of those who bore testimony to Jesus_

Who is this "woman" according to verse 18? *She is the great city that rules over the kings of the earth.*

One last question: Based on all we've considered today, can you think of possible reasons why Babylon is symbolically described as a prostitute? *She is a temptress. She lures people into sin. And she is Satan's vessel to pull Christians away from God*

We survived, didn't we? And don't we have a little better understanding of all Babylon represents in Scripture? The glitter of Daniel's Babylon was no less a ploy by the enemy of God to lure away the faithful. Even in the lesser splendor that wooed the Medes and Persians, her cup was full and intoxicating.

Only a true Daniel could resist. May God make us Daniels.

Great job today! See you tomorrow!

DAY THREE THE FALL OF REVELATION'S BABYLON

Today's Treasure: *"Woe! Woe, O great city, O Babylon, city of power! In one hour your doom has come." Revelation 18:10*

This week in our study of the Book of Daniel, we arrived at the critical transition from the Babylonian Empire to the silver-armed Medo-Persians. The fall of Daniel's Babylon offers the irresistible opportunity to compare the fall of the final Babylon depicted in the Book of Revelation. We can draw insight from Revelation 17 and 18 to help us understand Babylon as a mentality in our current surroundings and as a location in history and prophecy.

What was the most interesting thing you learned about Babylon—in Genesis or Revelation—in yesterday's lesson? *That Nimrod who was the 1st ruler in scripture and He ruled Babylon. His wife Simaramis had a son supposed by miraculous conception which was the FALSE fulfillment of the promised seed*

We drew day 2 to a conclusion by questioning why Babylon is symbolically described as a prostitute in Revelation 17. Perhaps you mentioned something about her ability to seductively lure people away from God by offering false—and instant—fulfillment. Today in Revelation 18, we will get to see the form some of those allurements took. The chapter records Babylon's fall, but in doing so it describes her powerful art of seduction that will ultimately earn God's wrath.

Please read Revelation 18 and complete the following:

🦁 In brief phrases, list every way Revelation 18 describes Babylon's
excessiveness and wealth. Be sure to record the verse locations.

Cargoes of gold, silver, precious
stones & pearls; fine linen, purple
silk and violet cloth, every
sort of citron wood & articles of every
kind made of ivory, costly wood   _vs 12-13_
bronze, iron & myrrh and frankincense, of wine.....

How are her sins depicted in verse 5? _her sins are piled up to_
heaven and God has remembered her crimes

Compare Genesis 11:4, recalling that "Babylon" was the name given to the place
where this occurred. Describe any symbolic comparison you see between Genesis
11:4 and Revelation 18:5. _The people wanted to build the tower of_
Babel to the heavens to make a name for themselves &
Babylon's sins were piled up to heaven

What had Babylon given herself according to verse 7?

☐ sorrow   ☐ pleasure   ☒ luxury   ☐ sponge baths

What did she boast in her heart (v. 7)? _"I sit as a queen; I am_
not a widow, and I will never mourn"

Based on the message of verse 17, how stable is the great wealth of Babylon-
like societies? _Not very. In one hour great_
wealth will be brought to ruin

Why do the "saints and apostles and prophets" have cause to rejoice (v. 20)?

☐ God has made them wealthy.   ☐ God has promised hope.
☒ God has judged Babylon.   ☐ God has raised the dead.

In Daniel's Babylon and in Revelation's Babylon, the very lives of God's righteous are
at stake. The Babylon that surrounds us is figurative and cultural in nature, but it is
neither less seductive nor destructive.

Name one way you've noticed our Babylon-like culture growing increasingly
less tolerant of Christians. _Can't pray in schools, can't_
pray at graduation ceremonies. Can put
nativities up in public places have taken
Christmas out of Christmas - Stores wish "Happy
Holidays"
Verse 23 paints a vivid picture of Babylon's seductive power. How were the
nations led astray?

By her magic spell.

Surely we've all felt figuratively spellbound over the seductive beauty of worldly merchandise. My temptations are not necessarily yours. If you're willing, please share what seems to lure you most in the marketplace.

Sweets

Of all the cultural comparisons we've drawn between the biblical depictions of Babylon and our Western culture, "excessive luxuries" keeps rising to the surface. In fact, we might say, "It pile[s] up to heaven."

Excess was one of the first comparisons we drew between Nebuchadnezzar's Babylon and our own societal surroundings. Our fourth week of study offered a perfect opportunity to camp on the word *luxury*. You will recall that Daniel pleaded with Nebuchadnezzar to renounce his sins and show kindness to the poor and oppressed. The king had grown proud in his prosperity and power, taking credit for all his success. He'd also bathed himself in luxury; he detached himself completely from those in need and those he had hurt. So, as you can see, both "Babylons" are characterized by excessive luxuries.

The point is not that God only honors a vow of poverty. The point is avoiding the corruption of gross excess that catapults us so far into our wants that we cease to recognize need. Let's face it. Sometimes moderation in a culture of excess can be more challenging than abstinence.

> **GROSS EXCESS CATAPULTS US SO FAR INTO OUR WANTS THAT WE CEASE TO RECOGNIZE NEED.**

If you agree with that last statement, why do you think this is true?

If you haven't tasted something it doesn't have the draw of something we have freely enjoyed

The endless addictions of our culture betray our trouble with "some" in a land of much. Revelation 18:9 talks about the "kings of the earth who committed adultery with her and shared her luxury." One definition for the Greek word for luxury is "to act with wantonness from abundance."[8]

If abundance leads us to pride, decadence, or an insatiable lust for more, we, like the kings described in Revelation 18, are being corrupted by it. "In her hand [Babylon] holds a golden cup that promises a heady draught of carnal satisfaction. Its contents, however, are quite otherwise. … Moral corruption and all manner of ceremonial uncleanness are what she offers."[9]

As we begin to wrap up, look at verse 22. What will be silenced in Revelation's Babylon? *The music of the musicians, noise from workmen, the sound of a millstone*

The portrait of Babylon isn't complete without colorful brush strokes depicting its entertainment industry. Needless to say, nothing is wrong with music. Indeed, what a gift from God! Furthermore, nothing is wrong with wholesome entertainment. A Babylonian musician, however, plays a Babylonian tune. And what is more intoxicating, more luring than music? Why are some of us moms so particular about our children's taste in music if not its profound influence? Perhaps Babylon's musicians—not unlike our own—played the loud, rhythmic melodies of carnal pleasures, warping the listener's sense of reality. Can we spell MTV?

Who can blame us for listening? We just want to feel *something*. Something good. Something full. Eugene Peterson words our attempts well:

> We try to get [joy] through entertainment. We pay someone to make jokes, tell stories, perform dramatic actions, sing songs. We buy the vitality of another's imagination to divert and enliven our own poor lives. The enormous entertainment industry in America is a sign of the depletion of joy in our culture. Society is a bored, gluttonous king employing a court jester to divert it after an overindulgent meal. But that kind of joy never penetrates our lives, never changes our basic constitution. The effects are extremely temporary—a few minutes, a few hours, a few days at most. When we run out of money, the joy trickles away.[10]

How do his words strike a chord in you concerning our generation?

That all they see is movies, TV, that cause them to be unsensitive to sin. They listen to music & read books that cause them to think.

Respond to God about whatever He's been showing you in a written prayer.

Lord, I pray that my family would be very careful of what we allow to come into our minds. Protect little Bradyn. Thank You Jesus—

From Satan's first entrance on the stage of earth in Genesis 3, he's tried to convince believers that God is holding out on them. Cheating them. Satan tries to suggest that this life is all we can be sure of: live it sacrificially and we've lost it all. He mocks, "How gullible—how stupid—could you be? Live it up while you've got the chance!" As we walk up and down the sidewalks of our present Babylons, stay alert to his seductions and to the songs in his town squares.

In reality, Satan is the cheater and Babylon is his queen, offering false fulfillments for any taker.

Buyer beware.

STAY ALERT TO SATAN'S SEDUCTIONS AND TO THE SONGS IN HIS TOWN SQUARES.

DAY FOUR NEITHER CORRUPT NOR NEGLIGENT

Today's Treasure: *They could find no corruption in him, because he was trustworthy and neither corrupt nor negligent. Daniel 6:4*

Today we return to the opening scenes of Daniel 6. So far this week we've discussed the fall of the Babylonian Empire and compared it to the fall of Revelation's Babylon. The sixth chapter of Daniel unfolds with the appointment of a new administration under the authority of Darius. Earlier in the week we established the approximate age of Daniel at this point in the story line.

About how old was he? *early 80's*

Fill in the following blanks: Daniel 6:3 (NIV) tells us he " *so* *distinguished himself* among the administrators and the satraps by his *exceptional* *qualities* that the king planned to set him over the whole kingdom."

Remember that Belshazzar, the last Babylonian ruler in residence, seemed to have little familiarity with Daniel. We supposed that he probably served in relative obscurity during the frenetic changes of authority after Nebuchadnezzar's death. With Belshazzar dead and buried, Daniel 6 returns him to a place of trust very close to King Darius.

Glance at the end of Daniel 5. How old was Darius when he "received" the kingdom? (Check one.) ☐ 7 ☐ 21 ☐ 47 ☒ 62

Perhaps he'd been around the block enough times to know that, as he faced a foreign populace, he needed the assistance of someone who knew the city and people of Babylon like the back of his hand. Daniel was such a man.

Please read Daniel 6:3-13. Why did the conspirators have to trap Daniel with a plan that had "something to do with the law of his God" (v. 4)? *Because they would never find any basis for charges against him unless it had to do w/the law of his God.*

Verse 4 contains our key word as we seek to live with integrity in an enticing world. We stated from the very beginning that God's desire is not for us to turn our churches and Christian gatherings into hideouts from the world. Rather, they're meant to be places where we become equipped and fortified to minister out in the world. God desires for us to be light-bearers in this dark culture and to be highly effective fruit-bearers for the glory of His Name.

Our study raises these questions: Can we be culturally relevant for the cause of Christ without becoming spiritually irrelevant? Can we serve the world in the name of Christ without becoming a servant to the world? And, finally, the key question: Can we live in this excessive, self-absorbed culture without becoming *corrupted* by it?

Read verse 4 again carefully. In the NIV, NASB®, and HCSB® you see forms of the word "corrupt." What is the context? *That there was no dishonesty in him. No wrong behavior would be found in Daniel*

Compare Revelation 19:1-3. You may be surprised to realize that this "Hallelujah Chorus" is the praise that comes to God as a direct result of Babylon's apocalyptic fall. Take a good look at verse 2. What had "the great prostitute" done? *She had corrupted the earth by her adulteries and the blood of God's servants was on her hands*

In each of the major Bible translations, you'll find renderings of the word "corrupt." In Revelation 19:2 the NIV offers wording adequately representative of them all: "He has condemned the great prostitute who *corrupted* the earth by her adulteries" (emphasis mine). Satan uses Babylon, the symbolic persona of all that seems beautiful, enticing, and instantly gratifying in the world, as a puppet to corrupt people. *Babylon*

You and I often think of puppets as innocent and playful. This puppet is a prostitute, and, if you'll allow me to make the point bluntly, her pimp is the Devil. Forgive any offense, but I want you to see the connection.

Daniel is proof that corruption in Babylon is not compulsory. We really can make it here, Sister. We really can live out life with integrity. But we will never do it by accident. In fact, perhaps nothing in our lives will have to be more deliberate. Daniel walked a tightrope upon which God alone could have secured him.

Fill in the blank from Daniel 6:4:

We are told he was "neither corrupt nor _____*negligent*_____."

That Daniel wasn't negligent tells us he did his job. Stay with me here. If we are in a workplace where we have to be negligent in our positions in order to keep from being corrupted by our environment, we need a new job.

I believe with all my heart that God wants His representatives to be Daniels in our worlds: distinguishing ourselves with exceptional God-given qualities (v. 3) and performing our tasks as if God Himself were our boss. Colossians 3:23 says it beautifully: "Whatever you do, work at it with all your heart, as working for the Lord, not for men."

"At this, the administrators and the satraps tried to find grounds for charges against Daniel in his conduct of government affairs, but they were unable to do so. They could find no corruption in him, because he was trustworthy and neither corrupt nor negligent."

📖 DANIEL 6:4

In the process, we must guard ourselves voraciously from *both* corruption and negligence. Some environments make the tightrope—that fine line—virtually impossible to find, let alone walk. An environment that might corrupt me might not corrupt you. The reverse is also true.

Have you ever found yourself in a work environment where you could not do your job well without being corrupted by it? If so, explain.

_____No_____

If negligence is the only way we can avoid corruption in a job or service environment (yes, even a church or charity organization), let's consider that God may have our names on a transfer list. Our goal is becoming Daniels in our generation: people void of corruption *and* negligence. You've got it in you, and so do I. Those of us who have received Christ as our Savior are inhabited by the empowering, consecrating Spirit of the living God.

We're extraordinary because He's extraordinary. Let's start living like it.

DAY FIVE KEEP SINGING

Today's Treasure: *How can we sing the songs of the Lord while in a foreign land?*
Psalm 137:4

In Daniel's 80 years he'd had enough excitement for 10 lifetimes. He was a privileged teenager and the son of Hebrew nobles when the Babylonians crashed through Jerusalem and stole him from his homeland. After what must have seemed like endless miles and hopeless days, he stared bug-eyed and slack jawed as the infamous city of Babylon rose up in the horizon.

King Nebuchadnezzar had plundered the cream of Israel's crop. Daniel and other young Hebrews like him—handsome, intelligent, gifted, and talented—were swept immediately into the wind of Babylonian indoctrination and cultural seduction. Presumably, all but a handful of them were absorbed into virtual irrelevance. Those who chose not to be defiled by Babylon's excess experienced some of the greatest adventure engraved in Holy Writ.

Reflect back on all we've studied. What kinds of things would Daniel and his friends have missed had they chosen instead to blend in?

The fiery furnace, the lions
in the lions den, the exiles
being freed and allowed to
go back to Jerusalem

Daniel served among the chief counselors under the 43-year reign of Babylon's mightiest king. He no doubt saw the flagrant activity of a miraculous and mighty God more vividly within the walls of that pagan city than in Jerusalem. He learned that God's presence accompanied His faithful children no matter where life took them. He watched firsthand the prosperity a sovereign God could assign a polytheistic king. From an equally close vantage point, he also watched the insanity that same sovereign God could give a king who took too much credit. Daniel saw Babylon's greatest monarch proudly bow his back and then humbly bend his knees.

Surely a thousand images danced through Daniel's head as he witnessed the funeral festivities following Nebuchadnezzar's death. Violence and betrayal kept four other kings from occupying Babylon's seat of power for long. In the meantime, Daniel aged and continued his civil service with relative obscurity.

A party gone awry led to Daniel's summons to interpret handwriting on the wall for a baffled Belshazzar: *mene, mene, tekel, parsin.* The basic message from God? "I've seen. And you're done." Before the night was over, the Medo-Persian army flooded the city through the riverbed and slew the king who'd profaned the holy. Mighty Babylon fell to the strong arms of the silver kingdom.

Over the coming weeks, Daniel watched the establishment of a new administration and gained the favor of Darius the Mede. The leadership had changed, but human nature proved the same. In no time at all, jealous colleagues conspired against Daniel and placed a dismayed Darius in the position to follow through with a hasty edict. Instead of meeting his death in the lions' den, Daniel met God's angel.

> Complete the following sentence based on Daniel 6:23. "When Daniel was lifted from the den, no wound was found on him, because

☐ the angel shut the lions' mouths. ☒ he had trusted in his God.

King Darius issued a decree throughout his kingdom that Daniel's God must be feared and reverenced. "So Daniel prospered during the reign of Darius and the reign of Cyrus the Persian" (Dan. 6:28).

Daniel also witnessed other welcome changes. "After the Persians took over Babylon in 539 B.C., they discouraged the continuation of the mystery religions of Babylon. Subsequently the Babylonian cultists moved" elsewhere.[11] Overall, however, the Persians treated the Babylonians kindly. In fact, they may have embittered some of the Hebrews for "an insufficient judgment on those who devastated Israel."[12] Within a year, Cyrus the Great issued a decree to free the exiles and allow them to return to their homeland of Jerusalem … just as God foretold through the prophet Isaiah. Seventy years had come and gone. Some lived to see their homeland. Others died in exile.

Today we conclude part 1 of our series on the Book of Daniel. I hope so much you'll stick around for part 2. There we'll consider *The Ancient of Days and the End of Times.* Daniel will remain our saga's protagonist as the book shifts to prophecies he received during the reigns of Belshazzar, Darius, and Cyrus. I assure you, the excitement in the Book of Daniel is just beginning. I have been greatly moved by our study of the first half; however, I look at life differently now as an exile of sorts in this

GOD'S PRESENCE ACCOMPANIES HIS FAITHFUL CHILDREN NO MATTER WHERE LIFE TAKES THEM.

Babylon-like culture. I'm not ready for our present emphasis to end, but God tucked a telling chapter into the pages of the psalms that will provide a fitting benediction.

Please read Psalm 137:1-6. What does this segment of Scripture describe?

the exiled people in Babylon

This psalm is not from the pen of King David. The ink in this pen was the broken and bleeding heart of one of Israel's exiles in Babylon. The rivers by which the Hebrew people sat and wept "refer to the Euphrates and the canals and waterways stemming from it."[13] You'll recall that the Euphrates ran straight through the city. God had parted waters before and used them as ways of escape for the people of Israel (the Red Sea in Ex. 14 and the Jordan River in Josh. 3). Perhaps that's why the exiles sat at the banks of Babylon's river and wept. Escape seemed to elude them this time. Little did they know God would use a riverbed once again to lead to their escape by allowing an entryway for the Persians under the walls of Babylon.

Look at Psalm 137 again. Listen to the emotion of the exiles. _Feel it._ Imagine being taunted by mockers of your faith and told to sing one of your silly God-songs. Imagine being made fun of, or perhaps you don't have to imagine. Perhaps you already know what it's like for people to make fun of you for your faith. For the self-proclaimed intelligentsia to act as if you're stupid and gullible for believing the Bible. At times we may feel so outnumbered and outclassed that we're tempted to "hang up our harps." We can't do it, Sweet One. We can't keep quiet. We have to keep singing the songs of the Lord in this foreign land.

We must remember that we have a new and heavenly Jerusalem coming where we'll make ourselves right at home. But until then, our job is to keep singing the songs of our God by the rivers of Babylon until all who have ears to hear can listen.

How can _you_ keep singing the songs of God in your own Babylon? In other words, how can you draw a practical parallel from Psalm 137:1-6 for your own life?

Be a witness always for the Lord. Even when trials come into our life – we need to count it all joy as God allowed it and He is all-sufficient – so we don't need to worry.

The Apostle Paul posed a wonderful answer in Philippians 4:4. "Rejoice in the Lord always. I will say it again: Rejoice!" The world can't help but notice those accosted by joy. The world also can't help noticing a life that seems to work. Our lives can become flesh-and-blood felt boards of the great and glorious paradox: life is found by losing it for the sake of Christ. A vessel is filled by pouring out. The key to receiving is giving. The key to living is dying to self. The greatest in the kingdom is the servant of all. God has been right all along. His upside-down path is the only way to true contentment and satisfaction. The world's claim of happiness is betrayed by an ever-increasing lust for more. Nothing ever suffices. Nothing ever will. Christ alone satisfies the ailing human soul.

Cyrus the Great freed the captives of Babylon, but until further notice, you and I are still here. We remain exiles, chosen like Daniel to influence our overindulged, self-absorbed culture for the kingdom of God. We—believers in Christ in a post-modern, increasingly profane western culture—may feel like a small handful amid a scorning populous; but Daniel, Hananiah, Mishael, and Azariah were four in the midst of thousands. Our path to success is theirs: uncompromising resolve in big and small things alike. As we conclude part 1, the following quote offers thought:

> It's highly probable that if Daniel had compromised by eating the king's food, he would have compromised about other things too, like bowing to his image. "Oh, I'll still pray to God, but I'll just bow to this thing to spare my life, because, after all, I can do a lot of ministry for God if I survive." That wasn't Daniel or his uncompromising buddies Shadrach, Meshach, and Abednego. When you obey God in the small things, it becomes a lot easier to obey Him in the big things. That's when God shows up. He can shut the mouths of lions and protect you from the flames.[14]

Do you have a nagging feeling in an area that appears relatively insignificant? Does it seem like a small thing, but you can't shake the feeling that you're supposed to act on it? Could God be insisting on obedience in what seems like a small matter to prepare you for obedience in matters that aren't?

If your answers are "yes," describe the relatively insignificant matter and consider why it may not be as insignificant to God.

I need to be doing for others

Amid a tidal wave of temptation, Daniel and his friends stood firm, and so can we. We cannot seclude ourselves indefinitely in Christian hideouts. Our lives must be poured out like healing ointment on this injured land. We must not forsake meeting together and jealously holding one another accountable to walk in truth and remain fortified. For now, we live in this Babylon-like culture, but we can proactively guard ourselves from being corrupted by it. Otherwise, like the masses in Daniel's day, we, too, will be absorbed into virtual irrelevance.

This study has gotten to me, Beloved. I hope it has gotten to you, too. I am convinced that certain concepts we've studied together for the last six weeks will remain as pillars of fortification for me for the rest of my days. May God stir my remembrance with deep conviction should I forget. I want to ask you to participate in a very important exercise as a conclusion to part 1. Meditate on the concepts you've learned most vividly in the last six weeks. Recall the signs of corruption and ways we learned to guard ourselves against it.

OUR PATH TO SUCCESS IS UNCOMPROMISING RESOLVE IN BIG AND SMALL THINGS ALIKE.

Conclude by writing a very personal prayer to God in the space remaining. Voice your requests and your own heart's desires reflecting the concepts we've studied. Talk to God about your remaining time in Babylon. Pour out your heart to Him. He is a refuge for you. He is listening. He is your God. Your ever-present help in times of trouble.

_____

_____

_____

_____

_____

_____

_____

_____

Thank you for allowing me the unspeakable privilege of walking beside you to the shore of Babylon. When you've finished writing your prayer, go over to that poplar tree, take down your harp, and start singing the songs of the Lord with all your might … and for all your days. Not one will go unheard.

1. John F. Walvoord and Roy B. Zuck, eds., *The Bible Knowledge Commentary of the Old Testament* (Wheaton, IL: SP Publications, Inc., 1985), 1346-47.
2. Ibid., 1327.
3. Ibid., 1347.
4. Joyce G. Baldwin, *Daniel* (Downers Grove, IL: InterVarsity Press, 1978), 132.
5. Mark Hitchcock, *The Complete Book of Bible Prophecy* (Wheaton, IL: Tyndale House Publishers, 1999), 97.
6. Walvoord and Zuck, 970.
7. Hitchcock, 97.
8. Spiros Zodhiates, ThD., gen. ed., *Lexical Aids to the New Testament, Hebrew-Greek Key Word Study Bible, New International Version* (Chattanooga, TN: AMG Publishers), #5139, 1674.
9. Robert H. Mounce, *The Book of Revelation* (Grand Rapids, MI: William B. Eerdmans Publishing Company), 310-11.
10. Eugene H. Peterson, *A Long Obedience in the Same Direction,* 2nd ed. (Downers Grove, IL: InterVarsity Press, 2000), 96-97.
11. John F. Walvoord and Roy B. Zuck, eds., *The Bible Knowledge Commentary of the New Testament* (Wheaton, IL: SP Publications, Inc., 1983), 970.
12. Walvoord and Zuck, 890.
13. Ibid.
14. Janet Folger, *The Criminalization of Christianity* (Sisters, OR: Multnomah, 2005), 192.

DANIEL

PART TWO
WORDS OF PROPHECY

DEDICATION

In memory of Buddy Walters, an unparalleled mentor to me in the study of God's Word—

Within the four walls of a Bible doctrine class, I caught a burning passion for Scripture that no amount of time, trouble, or ease has been able to douse. His handprints are on every single Bible study that has come from my keyboard.

Perhaps Buddy's life is summed best in a story a friend of his told me after Buddy's unexpected death. As the two of them waited for praise team practice to begin, having no idea that one would worship Jesus face-to-face in just a few hours, Buddy shared with him what God was teaching him from the Book of Ephesians … and wept. I'd seen him do it so many times. He just never got over the wonder of God's Word. I never want to either. In his memory I will remind students as long as I live that "all Scripture is God-breathed."

Debbie, Winston, and Andrew, thank you for sharing him with hungry people like me.

Keith and I love you so much.

Beth

THE
ANCIENT
OF DAYS

7

SESSION SEVEN
THE ANCIENT OF DAYS

We launch part 2 of our series on the Book of Daniel with a chapter that could not have greater importance.

Our session as well as the five daily assignments ahead will center on the seventh chapter of Daniel. The clock rewinds to the first year of Belshazzar's reign at the time when our protagonist is about 67 years old.

Read Daniel 7:1-14 and consider the following participants in the dream scene:

1. _Daniel_ himself (vv. 15-16).

2. The _little_ _horn_ (v. 8). (ANti-Christ)

• He had "eyes like the _eyes_ of a _Man_."

• He spoke _boastfully_. *Word Biblical Commentary* translates the Aramaic, "and a mouth _Making_ _great_ _Statements_."

Read Revelation 13:4-9.

3. The _Ancient_ of _Days_ (Dan. 7:9-10). (God, the Father)

• He entered the scene as _Chief_ _Justice_ of the _Universe_

• He _Sat_ on a _Chariot_ _throne_.

• The _books_ were _opened_ before Him.

The significance of Daniel's name: God is _My_ _Judge_ or God _has_ _judged_ .

The significance of God's specific title in this scene …

- The Ancient of Days judged _in_ _favor_ of the _Saints_ then the _beast was slain_ .

4. One _like_ a _Son of Man_ (vv. 13-14. Compare Mark 14:60-65).

- Daniel saw the _Coronation_ of the _Messiah King_

- *The New American Commentary* reads, "The Son is presented to the Ancient of Days that he might receive his _Father's gift_ , namely, a _universal kingdom_ ."

"The saints of the Most High will receive the kingdom and will possess it forever— yes, for ever and ever" (v. 18).

Literally, "to the forever and to the _forever_ of _forevers_ ."[1]

---

1. Stephen R. Miller, *The New American Commentary: Daniel, vol. 18* (Nashville: Broadman & Holman, 1994), 211.

Part 2 of our series is officially off the ground, launching us into the prophetic and eschatological second half of the book. I want to encourage you to strengthen your resolve to participate fully in the remaining sessions and all the daily assignments. The six video sessions in part 2 will allow us only enough time to hit the high points. The daily assignments will play a significantly greater role than those in part 1.

Our primary goal is to come to know the Most High more deeply by developing a stronger grasp of the Book of Daniel. Part 2 presents additional secondary goals. One is to develop a working knowledge of the dispensational-premillennial model of understanding end-time events. Don't let those big words frighten you. We'll learn what they mean. My hope is that you'll be able to chart end-time events on a time line in potential chronological order by the conclusion of our series. I also want you to know them well enough to explain them to someone else.

You can do it! In fact, I think you're going to love it! However, reaching the goal will demand work, especially if the concepts are new to you. Rest assured the work will be satisfying, Dear One, and your added investment will bring an incomparable return. When our study is over, I also encourage you to do further research into other interpretations and sit under other teachers. Remember, brilliant scholars through the centuries have held very different views and interpretations of end-time events. We are going to be dealing with some very difficult texts. Check with your pastor and other teachers. Ask their views and their recommendations of sound materials they'd suggest. The study of eschatology is thrilling! Explore it thoroughly with your Bible and your mind wide open. In the meantime, keep this ever before you: no matter which interpretation gets our vote of confidence, in the end God will do what He wants, how He wants, and when He wants. He is the King of glory.

THIS WEEK'S PRINCIPAL QUESTIONS

DAY 1 According to Daniel 2, what are the names of the four empires, and which part of the statue represents each empire?

DAY 2 What event does Daniel 7:22 foretell?

DAY 3 What is the most well-known title of the little horn (see 1 John 2:18)?

DAY 4 What does Daniel 7:25 specifically say will happen to the "saints"?

DAY 5 Briefly define *amillennialism* and *premillennialism*.

DAY ONE FOUR BEASTS OUT OF THE SEA

Today's Treasure: *Four great beasts, each different from the others, came up out of the sea. Daniel 7:3*

In today's lesson we explore the four beasts in Daniel's dream (Dan. 7) and their parallels to Nebuchadnezzar's dream statue (Dan. 2). Aren't you glad we've already dipped our toes in the prophetic waters of chapter 2? Daniel 7 is so chock-full of complex and crucial information that any measure of familiarity is a relief.

Daniel's role in the two dreams drastically differs. In Daniel 2, he was the interpreter. In Daniel 7, he was the dreamer. Though the two dreams have parallels, we don't have to wonder why God would entrust a certain heavenly scene to Daniel that wasn't conveyed to Nebuchadnezzar. God's faithful servant and child got to glance into heaven while God limited Nebuchadnezzar's visions to scenes that would play out on earth. Session 7 cast the spotlight on the court scene of the Ancient of Days and the Son of man.

Reread Daniel 7:9-14. If you participated in the session, what was most meaningful to you about the court scene? If you didn't view the session, which part of this segment intrigues you most?

God sitting on the throne.

Our seventh session thrilled me. Seeing God as the Ancient of Days brings both untold comfort and answered questions in a world filled with injustice. Take heart, Dear One. Time doesn't diminish God's judgment.

Now, take a good look at Daniel 7:1. According to this verse, Daniel had one dream containing multiple visions. The court scene was preceded by Daniel's vision of four beasts. Please read Daniel 7:2-8.

How did these beasts emerge (vv. 2-3)? *The four winds of heaven were churning up the sea and the beasts emerged from the sea.*

This portion of Daniel's vision is symbolic. The four winds probably represent powerful forces coming from the four points of the compass to stir up this sea. Scholars disagree on the meaning of the "sea" from which the beasts emerged. *The Bible Knowledge Commentary* says, "Throughout the Old Testament the Mediterranean Sea is referred to as the Great Sea. This vision then related specifically to the Mediterranean world."[1] *The New American Commentary* adds another point of view based on Daniel 7:17.

Look ahead to 7:17. What do the four great beasts represent?

Four kingdoms

From where will the four beasts rise? *from the earth*

"Thus v. 17 interprets the 'sea' to be symbolic of the 'earth,' and the beasts that rise out of this 'sea' are interpreted later in the chapter as being great 'earthly kingdoms.'"[2] Both interpretations work in Daniel 7 since all four earthly kingdoms represented by the beasts did emerge in the lands surrounding the Mediterranean Sea. Of course, their greater common denominator was domination over Israel.

Our look ahead at verse 17 confirmed that "the four great beasts are four kingdoms." Thankfully, their identities are already familiar to us. They are the same Gentile empires prophesied by the statue in Nebuchadnezzar's dream (Dan. 2), now described in greater detail in Daniel's dream (Dan. 7).

In the left column, please write in proper order the name of the four empires we discussed in session 2 and week 2. In the center column, document the part of the statue (and corresponding material) representing each empire according to Daniel 2. We'll fill in the third column later.

Gentile Empires	Symbolized in Daniel 2	Symbolized in Daniel 7
Babylonian	Head (Gold)	The lion w/ eagle wings
Medo-Persia	Chest & arms (silver)	Bear was raised up on one side w/ 3 ribs in his teeth
Grecian	Belly & Thighs (Bronze)	leopard w/ 4 wings & 4 heads
Roman	Legs (Iron)	unidentified beast w/ 10 horns

Now, let's concentrate on the third column. Each of the first three beasts in Daniel 7 has peculiarities. Look carefully in verses 4-6. Note each peculiarity:

The lion had _eagle wings_

The bear _lopsided - had 3 ribs in his mouth_

The leopard had _4 wings & 4 heads_

We'll begin with the lion with eagle's wings. Elsewhere, the Word of God symbolizes Nebuchadnezzar and/or Babylon as both an eagle (Jer. 49:22; Lam. 4:19; Ezek. 17:3) and a lion (Jer. 4:7; 49:19; 50:17,44). "Statues of winged lions, which are believed to have been representative of the empire, have been found in the ruins of Babylon."[3] The tearing off of the eagle's wings probably represents the king's season of insanity. That the lion "stood on two feet like a man, and the heart of a man was given to it" reflects Nebuchadnezzar's restoration and human heart thereafter.

Please record this symbol (the lion with eagle's wings) in the third column alongside the Babylonian Empire and the head of gold (Dan. 2).

The second beast was a bear "raised up on one of its sides" (v. 5). It represents the Medo-Persian Empire. The lopsided stature of the beast "suggests that though Persia rose later than Media, Persia soon overshadowed the Medes in their united kingdom."[4] The kingdoms united against the great Babylon, but the resultant empire was lopsided toward the greater strength of the Persians. The three ribs probably symbolize "Medo-Persia's three major conquests—Babylon (539 B.C.), Lydia (546 B.C.), and

Egypt (525 B.C.)."[5] Please record this symbol (the lopsided bear) in the third column alongside the Medo-Persian Empire and the chest and arms of silver (Dan. 2).

The third beast was a leopard with four wings and four heads. Both the leopard and the wings symbolize swiftness. Together they illustrate exceeding sleekness and speed. Alexander the Great conquered the entire Medo-Persian Empire between 334 and 330 B.C. The four heads of the leopard foretold with stunning accuracy the division of Alexander's great empire into four parts after his death. Please record this symbol in the third column alongside the Grecian Empire and the belly and thighs of bronze (Dan. 2).

Daniel leaves the fourth beast lacking description in chapter 7. Perhaps the vision defied any earthly comparison. While Keith and I were in Africa, I was stunned to see several kinds of animals that I didn't know existed. At least I could describe one of them to my daughters as catlike. Daniel, on the other hand, had nothing with which to compare the fourth beast.

According to Daniel 7:7, what made this beast "different from all the former beasts"?

_____

How does Daniel 7:24 identify the 10 horns? *The 10 horns are 10 kings*

You probably recall the iron legs on the statue in Daniel 2. The two legs or feet likely represented the Roman Empire's division east to west. We characterized the 10 toes as future kings (heads of state) or kingdoms with roots in the Roman Empire that would form a confederation. We'll talk about the little horn that rose up among them tomorrow. For now, please record an unidentified beast with 10 horns in the third column alongside the Roman Empire and the legs of iron (Dan. 2).

The fourth beast lacks something the first three beasts have in common. We pointed this out in session 7, but let's reiterate. Look at verse 12. The first three beasts lost their authority, but they were "allowed to live for a period of time." This means that each of the cultures was absorbed to some degree by the next empire, so parts of them lived on for a while. When the fourth empire is destroyed, nothing of it will linger in the kingdom without end.

The most obvious question is why were the four empires represented by a statue of metals in Daniel 2 and great beasts in Daniel 7. The explanation I found most plausible is described in *The New American Commentary*: "There may be truth to the idea that the image with its glittering metals portrays the world's kingdoms from humanity's viewpoint—impressive and great, whereas the beasts depict these earthly kingdoms from God's perspective—vicious and destructive."[6]

Whew! What a way to begin a week! Perhaps you can already tell that we have a wild ride ahead of us. Hang on, and hang in there! Our study will only grow more fascinating. Fabulous job, Sister! Rest assured, God is accomplishing something deep in you.

WHEN THE FOURTH EMPIRE IS DESTROYED, NOTHING OF IT WILL LINGER IN THE KINGDOM WITHOUT END.

DAY TWO THE LITTLE HORN

Today's Treasure: *This horn had eyes like the eyes of a man and a mouth that spoke boastfully. Daniel 7:8*

Yesterday I hiked the mountain behind my writing cabin with all of you on my mind. Though small by Teton standards, its climb was steep enough to burn my lungs and test my endurance. The payoff never fails, however. I could see the river for several miles and reveled in the vivid reminder of why it's called the Snake. I could hear the flap of a falcon's wings and the whistle of the bird soaring over my head.

Many of us have taken Bible study journeys together before. Few of them demanded the steep mind-climb this one will. Our spiritual lungs will burn, and at times we'll think we want to head back down and do something easier. Please don't! If we stick with this, God will give us a view of His glory and His sovereign plan that could well be unmatched.

Remember, we're giving up the Babylonian approach to Bible study that says it has to be all about me to interest me. Lessons like the ones this week increase our working knowledge of God's Word *and* build our faith. Today our attentions will be drawn to the little horn introduced in Daniel 7:8. Please ask God to give you particular focus as you scour every word the seventh chapter of Daniel offers about this little horn. Daniel 7:7-28 describes the evil successes of the little horn as well as ways he'll be defeated. The two columns below will help you keep your thoughts organized.

Please read Daniel 7:7-28 carefully and list every fact about the little horn under its proper heading. These "successes" or "failures" may be implied or obvious. Be sure to note the verse location with each fact.

The little horn's successes	The little horn's defeats
vs 7 { crushed & devoured its victims / Trampled underfoot what was left	was slain, body destroyed thrown in blazing fire
vs 21 waging war against the saints & defeating them	Power taken away
Boasted	

🦁 What event does verse 22 foretell?

Judgment Day (Judgement Seat of Christ)

👜 How does this "judgment" encourage you in your temptations and struggles?

Encourages us to walk w/ the Lord (I want to do better)

Daniel 7:24 tells us that "the ten horns are ten kings who will come" from the fourth kingdom. We've already identified the fourth kingdom in both Daniel 2 and Daniel 7. What is this fourth Gentile empire?

The Roman Empire

Time would reveal the fulfillment of Daniel's prophecy centuries after his death. The Roman Empire stomped and trampled every inch of available ground with particular viciousness. Division and weak leadership finally led to its decline and ultimate demise. Interestingly, no other comparable world power or empire has since risen. "When the hordes from the north conquered the Roman Empire in the fifth century A.D., they did not unite to form another empire. Instead individual nations emerged out of the old Roman Empire. Some of those nations and others stemming from them have continued till the present day."[7] Some scholars believe the present age, then, is the 10-horned era of the fourth beast."[8]

Basically, two possibilities exist for fulfillment of this prophecy. It must either apply to ancient Rome or it must be yet future. Some believe that the fourth beast and 10 horns applies to first-century Rome. They point to the persecution under the Roman emperors Nero and Domitian. However, no historical 10 kingdoms seem to fit. I believe the precision of the prophecy calls for fulfillment yet to come in our future.

We call the era in which we live the *church age*. It began with the birth of the New Testament church in Acts 2 when God poured out His Spirit upon the disciples and added about three thousand to their number (see Acts 2:41). For clarity's sake, we will adopt the same terminology. Sometimes you'll hear this era called the *age of grace* as opposed to the Old Testament *age of law*, but we won't often use this terminology because God extended lavish grace in the Old Testament as well as the New.

Look back over this paragraph to make sure this information is sticking. To what does the church age refer?

We presently live in the church age, but the 10 kings prophesied in Daniel 7 may emerge in the future. Many scholars "hold that the time of the 10 horns is yet future, that the present church age is not seen in this vision, and that 10 kings will coexist over a future revived [or realigned] Roman Empire."[9] If the 10-horned era of

TIME WOULD REVEAL THE FULFILLMENT OF DANIEL'S PROPHECY CENTURIES AFTER HIS DEATH.

DANIEL
PROPHESIED
EXACTLY
FOUR GENTILE
EMPIRES,
AND HISTORY
UNVEILED NO
MORE AND
NO LESS.

the fourth beast *does* overlap with the present age, it must be toward the end of it. Remember, we learned in session 2 that the coming of Christ's kingdom will put an end to the rule of these kings. We cannot know whether these kings and nations have begun emerging until the events prophesied actually come to pass. Our goal is to learn the possible scenarios rather than claim a certainty that has escaped the best scholars for centuries.

I believe that these events *will* happen. When and in what order remain the questions. Daniel prophesied exactly four Gentile empires, and history unveiled no more and no less. Will 10 kings or heads of states that have ties to the old Roman Empire emerge in the future? The intrigue heightens as we recognize that to a degree, the Roman Empire lives on today. Many of the countries of Europe and even the United States are the philosophical offspring of Rome. Are these events presently unfolding? God alone wears the royal Timex. Be assured He can tell time.

DAY THREE OTHER NAMES FOR THE LITTLE HORN

Today's Treasure: *After them another king will arise, different from the earlier ones.* Daniel 7:24

Today, under the lamp of New Testament Scriptures, we'll learn much more about the little horn in Daniel 7. Before we turn to our New Testaments, let's make sure we understand a significant prophecy concerning the little horn based on a comparison of Daniel 7:8 and 7:24.

How does verse 24 explain the uprooting of the other three horns in verse 8?

_____

_____

At some point during the 10-king confederacy, another Gentile king or head of state will emerge. Though at first he appears to be a "little" horn, he will prove incomparably powerful. The text intimates that he will also exceed the others in intelligence and arrogance. Three kings or kingdoms will apparently resist his power and be conquered by force. The other kings will then likely submit out of fear or a sense of inevitability.[10] "These will continue to be separate nations but will come under" the little horn's control.[11]

Now, let's take a look at three sketches in the New Testament. They will help us draw a much better picture of the little horn because they give him additional names and descriptions. The first two sketches will take a little extra time, but the third sketch is brief and to the point.

Please read each segment, identify the title given to the figure many scholars identify with the little horn, and note all additional facts underneath.

Sketch One: 2 Thessalonians 2:1-10. Title: Man of _____
Additional information: (Always document Scripture locations.)

_____

_____

_____

_____

_____

_____

Many associate "the man of lawlessness" with Daniel 7's "little horn." When I first studied eschatology, my wonderful teacher taught us that the "restrainer" inferred in 2 Thessalonians 2 is the Holy Spirit. If this is accurate, we could find the thought of Him being "taken out of the way" (v. 7) at some point a little disturbing. Rest assured, God's omnipresence never changes. As the Holy Spirit acts in the role of Restrainer, however, He could conceivably pull back His restraining presence for a time and allow evil to be temporarily unleashed until it fulfills its purpose.

Other theologians believe the restrainer is the church. When we speak of the church in our study of eschatology, we mean the corporate body consisting of every person who has placed his or her faith in Jesus Christ, regardless of denomination or Jewish or Gentile descent. Every Christian is part of the church. Most of the theologians interpreting the restrainer as the church believe that the reference to it being "taken out of the way" is an event commonly called the rapture. We will save our discussions on the rapture for a later time in our study.

We cannot be positive about the identity of the restrainer, but we do know that the Holy Spirit abides in all Christians. Therefore, if the church is removed from the picture, the restraining working of the Spirit would naturally be removed. The result would be an intensifying of evil in the world reaching its pinnacle with the emergence of the "man of lawlessness."

Sketch Two: Revelation 13:1-8. Title: (v. 1) _____

Before you compile the additional facts, please identify the "dragon" that "gave the beast his power." Who is the dragon according to Revelation 12:9?

_____

Now, proceed with the additional information Revelation 13:1-8 gives you concerning the one many identify with Daniel 7's "little horn."

_____

_____

_____

_____

_____

You've discovered that the "little horn," called the "man of lawlessness" in 2 Thessalonians 2, is called "the beast" in Revelation 13. Did your eyebrows raise over the familiar reference to the leopard, bear, and lion?

Based on our studies in day 1, what does each of these animals represent in Daniel 7?

Lion: _____

Bear: _____

Leopard: _____

This beast's empire "will combine the greatness of the kingdoms of the past."[12] You likely found the reference to the seemingly fatal wound very intriguing. Keep in mind Satan's greatest issue—he didn't get to be God. In blasphemous arrogance, he wanted more than anything to "make [himself] like the Most High" (Isa. 14:14). He couldn't be God, so he set out to counterfeit the actions of God. Therefore, anything God does, Satan tries to counterfeit. We have a prime example in Revelation 13. The beast plays the role of son to the dragon (Satan). His wound and healing counterfeit the death and resurrection of Christ.

Oh, that time and space would allow us to explore every facet of eschatology! We must stay on task, however, and lay only a basic foundation for understanding the little horn for now. Let's conclude today's lesson with a final sketch.

Sketch Three: 1 John 2:18. Title: The ___Antichrist___

Additional information:

_____

_____

_____

Beast
Man of Lawlessness (sin)
Antichrist
Little Horn

Perhaps the most well-known title of the little horn is *antichrist*. John's reference to many antichrists meant that many would and have come who powerfully opposed Christ. *The* Antichrist, however, is the one figure—unparalleled in earthly power—who will fulfill all the prophecies concerning the little horn, the beast, and the man of lawlessness. Remember, Satan doesn't know when Christ's kingdom will come. He is left to read the signs of the times and coinciding Bible prophecies just as we are. I believe Satan has to have potential candidates ready in every generation so that when the time comes, he can inhabit and use his prime choice.

What did you learn new about this figure in today's lesson?

There are four names for the antichrist

Great work today, Sister! Your mind may be spinning, but I dare say you aren't bored! Ask the Lord to continue to give you added insight and understanding. He is so pleased that you are studying His Word, Dear One! Be blessed!

DAY FOUR OPPRESSION OF THE SAINTS

Today's Treasure: *He will speak against the Most High and oppress his saints. Daniel 7:25*

I can't begin this lesson without telling you how proud I am of you. I highly esteem you, Dear Fellow Sojourner. Far more importantly, God esteems you and will undoubtedly bless your diligence. Let me remind you that at almost every turn in our journey many good Bible scholars hold different views. If we tried to compare all of these opinions, you would probably lose your mind—and your teacher most certainly would. So remember for the most part that we are taking one approach to understanding these Scriptures. We are following the dispensational-premillennial view.

> Let's start with a recap of yesterday's lesson. Please list the three additional names/titles for the "little horn."

_____   _____   _____

Do your best to memorize all four titles. In fact, try looking away from your notes now and saying each name aloud several times from memory. You're such a good sport. Deliberate recollection will always be our most effective way to retain information.

Scripture also has other titles or references some interpreters link to the little horn, such as the rider on a white horse in Revelation 6:2. For simplicity's sake, we will primarily refer to the one bearing all these titles as the antichrist. One of the most

Dispensational premillennialism
The view of Scripture that sees: Israel and the church as two separate peoples of God, the rapture of the church before the great tribulation, and God fulfilling His promises to Israel through the thousand-year earthly reign of Christ.

notable characteristics of the antichrist is his genius. I believe he will be a Gentile (Rev. 13:1) emerging from a reunited Roman Empire (Dan. 7:8; 9:26) who is an intellectual genius (Dan. 8:23), an oratorical genius (Dan. 11:36), a political genius (Rev. 17:11-12), a commercial genius (Dan. 11:43; Rev. 13:16-17), a military genius (Rev. 6:2; 13:2), and a religious genius (2 Thess. 2:4; Rev. 13:8).[13]

Perhaps nothing is more dangerous than an evil genius. Why do you suppose evil and intelligence form such a deadly combination?

_____

_____

Among your reasons, you might have noted an evil genius would have exceeding abilities to manipulate, seduce, and contrive to get what he wants. Unfortunately, people in our world place such a premium on intelligence that they mistakenly assume those who are smart are also *right*. Such a philosophy will prove fatal during the last days.

Let's turn our attention now to the antichrist's (the little horn's) treatment of the saints. What does Daniel 7:25 specifically say will happen to the "saints"?

They will be oppressed.

Who are these saints? The Aramaic word translated "saints" is the equivalent of the Hebrew *qados,* meaning "holy (one), saint."[14] Many scholars believe the saints in Daniel 7 refer specifically to the people of Israel and that Israel will be the focus of unparalleled persecution in the last days.[15] Others refer to the saints in Daniel 7 as "believers," meaning people who place their faith in Christ during the terrible times of the last days, many of whom will be Jewish by heritage. The New American Commentary identifies these as "the followers of the 'son of man,' Jesus Christ described in vv. 13-14."[16]

Daniel 7:27 offers the most helpful generalization. The saints are the people

of the _____ _____.

Whatever their specific identity, we can know for certain they are God's people: "the people of the Most High." This could be the nation of Israel (as His covenant and chosen people), Christians, or both.

In verse 25 you noted that the antichrist will "oppress" the saints. *Oppress* "literally means 'to wear away' or 'to wear out,' as one would wear out a garment."[17] Though Satan's persecutions of God's people will reach full measure in the last days, he certainly oppresses Christians today. Meditate for a moment on the definition for the word *oppress* offered in this paragraph.

How does Satan attempt to oppress you as described in this definition?

_____

_____

One of Satan's most effective schemes is simply to wear God's people out. Satan uses exhaustion and profound discouragement to persuade us to give up opposing him. We must not give up! As believers in Christ in whom the Spirit of God dwells, Satan may be able to wear out our human strength, but he cannot wear out the Holy Spirit's. We can call upon God's supernatural strength to fight the good fight of faith and persist in our proclamation of Christ, the son of the Most High God.

The Apostle Paul said in Colossians 1:29, "To this end I labor, struggling *with all his energy,* which so powerfully works in me" (emphasis mine). We who are Christians have God's "all surpassing power" in our "jars of clay" (2 Cor. 4:7). Let's not wait until we're at the end of our strength to utilize it! Let's call on God to fill us with His all-surpassing power day in and day out. His "incomparably great power" is accessible daily for those who believe! This power is the same power He used to raise Jesus from the dead (see Eph. 1:19-20). What more could we need?

Those of us who have felt terribly worn down and worn out by the enemy can hardly imagine the oppression Daniel 7 describes. The people of God "will daily be harassed until their lives become miserable."[18]

Have you ever felt "harassed" by the enemy until you were miserable? If so, what form did this harassment seem to take?

_____

LET'S NOT WAIT UNTIL WE'RE AT THE END OF OUR STRENGTH TO UTILIZE GOD'S POWER.

God uses circumstances to help us develop compassion. Just imagine the suffering of the saints of the last days who will endure the virtually unendurable.

We also learn from Daniel 7:25 that the antichrist will "try to change the

_____ and the _____." (Fill in the blanks.)

The context of the antichrist's persecution of the saints suggests to many scholars that these set times and laws are either religious or greatly impact the practice of religion. Earlier we noted antichrist will be a "religious genius." Never lose sight of the fact that Satan's ultimate goal is to set himself up to be worshiped via the antichrist. *The New American Commentary* suggests that the "'set times' are best understood to be religious holidays, which the Antichrist will attempt to eliminate."[19]

Let's imagine that our country somehow ended up with a dictator who eliminated our religious holidays and made any observance of them a punishable offense. What impact would the elimination of your most meaningful religious holidays mean to you?

Really give this question some thought and then offer your answer.

_____

_____

ALL THINGS IN HEAVEN AND EARTH ARE UNDER CHRIST'S FEET.

"Denying religious liberty is characteristic of dictators (e.g., Antiochus IV, Nero, Domitian, Stalin, Hitler, and others), but Antichrist will go beyond what anyone has done before in his attempt to create a thoroughly secular world. Even now there are those seeking to rid society of all vestiges of religion."[20]

Other scholars do not interpret these laws as purely religious in nature or impact. They believe that the antichrist "will introduce an entirely new era in which he will abandon all previous laws and institute his own system."[21] One thing is certain: he will force changes for the purpose of pure demoralization, and his target group will be the people of the Most High God. Step-by-step he will attempt to crack every foundation under the saints' feet. Thank goodness, all things in heaven and earth are under Christ's feet. The ancient serpent may have struck our Savior's heel, but Christ will most assuredly crush the serpent's head (Gen. 3:15). Before you're tempted to wearily cast aside your jersey and quit, keep in mind our team wins. If you've been oppressed, let these truths energize you from the sidelines back onto the field.

DAY FIVE TIME, TIMES AND HALF A TIME

Today's Treasure: *The saints will be handed over to him for a time, times and half a time. Daniel 7:25*

We've broadened our knowledge about the Antichrist considerably this week. As you continue to develop a mental sketch, don't picture him coming on the scene in a repulsive form. He will likely be a magnetic and heroic figure, and people will feel they can trust him. Ezekiel 28:17 tells us that the "anointed cherub" (now called Satan) became proud because of his beauty. You can be fairly certain that his chosen one—the antichrist—will be beautiful.

By contrast, God sent His own Son to earth in His first advent with "no beauty or majesty to attract us to him, nothing in his appearance that we should desire him" (Isa. 53:2). This passage does not mean Jesus was ugly, but God purposed that people would choose Him based on His love and His truth. They were not to be swayed by His physical beauty. We can rest assured that when all is said and done, we will see Christ our Savior in His inexpressible splendor and Satan, our adversary, in his hideous reality.

However, the world will know terrible times before the coming day of the Lord. Today we will focus on the very important time reference found in Daniel 7:25.

How long does this Scripture say the saints will be handed over to this evil king we've identified as the Antichrist?

_____

Strange reference, isn't it? Thank goodness we have the companion Book of Revelation to offer some clues to its meaning. Please look up the following Scriptures and record each reference to time periods.

Revelation 11:2 _____

Revelation 12:6 _____
(The "woman" symbolizes the nation of Israel.)

Revelation 13:5-7 _____

All three of these time references can reflect three and one-half years. Compared in their contexts, they refer to a horrific season of unparalleled persecution through which God will sustain Israel as a nation.

Look back at the time reference in Daniel 7:25. How could the wording speak figuratively of three and a half years?

_____

Daniel 4:25 offers a parallel that may help us interpret the word "times." How long did he say the king would remain in an animal-like state?

_____

Many believe the reference to seven times means seven years.[22] A "time" could refer to the passing of one set of annual seasons. If this interpretation is accurate, the time reference in Daniel 7:25 could mean: a "time" one year; "times" two years, a "half a time," six months. Together they could very well describe three and one half years.

We've arrived at the point of our study where a potential time line of events will be helpful. When placed beside other time references in prophetic Scripture, Daniel 7:25 and its possible companion references in the Revelation invite us to consider potential sequences. All who profess the Apostles' Creed and all evangelicals hold doctrinally to a belief in Christ's return. Most of us term this event the second coming. The primary question dividing many believers is whether He will set up a kingdom on this earth and, if so, when and in what form.

Please read Revelation 20:1-10. Record any reference to a time period in verses 4 and 5.

_____

Amillennialists believe the present church age will continue until Christ's return.

The Latin word for one thousand years is *millennium*. Christians have held several major views concerning references to the millennium. I cannot stress strongly enough that brilliant scholars interpret these Scriptures very differently. The wisdom of considering several views will make necessary a lengthening of today's lesson. For our purposes, we will briefly present the amillennial and premillennial approaches.* Keep in mind each model has variations:

Amillennialism: The prefix "a" means "no," resulting in a word that means "no millennium," but adherents to this view don't actually believe in no millennium. They rather understand Revelation 20 to be describing the binding of Satan now being fulfilled in the church age, so some call themselves realized millennialists. They believe the present church age will continue until Christ's return. Then they expect one resurrection of both believers and unbelievers followed by judgments and rewards. Unbelievers will be raised to judgment and eternal condemnation. Believers will enter eternal bliss in the new heavens and new earth. This model is the simplest because all of the end-time events follow directly after Christ's return.

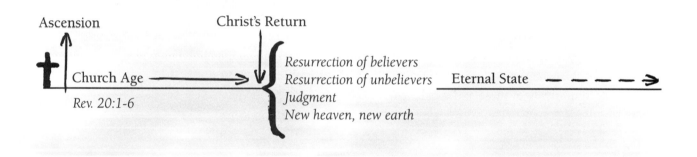

What do you find most interesting about amillennialism?

no tribulation

Premillennialism: Amillennialists take the thousand years as a symbolic reference to something that happens before the second coming of Christ. Premillennialists take the thousand years as referring to Christ's physical kingdom set up on earth after His return. Premillennialists ("pre" meaning "before") believe that "the present church age will continue until, as it nears the end, a time of great tribulation and suffering comes on the earth."[23] Many premillennialists believe this time of "great tribulation and suffering" coincides with the three and a half year period in Daniel. However, premillennialists divide into two very different models of understanding the future. We will discuss them as historic premillennialism and dispensational premillennialism.

Historic premillennialism: Wayne Grudem's *Systematic Theology* calls this view "Classic or Historic Premillennialism" because "this viewpoint has a long history from the earliest centuries onward."[24] Advocates of this view expect the church to go through the tribulation period. "After that time of tribulation *at the end of the church age, Christ will return to earth to establish a millennial kingdom*. When he comes back, believers who have died will be raised from the dead, their bodies will be reunited with their spirits, and *these believers will reign with Christ on earth for one thousand years*."[25]

Historic premillennialists expect the church to go through the tribulation period.

The distinction of the historic premillennial position is that they see the tribulation and subsequent thousand-year reign as essentially Christian in nature. Like the amillennialists, they understand God's people to be one continuing people of faith. They emphasize the New Testament church grafted into Old Testament Israel making one people of God. That distinction will become clearer as we turn to the remaining view.

Dispensational premillennialism is the view we are following in our Bible study. Dispensationalists understand Israel to be a people of God distinct from the church. The tribulation period—and particularly the millennium—fulfills God's promises and dealing with the nation of Israel. The rapture of the church happens either before the seven-year tribulation period or at the three and one-half year midpoint. At the rapture the church is taken to heaven leaving the judgments and promises of God to fall on unrepentant humanity and national Israel. Do you see how this fits at this point in our discussion of Daniel chapter 7?

The two forms of premillennialism agree about the events at the end of the thousand years.* "Satan will be loosed from the bottomless pit and will join forces with many unbelievers who have submitted outwardly to Christ's reign but have inwardly been seething in rebellion against him. Satan will gather these rebellious people for battle against Christ, but they will be decisively defeated. Christ will then raise from the dead all the unbelievers who have died throughout history, and they will stand before him for final judgment. After the final judgment has occurred, believers will enter into the eternal state."[26]

*Be aware that another view called postmillennialism does exist. It was the view of many 19th-century Christians who believed the progress of the gospel and the growth of the church would gradually bring in a millennial age of peace and righteousness. Two world wars and the tumult of the 20th century effectively killed this optimistic view.

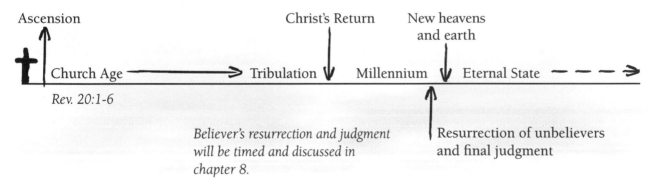

I know this information seems overwhelming right now, but we will echo the basic tenets of the four views until we can reach these goals. I want you to be able to:

1. give a very basic definition of amillennialism.
2. distinguish between historic and dispensational premillennialism.
3. form a working knowledge of dispensational premillennialism.

As I have explained, I understand the dispensational view to most closely fit the total teaching of Scripture. For that reason and to keep your head from exploding, I will not attempt to teach all the views. Remember that at almost every point of the study of eschatology you will encounter several competing ideas with honest Bible scholars who adhere to the different views. As my grandmother would say, we'll just stick to our knitting. I hope you'll know this premillennial view virtually by heart when this series ends. After its conclusion, by all means study other views just as thoroughly!

ASK GOD FOR FOCUS AND FOR A SUPERNATURAL ABILITY TO LEARN.

You can do this, Dear One! Ask God for focus and for a supernatural ability to learn. Those of you who are young have a great capacity to expand your mind in these areas. Your understanding of prophetic Scripture will likely explode. Those of us who are older can do nothing wiser than force our minds to learn new things. Where the healthy mind is concerned, exercise prolongs sharpness. If Scripture is brain food, eschatology is an energy bar on steroids.

Conclude today by writing the briefest possible definitions of the terms below based on their prefixes:

Amillennialism basically means ... *Church age continues until Christ comes*

Premillennialism basically means ... *1000 years before the new heavens & the earth*

Way to go! You have accomplished a hard week of study. I'd treat you to an energy bar right now if I could. May every inch our minds are being stretched broaden our capacity to know and love Jesus, the coming King!

1. John F. Walvoord and Roy B. Zuck, eds., *The Bible Knowledge Commentary of the Old Testament* (Wheaton, IL: SP Publications, Inc., 1985), 1350.
2. Stephen R. Miller, *Daniel*, vol. 18 in *The New American Commentary* (Nashville: Broadman & Holman, 2001), 195.
3. Ibid., 197.
4. Walvoord and Zuck, 1350.
5. Miller, 199.
6. Ibid., 218.
7. Walvoord and Zuck, 1354.
8. Ibid.
9. Ibid.
10. Miller, 213.
11. Ibid.
12. Charles R. Swindoll and Bryce Klabunde, *God's Pattern for the Future, Insight for Living Bible Study Guide, From the Bible Teaching of Charles R. Swindoll* (Insight for Living, 1996), 90.
13. Mark Hitchcock, *The Complete Book of Bible Prophecy* (Wheaton, IL: Tyndale House Publishers, 1999), 131.
14. Spiros Zodhiates, ThD., gen. ed., *Lexical Aids to the Old Testament, Hebrew-Greek Key Word Study Bible, New International Version* (Chattanooga, TN: AMG Publishers), #10620, 1566.
15. Walvoord and Zuck, 1353.
16. Miller, 216.
17. Ibid., 214.
18. Ibid.
19. Ibid.
20. Ibid.
21. Walvoord and Zuck, 1354.
22. Miller, 137; Swindoll, 49; Walvoord and Zuck, 1342.
23. Wayne Grudem, *Systematic Theology* (Grand Rapids, MI: Zondervan, 1995), 1111.
24. Ibid.
25. Ibid., 1111-12.
26. Ibid.

FORE-SHADOWING THE LITTLE HORN

8

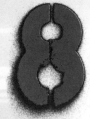

SESSION EIGHT
FORESHADOWING THE LITTLE HORN

As we continue part 2 of our study on the Book of Daniel, we will focus on an additional vision recorded in Daniel 8. Several common denominators will offer us a familiar canvas on which to paint an entirely new portrait. Thankfully, much of the prophecy in this chapter has become history.

Overview Daniel 8:1-8 then read verses 9 through 27. Fill in the following diagram accordingly:

The Two-Horned Ram

Medo-Persians

The Shaggy Goat

Large horn: Alex the Great   Four horns: {

Cassander
(Macedonia and Greece)

Lysimacus
(Thrace and parts of Asia Minor)

Ptolemy
(Egypt and parts of Asia Minor)

Seleucus
(Syria, Israel, Mesopotamia)

The name "Epiphanes" means " the Illustrious one ."

The Jews called him "Epimanes," meaning " The Madman ."

According to *The Bible Knowledge Commentary,* this portion of prophecy in Daniel 8 "reveals

Israel's history under the Seleucids and particularly under Antiochus during the time of

Greek domination, but it also looks forward to Israel's experiences under __Antichrist__

whom Antiochus __foreshadows__."[1] Because much can be learned about the

"forthcoming desecrator" from the former desecrator, "it may be concluded

that there is a __dual reference__ in this striking prophecy."[2]

When "the near fulfillment of the prophecy foreshadows the far," Dr. Charles R. Swindoll

terms the occasion a __double fulfillment__.[3]

HINTS OF FORESHADOWING IN DANIEL 8:

Compare verse 13 and Matthew 24:15-18. According to Christ, the __abomination__

that causes __desolation__ is ultimately __yet to come__.

"he will become very strong but not by __his own power__" (vv. 23-24).

"he will ... take his stand against the __Prince__ of __princes__" (v. 25).

"he will be destroyed, but not by __human power__" (v. 25).

1. John F. Walvoord and Roy B. Zuck, *The Bible Knowledge Commentary* (Wheaton, IL: Victor Books, 1985), 1359.
2. Ibid.
3. Charles R. Swindoll, *Daniel: God's Pattern for the Future* (Plano, TX: Insight for Living, 1996), 97.

WEEK EIGHT
FORESHADOWING THE LITTLE HORN

DAY 1

An Uncommon Conqueror, A Common Language

DAY 2

A Master of Intrigue

DAY 3

The Record of the Maccabees

DAY 4

Important Distinctions

DAY 5

What on Earth Is a "Rapture"?

Two years had passed since Daniel received the vision of the four creature-like empires, the Little Horn, and the court scene of the Ancient of Days. Surely a rare day passed without Daniel's mind replaying the images of chapter 7. He must have wondered if he'd ever receive another vision. Did he ever! This week our attention turns to a detailed vision God gave Daniel in the third year of Belshazzar's reign.

From the time Nebuchadnezzar received the first dream of Gentile empires, each subsequent dream built on that familiar foundation. If each new vision were completely unrelated, I fear we'd succumb to information overload and quit. Whatever you do, don't quit! The Book of Daniel offers repetitive streams to help us navigate the dark, new waters. Even if we don't absorb every detail and some go over our heads, we are still learning volumes about God and His Word. New truths are abiding in us that we'd never even thought about eight weeks ago!

Glance all the way back at the commitment we made at the conclusion of session 1.

To what did you commit? _____To learn_____

Have you learned anything about …

God, His Word, and His work? ☒ yes ☐ no
The history of God's people during Babylonian exile? ☒ yes ☐ no
Divine prophecy? ☒ yes ☐ no

Do you feel as if your time in God's Word has been wasted? ☐ yes ☒ no

Then persevere!

We don't have to learn *everything* to learn many things. Continue to approach every lesson with prayer for supernatural understanding. Stretch your mind! Just think. In the time one daily assignment takes, we could watch or read something that would undoubtedly—as Melissa said—make us dumber. In Jesus' Name, we're getting smarter! Hang in there, Sweet One. God is so pleased.

THIS WEEK'S PRINCIPAL QUESTIONS

DAY 1 When was Alexander, represented as the "large horn," "broken off"?

DAY 2 What are several horrific effects the more immediate small horn (Antiochus IV) would have upon Israel?

DAY 3 Who was Judas Maccabeus, and what did his name probably mean?

DAY 4 What does Romans 11:25-32 suggest to you about God's continuing concern/plans for Israel?

DAY 5 How do 1 Corinthians 15:51-53 and 1 Thessalonians 4:13-18 describe the rapture?

DAY ONE AN UNCOMMON CONQUEROR, A COMMON LANGUAGE

Today's Treasure: *The shaggy goat is the king of Greece, and the large horn between his eyes is the first king. Daniel 8:21*

Beloved, if you're on the suggested time-trek, you have two months of in-depth Bible study behind you. We have some exciting days ahead in the Book of Daniel. I'm praying that your passion to study this fascinating book will continue to grow and your life will bear much fruit as a result. Your God is accomplishing awesome purposes in you, Dear One. Have the confidence to thank Him for it. Nothing about this adventure is accidental in your life.

In the original language the opening words of Daniel's eighth chapter provide a significant transition. The Hebrew language resumes. You may recall that the Book of Daniel was penned in both Hebrew and Aramaic. The book opens in Hebrew and transitions to Aramaic in Daniel 2:4. Daniel 8:1 reverts to the Hebrew language and retains it through the end of the book. This language change may take place because chapters 8-12 focus on specifically Jewish concerns while the segments in Aramaic include Gentile concerns. Actually, language happens to be the theme of our lesson today. Follow me to the place where we'll discover why.

Please read Daniel 8:1-8. Compare Daniel 8:20-21 and identify the following representations in the vision:

The two-horned ram: *The Kings of Media & Persia*

The shaggy goat: *King of Greece*

The large horn between his eyes: *The first King*

Recall session 8 and our previous discussions of the Grecian Empire. Who did history reveal this "first king" to be? *Alex the Great*

Philip II of Macedonia was a powerful leader/warrior, uniting nearly all the Greek city-states. He was planning an attack on Persia when he was murdered. His son Alexander, a student of the famed Aristotle, was only 20 years old when he succeeded his father as king in 336 B.C. Approximately 18 months later he launched an attack against the mighty Persians and within three short years he had conquered the entire Near East. Alexander ultimately conquered most of the known world, and Greece became the greatest nation on the planet. His empire encompassed 1.5 million square miles.[1]

🦁 When was Alexander, represented as the "large horn," "broken off" (v. 8)?

at the height of his power

If we're not careful, we can start reading Daniel like a history book of Gentile empires. Remember, these visions were prophetic! Everything Daniel envisioned was future to him. Some of it played out in history that is past to us. Some remains in our future.

At the pinnacle of Alexander's success—"at the height of his power"—he contracted a terrible fever (perhaps malaria) and died on June 13, 323 B.C., at a mere 32 years of age. As a matter of fact, he drew his last breath in Babylon. Before he died, however, he let success go to his head. You might say he believed his own press. He convinced himself that "Achilles (the mightiest warrior on the Greek side in the Trojan War)" and "the god Hercules were his ancestors. Whether out of pride or for political reasons or both, Alexander required the provinces to worship him as a god. Quite naturally the Greek troops resented such an order."[2]

Word Biblical Commentary offers wisdom worthy of our meditation: "There is nothing inherently wrong about 'doing great things' but the expression is only used in an unequivocally good sense of God (1 Sam. 12:24; Ps. 126:2,3); of human beings it tends to suggest arrogance (Jer. 48:26; Joel 2:20; Zeph. 2:10; Ps. 35:26; Ps. 55:13), or at least achievement at someone else's expense (Zeph. 2:8; Lam. 1:9)—here achievement that presages calamity."[3]

🛍 Can you think of several reasons why asking God to cause us to "do great things" might not be wise?

He won't be happy w/us just as He wasn't happy w/those who wanted to build the tower of Babel so they would be great. He is prideful & we are to be humble

THE POINT OF OUR BEING HERE IS FOR GOD TO USE US FOR HIS GREATNESS.

We walk a very fine line when we ask God to cause us to do great things for Him. If we're not careful, the deeper motive could become using God as a means toward our own greatness. The point of our being here is for God to use *us* for *His* greatness. A wiser prayer is probably to ask God to do great things. Then, we can be profoundly humbled if we get to participate in the process in any small way. Yes, our lives are meant to bear much fruit, but asking God to bear much fruit in us to His glory differs from asking God to make us do great things.

What did Christ tell His disciples they would do (John 14:12-13)?

He said anyone who had faith in him would do what he did and even do greater things

According to verse 13, what was the point of these great works and the answered prayer that would accomplish them?

So that the Son would bring glory to the Father

Think about this with me for a moment. When we pass an orange orchard in Florida, we don't exclaim, "Behold what great things those trees have done!" They're doing what they were created for. Your life and mine will be well lived and greatly influential if we simply ask God to empower us to do that for which we were created.

How do you think what Jesus taught in Luke 17:7-10 might have spoken to Alexander the Great if he had stumbled upon the story?

_____

In connection with our discussion of pride, how might Luke 17:10 be seen as words to protect us from ourselves?

_____

Alexander the Great would have been greater had he seen himself smaller. No human being is wise or powerful enough to attain the swift feats of Alexander the Great. The sovereign God who "sets up kings and deposes them" (Dan. 2:21) had an agenda. Among other things, God used Alexander the Great to "spread the Greek language and culture all over the world, an act that prepared the world for the gospel by giving it a common speech, Koine Greek, the language of the New Testament."[4]

In the third century B.C., not many years after Alexander's death and while Greece still dominated the world, Hebrew scholars in Alexandria began translating the Old Testament Scriptures into the Greek language. This translation became known as the "Septuagint" because the story circulated that the number of scholars who worked on the translation was 70 or 72 and that they miraculously did the translation in 70 days. (*Septuaginta* is Latin for 70.) In Bible study research, when you see the abbreviation LXX, you're seeing a reference to the Septuagint. Why was this translation so critical? The outside world was introduced to the history, religion, and doctrine of the Hebrew people, greatly spreading their belief system. The Septuagint was the Bible of most of the writers of the New Testament.

Quick review: Why is the third-century-before-Christ Greek translation of the Old Testament called the Septuagint? *Because the story circulated that the number of scholars who worked on the translation was 70 or 72 and they miraculously did the translation in 70 days & Septuaginta is Latin for 70*

Alexander's conquests "paved" roads for the circulation of Scripture. How amazing is our God? He can "set up" a pagan king to accomplish His purposes. Likewise, God can depose him when his heart becomes proud and God's purpose is served.

Shaggy goats come and go. Greatness belongs to our God.

DAY TWO A MASTER OF INTRIGUE

Today's Treasure: *In the latter part of their reign, when rebels have become completely wicked, a stern-faced king, a master of intrigue, will arise. Daniel 8:23*

I so hope you were able to participate in session 8 because we studied a divine teaching method God employs in the eighth chapter of Daniel. If you were part of our session, please glance back at your listening guide for a refresher.

Briefly describe the concept of a dual reference. *Dual reference is when prophecy talks about two different time*

We drew the concept from a helpful statement in *The Bible Knowledge Commentary*. After drawing many parallels between Antiochus IV Epiphanes and the coming Antichrist, J. Dwight Pentecost suggests, "So it may be concluded that there is a dual reference in this striking prophecy."[5] In our session, we discussed how dual references help us better picture the unfamiliar through a portrayal of something more familiar. Dual references have something in common with parables as a teaching method.

Before I tell you the meaning of the Greek word translated "parable," let's recap yesterday's lesson. Based on our previous study, briefly explain why the Old Testament was translated into Greek from Hebrew. *So that the outside world be introduced to the history, religion & doctrine of the Hebrew people*

While we're on the subject, to what does the abbreviation "LXX" refer?

It is a reference to the Septuagint

A PARABLE USES SOMETHING FAMILIAR TO HELP US UNDERSTAND SOMETHING HEAVENLY OR SPIRITUAL.

You can see why Greek definitions matter even in the Hebrew Old Testament. The word *parable* comes from the Greek *paraballo*. *Para* means "near" and *ballo* means "to cast, put. To cast or put near."[6] A parable uses something familiar to help us understand something heavenly or spiritual. In the Book of Daniel, Antiochus Epiphanes becomes the example through whom we get a glimpse of a figure yet in our future. Daniel's prophecies add the element of time to the comparison seen in parables.

We ultimately come to know this "Little Horn" of Daniel 7 by additional New Testament names. Please recall several of them in this space:

Anti-Christ, Beast, Man of lawlessness or man of sin

God knew that this Little Horn (identified in the New Testament as the Antichrist) would exceed man's range of understanding. Therefore, after introducing him in Daniel 7, God prefigured him in the very next segment of Scripture (Dan. 8) through a nearer "small horn" history would name Antiochus IV Epiphanes. God seemed to say, "As you try to picture what this ultimate Little Horn will be like, take a good look at a figure history will reveal much sooner who meets these qualifications." Imagine him rising to power much later with a fury far worse. There you'll discover the closest possible picture of Daniel 7's "Little Horn."

Please read Daniel 8:8-14. Record several horrific effects the more immediate small horn (Antiochus IV) would have on Israel, "the Beautiful Land."

① He threw some of the starry host down to the ground & trampled on them ② the sanctuary was brought low ③ rebellion which caused desolation ④ Took away the daily sacrifice.

Several times in our study of the prophecies in Daniel, we've talked about the identity of the four kingdoms that emerged from the first king of the Grecian Empire. In Daniel 7, they appear as the four heads of the leopard. In Daniel 8, they become "four prominent horns" that grew out of the "large horn" that was broken off "at the height of his power." After Alexander the Great died, his wife gave birth to his legitimate heir. Both of them were later killed in the following struggle for power. Alexander's four generals divided the Greek Empire as we noted in session 8.

If you attended the session, please glance at your notes and write their names for familiarity's sake: Cassander, Lysimacus, Ptolemy & Seleucus

We learned in session 8 that Antiochus IV came to power in 175 B.C. "after murdering his brother, who had inherited the throne in the Seleucid dynasty."[7] I'll tell you more about this murderous madman in week 11. For now note that the Seleucid Dynasty gained supremacy over the areas of Syria, Israel, and Mesopotamia. Thus Antiochus IV, the most heartless power broker in the world at the time, gained earthly control over God's chosen land. Because the people of God—both past and present—are Satan's unholy passion, we can be sure he fueled a vengeance in Antiochus to demoralize the Jews.

Where in Daniel 8:9-12 do you see hints that Satan himself was at work with his own agenda? threw some of the starry hosts down to earth & set himself up to be as great as the Prince of the host

No doubt, Satan and Antiochus IV were—as my daddy would say—in cahoots whether or not the "stern-faced king" (Dan. 8:23) ever realized it. Perhaps Satan could hardly wait for the end of times when he could raise up his counterfeit son, the

Antichrist, and, through him, demand to be worshiped. He seized a golden opportunity for a dress rehearsal starring Antiochus IV as the understudy. Gone were the days of Babylon's "friendly captivity" of Daniel and friends. Days of unparalleled sacrilege had come.

Look back at the time period when Daniel received this prophetic vision. When did the vision come to him (Dan. 8:1)?

In the 3rd year of Belshazzar's reign

God is a God of timing. What do you recall about this particular king regarding his use of the sacred vessels that had been stolen from Jerusalem's temple (Dan. 5:2-4)? *He had the sacred vessels brought into the banquet & they drank out of them at the same time they were praising the gods of gold & silver, bronze, iron, wood & stone*

Belshazzar didn't become evil and profane the morning of that feast. Daniel had very likely grown deeply concerned about King Belshazzar by the third year of his reign. Possibly God gave Daniel the vision of such sacrilege so he would know that …

- one exceedingly more sacrilegious than Belshazzar would come.
- God was in control and would not allow him to go unpunished.
- the sanctuary of God would indeed be reconsecrated (see Dan. 8:14).

Remember, by the time Antiochus IV seized power over the Beautiful Land, Jerusalem and its temple had been rebuilt by the exiles. Many Jews once again called Jerusalem home, and the temple services were resumed with great relief and rejoicing. Then came Antiochus IV who could not wait to wield his evil control.

As we conclude, imagine the kind of impact the forced cessation of daily sacrifice had on the Jews (see Dan. 8:12). Based on all the Jews understood, the atoning blood of the daily sacrifices enabled them to approach God in worship and relationship.

If God allowed Satan to stop them from offering their sacrifices, what might the Jews have concluded?

That they know longer would be able to approach the Lord - their relationship would be severed

Oh, how Satan wants the people of God to think God has abandoned them! Thank goodness, God is the initiator, enabler, and sustainer of relationship. Though He undoubtedly calls us to obedience, we can offer nothing that paves a path to the throne of grace. God alone makes the way, and the same God who calls us keeps us.

"No power of hell, no scheme of man
Can ever pluck me from His hand
'Til He returns or calls me home
Here in the power of Christ I'll stand."[8]

THE ATONING BLOOD OF THE DAILY SACRIFICES ENABLED JEWS TO APPROACH GOD IN WORSHIP AND RELATIONSHIP.

DAY THREE THE RECORD OF THE MACCABEES

Today's Treasure: *It grew until it reached the host of the heavens, and it threw some of the starry host down to the earth and trampled on them. Daniel 8:10*

History records eerily specific ways Antiochus IV Epiphanes fulfilled Daniel's vision (Dan. 8). He reigned for 11 years, aggressively attempting to strip the Jews of all things Jewish and turn them into Greeks. In other words, he wanted them Hellenized, not just in spite of their wishes to the contrary but because of them.

> *To Hellenize*
> to shape people into a Greek worldview

Please read Daniel 8:9-10 carefully. Using the same figurative language, record what the one fulfilling this prophecy would do.

_____

We'll limit our present comments on Daniel 12:3 because it has an important place in our conclusion. However, I do want you to see its reference to "stars." The "host of the heavens" and the "starry host" could refer to angelic warriors fighting the unseen battle surrounding the people of God during this terrible time. In context, we see a more likely interpretation.

To what do the "stars" and that which will "shine like the brightness of the heavens" refer in Daniel 12:3?

- ☒ wise advocates of righteousness
- ☐ followers of the Antichrist
- ☐ meek who inherit the earth
- ☐ physical objects in the night sky

The figurative language in Daniel 8:10 likely carries the same kind of meaning. The context in Daniel 8:10-12 "could suggest that the heavenly army is the Jewish people, or the priesthood in particular, viewed as of heavenly significance because of their relationship with the God of heaven."[9]

Perhaps Ephesians 2:6 implies the same kind of idea regarding believers in Christ. What is our position according to this New Testament verse?

We are seated w/ Christ in the heavenly realms

It doesn't say we will be seated. It says we are already seated in lofty places because of our relationship with God through Christ. In the same way, the "starry host" may refer to the people of Israel whose feet were still planted on planet Earth in Daniel 8:10 while holding a heavenly position.

Daniel 8:10 also tells us that the figure fulfilling these prophecies would "trample on" the saints of God. The trampling shoes of Antiochus IV fit, and history demonstrated him wearing them. Observe what the historians say about this Madman:

His "persecution of the Jews may be considered to have begun in 170 B.C. with the assassination of the high priest Onias III and terminated in 163 B.C. at his death … During this period he executed thousands of Jews who resisted his unfair regulations."[10] His soldiers reportedly slaughtered "eighty thousand men, women, boys, girls, even infants" during his attack upon Jerusalem.[11]

Antiochus "meddled in the appointment of high priests, forced Greek customs upon the Jews, looted the Temple, defiled the altar, and cruelly persecuted the pious Jews who wished to observe their religious laws and customs."[12] "In December 167 B.C. Antiochus committed his crowning act of sacrilege against the Jewish religion by erecting an altar to Zeus in the temple precincts and offering swine on it."[13]

Antiochus IV decreed "that sacrifice to the Greek deities be offered in every Judean city and village."[14] Officers sent to carry out his orders arrived in the "village of Modein where an aged priest by the name of Mattathias lived with his five sons. … When Mattathias, in an act of anger, killed both the first Jew who approached the pagan altar to offer sacrifice and the royal official who presided, he and his sons … were forced to flee to the hills. There they became the nucleus of a growing band of rebels against Antiochus. Mattathias died soon after the beginning of the revolt, leaving military leadership in the hands of Judas, whose surname 'Maccabeus' (probably from the Aramaic word *Maqqabah*, meaning 'hammer') became the source of the popular name given to the family and its followers."[15] (The proper name of this family was the Hasmoneans.)[16] "Under Judas's brilliant leadership, what had begun as a guerrilla war turned into full-scale military engagements in which smaller Jewish forces managed to defeat much more powerful Syrian armies."[17]

Quick review: Who began the revolt? *Antiochus IV*

Who was Maccabeus, and what did his name probably mean?

Judas / Hammer

Which army ultimately won? (Check one.) ☒ the smaller ☐ the greater

Sounds like the work of God, doesn't it? He often brings fame to His great Name by using a pitifully small army to defeat a vast one. He is the God who beats all odds.

Do you feel as if you're fighting a battle with odds stacked greatly against you? If so, what kind of battle is it? (Stay general if the specifics are private.)

_____

_____

_____

_____

Be encouraged, dear Sister! Beating great odds is God's specialty. It's one way He proves to us that He can do the impossible. Don't accept defeat if what you're standing for is consistent with God's Word and His ways. Persevere, believing God. Ask Him to fight for you and to show Himself mighty!

GOD CAN DO THE IMPOSSIBLE.

No one would have believed in advance that the Maccabees could be used of God to bring an end to the "astounding devastation" of Antiochus IV (see Dan. 8:24). Judas's crowning victory was the recapture of Jerusalem and the rededication of the temple that had been so terribly defiled by "Epimanes, the Madman."[18] The temple was officially rededicated on 25 Kislev of 164 B.C.[19] You are familiar with the celebration of this historical event. Christ Himself observed this great feast.

Read John 10:22-23. For what event was Christ in Jerusalem to celebrate?

Feast of Dedication (Hanukkah)

The Hebrew transliteration of this dedication is *Hanukkah*—the annual celebration observed by Jews around the world every December. If you didn't already, now you will associate the name of the celebration with its great historical significance. The books of First and Second Maccabees, contained in the Apocrypha, tells much of the history involving the persecution of the Jews under Antiochus IV and their astonishing revolt. Both books were written during the second and first centuries B.C. Though not part of the Protestant canon, for centuries historians have looked to these books with confidence regarding this terrible time of persecution.[20]

What is history to us was prophecy to Daniel. He would not live to see the devastation and humiliation of the Jews under the madman, but he received the revelation with such certainty that he "was exhausted and lay ill for several days … appalled by the vision" (Dan. 8:27).

Likewise, if you and I could fully grasp the devastation to come in the last days under the rule of the ultimate "master of intrigue," the thought would be almost unbearable. What is ahead for this world? And what part will the church play? We will busy ourselves with possible answers for the remainder of the week.

Good work today, Sister! Keep it up!

Today's Treasure: *Oh, the depths of the riches of the wisdom and knowledge of God!*
Romans 11:33

I'm so glad you keep tuning in. Our material is difficult, but it's intriguing, isn't it? You make the climb so much more fun. OK, take a look at the final paragraph in yesterday's lesson.

What questions did I tell you we'd seek to answer?

What is ahead for this _world_ ? And what part will the _Church_ play?

This week we've studied the persecution of Israel under Antiochus IV, the madman. We saw how God sustained Israel and caused her to prevail under terrible odds and horrendous circumstances. Today we're going to see that God will show His faithfulness even more dramatically as He brings Israel through the unparalleled tribulation awaiting her under the Antichrist. Remember, we're viewing the reign of Antiochus IV as a dress rehearsal with an evil understudy foreshadowing a time and a ruler who will be far worse. Tomorrow we will discuss the role of the church during the last days. To reach our goals we'll need to launch out of Daniel 8 to gain insight only the New Testament can provide.

As we lengthen our eschatological time line and consider all the players, let's have a quick and important refresher: to whom are we referring when we speak of the "church"? (If necessary see p. 143.)

Every person who has placed their faith in Jesus Christ

The model for understanding end-time events we'll study distinguishes between three vital groups of people: the people/nation of Israel (the covenant children of God), the church (defined as all believers in Christ, whether Jew or Gentile), and the lost. I do not in any sense believe the church has replaced the nation of Israel in God's heart or agenda. I believe God has two distinct peoples: national Israel and the church. Other interpreters believe that Israel and the church form a single covenant people of faith. I urge you to study their interpretations and scriptural support. I am utterly convinced that Israel as a nation will accept Jesus as Messiah and Savior during the time of great tribulation before the final judgment.

Chapters 9–11 of the Book of Romans contain very difficult passages to understand fully. Paul wrote them under the inspiration of the Holy Spirit, and yet I believe even he found them beyond human comprehension. He ended the segment with an appropriate and wonderful exclamation recorded in Romans 11:33-36.

Please read these verses in the margin and write in your own words Paul's conclusion to the problem of understanding Israel and the church.

_____

_____

_____

These words fall fresh on me today as I struggle to reconcile what I absolutely know about God with the ongoing struggles of a godly, fervently praying friend. I'm reminded that God's ways are often beyond us but His heart is always for us.

What about you? Do these words from Romans fall fresh on you today? Why?

_____

_____

_____

"Oh, the depth of the riches of the wisdom and knowledge of God! How unsearchable his judgments, and his paths beyond tracing out! 'Who has known the mind of the Lord? Or who has been his counselor?' 'Who has ever given to God, that God should repay him?' For from him and through him and to him are all things. To him be the glory forever! Amen."

ROMANS 11:33-36

Back to the future of Israel. Now we're going to read the segment in Romans 11 leading up to Paul's exclamation. Like him, we aren't likely to grasp how the concepts work together, but we can see a portion of the scriptural backing for the claim that Israel will be saved.

Please read Romans 11:25-32. The letter to the Romans was written to a predominantly Gentile audience. Keep in mind that Paul's reference to "you" was a reference to believers in Christ.

What does this segment suggest about God's continuing concern and plans for Israel?

All Israel will be saved

We have on several occasions referenced a future time of unparalleled tribulation. Perhaps you've heard the reference "the great tribulation" many times. The terminology is from Matthew 24:21-22 (KJV) where Christ spoke of " 'great tribulation, such as was not since the beginning of the world to this time, no, nor ever shall be. And except those days should be shortened, there should no flesh be saved: but for the elect's sake those days shall be shortened.' " Christ set the time of this tribulation just prior to His return: " 'Immediately after the tribulation of those days shall the sun be darkened, and the moon shall not give her light, and the stars shall fall from heaven, and the powers of the heavens shall be shaken: And then shall appear the sign of the Son of man in heaven: and then shall all the tribes of the earth mourn, and they shall see the Son of man coming in the clouds of heaven with power and great glory'" (Matt. 24:29-30, KJV).

We will learn far more about this time of tribulation in coming weeks. Recall Daniel's reference to "a time, times and half a time" (Dan. 7:25). We studied the reference and compared it to Revelation's "forty-two months" (11:2) and "1,260 days" (12:6). Many scholars believe each of these refer to the same period of three and a half years of "great tribulation." Don't confuse this time period with the "2,300 evenings and mornings" in Daniel 8:14. The 2,300 evenings and mornings referenced the reign of terror under Antiochus IV when he stopped the daily sacrifice (Dan. 8:11). "Most scholars believe that 2,300 evenings and mornings involve only a total of 1,150 days, since the 1,150 evening and 1,150 morning sacrifices (which would not be offered) equal a total of 2,300."[21] This calculation easily approximates the season stretching from the time Antiochus set up the altar to Zeus in Jerusalem's temple in December 167 B.C. to the rededication of the temple under Judas Maccabeus on December 14, 164 B.C.[22] So for clarity:

- "2,300 evenings and mornings" refers to the now-past terror of Antiochus.
- "A time, times and half a time," "forty-two months," and "1,260 days" refer to the future terror of the Antichrist.

Remember, we're viewing Daniel 8 as God's way of telling us about the former to help us better picture the latter. In session 8, we referred to this teaching method as "dual referencing." The nation of Israel will endure and emerge from the future terror of the Antichrist just as they endured and emerged from the past terror of Antiochus. Not unscathed, mind you. Will the church also endure the coming tribulation? Stay tuned for tomorrow's lesson.

DAY FIVE WHAT ON EARTH IS A "RAPTURE"?

Today's Treasure: *Therefore encourage each other with these words.*
1 Thessalonians 4:18

The concluding questions on days 3 and 4 were purposely posed to prepare us for today. Recall that in week 7 day 5 we introduced premillennialism. Today we'll expand this discussion by further exploring the two forms of premillennialism. Before we do, let's make sure we remember the basic definition of premillennialism.

By all means, glance at the segment on week 7, day 5, then write a brief synopsis of premillennialism in this space: *Premillennialists believe that the 1000 years refers to Christ's reign on earth after he returns. They believe the Rapture will be before the Tribulation or right in the middle (3½ yrs)*

A variety of premillennialism has gained increasing popularity since the nineteenth century. It is called pretribulational premillennialism or dispensationalism. Note that I will use these two terms interchangeably. I cannot stress strongly enough how many wonderful, sound scholars do not see eye to eye on this subject. Again, I offer you one view that I hope will heighten your appetite to study eschatology, then urge you to study others at the close of our journey. Those of us who hold to this view believe that the church age will continue until Christ suddenly and secretly draws believers in Christ out of this world to meet Him in the air. We'll see the scriptural support for this interpretation in a few minutes.

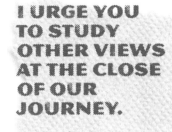

Dispensationalists believe that after Christ's secret return partway to the earth, He will "then return to heaven with the believers who have been removed from the earth. When that happens, there will be a great tribulation on the earth for a period of seven years."[23] What explanation the rest of the world will offer for the sudden disappearance of millions is unknown. We can be fairly certain that Satan, the father of lies and counterfeiter of facts, will find ways to suggest explanations that will blind many eyes from recognizing the fulfillment of Scripture.

The second half of this seven-year period will be far worse than the first. So we often refer to the entire seven years as the "seven year tribulation" and the second half (the 1,260 days or forty-two months) of the seven years as "the great tribulation."

"During this seven-year period of tribulation, many of the signs that were predicted to precede Christ's return will be fulfilled. The great ingathering of the fullness of the Jewish people will occur, as they trust Christ as their Messiah. In the midst of great suffering there will also be much effective evangelism, especially carried out by the new Jewish Christians. *At the end of the tribulation, Christ will then come back with his saints to reign on the earth for one thousand years.* After this millennial period there will be a rebellion, resulting in the final defeat of Satan and his forces, and then will come the resurrection of unbelievers, the last judgment, and the beginning of the eternal state."[24] Consider the following diagram of this interpretation (obviously not to scale):

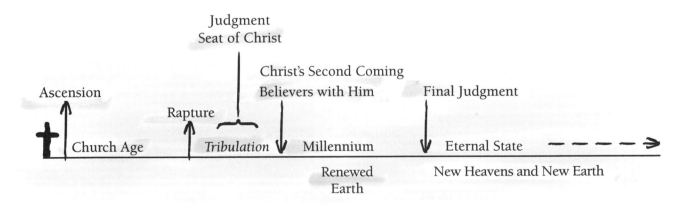

Pretribulationists make a distinction between a secret return of Christ in the air for believers and the return of Christ to the Mount of Olives that "every eye will see" (Zech. 14:3-4; Rev. 1:7).

🦁 Please read the following primary texts pretribulationists cite as their scriptural basis. Take down all pertinent descriptions of this event for both references:

1 Thessalonians 4:13-18

Jesus died & rose again
God will bring Jesus
& those who have died
Knowing him
He will return w/a
trumpet call.
The dead will rise
& then those who are
alive will be caught up
in the air to meet Christ

1 Corinthians 15:51-53

we will not all sleep
but we will be changed
in a flash. the
trumpet will sound
& the dead will be
raised imperishable
and we will be
changed

Amillennialists take these Scriptures to be descriptions of the resurrection, but premillennialists identify this event as the rapture. Search as you may, you will not find the term *rapture* in Scripture. "The words 'caught up' in 1 Thessalonians 4:17 translate from a Greek word that means 'to snatch, to seize suddenly, or to transport from one place to another.' It is also used of rescuing someone from a threatening danger (Acts 23:10; Jude 1:23). The Latin translation of this Greek word is *rapturo*. That's where we get the English word *rapture* to describe this future event of being caught up to meet Jesus Christ in the clouds."[25]

Keep in mind that we don't find the English words *Bible* and *Trinity* in Scripture either, but each is undeniably scriptural. The thing to remember is that pretribulationists understand the Scriptures to teach the rapture in which Christ will take away all the Christians on the earth before the terrible period called the tribulation. If a generalization helps to understand the different views, historic premillennialists believe the church will go through the tribulation period, and amillennialists believe both the tribulation and the millennium refer to aspects of present reality. Adherents to each of these views believe in the literal second coming of Christ. We just understand differently the details of how that coming will take place.

We can disagree all day long on end-time interpretations and still hold firmly to the foundations of our faith. What's important for unity's sake is that we exercise the freedom to disagree without being disagreeable. Some issues are spine issues. They are fundamental to our Christian belief system. Among eschatological subjects, belief in a second coming of Christ is a spine issue. Others are rib issues. On these our views can go in different directions, yet we can respect one another deeply. Interpretations of many end-time specifics are rib issues.

Even those who believe in the rapture don't agree on when it will take place. Are you ready for a mind-spinner? Here goes. Pretribulationists believe Christians will escape the entire seven-year period. Mid-tribulationists believe that Christians will endure the first half of the tribulation but will be drawn out before the second half, or great tribulation. Others hold to what is called a pre-wrath view in which believers endure all of the tribulation except the seventh seal of judgment (Rev. 8) when God pours out His wrath on earth. In other words, many pre-wrath interpreters believe Christians will endure Satan's wrath but not God's. Still others are

SOME ISSUES ARE SPINE ISSUES. OTHERS ARE RIB ISSUES.

"post-tributationists" who believe that Christians will go through the tribulation but will be seized by Christ just before His visible return. All of these views leave room for Christians to be with Christ by the time He visibly returns because Scripture teaches that we return *with* Him.

> Please read Revelation 19:11-16, one of the segments describing Christ's visible return. How are the "armies of heaven" dressed who will follow Christ on white horses? *They are dressed in clean, fine white linen*

> Now, read Revelation 19:7-8. Who was given identical dress? *The Bride of Christ*

The bride of Christ is made up of the same group of people called "the church." She is representative of all believers in Jesus Christ. Any group of students naturally wants to know what their teacher thinks. Believe me when I say that men and women far more knowledgeable than I strongly disagree on the rapture and its timing. I believe in a seizing away of believers in Christ. I am less dogmatic about the timing. Many of my fellow pretribulationists cite Christ's assurance in Revelation 3:10 as evidence that believers will be spared the tribulation.

> How do you think that Revelation 3:10 could suggest God will remove His people before the tribulation? *Because Jesus says that He will keep believers from the hour of trial that is going to come upon the whole earth to test those who live on earth.*

I lean heavily toward a pretribulational view, but not on the basis of Revelation 3:10. Those words were issued specifically to the church of Philadelphia. But I have to ask myself if the church of Philadelphia represents all Christians in this context. It's possible, but none of the other churches addressed in Revelation seem to represent all believers. Furthermore, I'm not sure we can interpret the "hour of trial" to which it refers as the entire seven-year tribulation period.

I think Revelation 3:10 is greatly encouraging but not totally convincing on its own. I lean toward a pretribulational seizing of believers far more strongly based on Christ's comparisons of the coming of the kingdom of God to the "days of Noah" and "the days of Lot" (Luke 17:26,28). In both cases, the "righteous" were removed or secured before the judgment of God fell. The imputed righteousness we have been granted in Christ (see 2 Cor. 5:21) may very well enable Christians to escape the time of tribulation. All I know for certain is this: whenever the trumpet sounds—before the tribulation, midway through, or at the end—I'm going to meet my Christ in the air. And if you're in Christ, I can't wait to see you there.

WHEN THE TRUMPET SOUNDS, I'M GOING TO MEET CHRIST IN THE AIR. IF YOU'RE IN CHRIST, I CAN'T WAIT TO SEE YOU THERE.

> Enough of my thoughts. Let's conclude with yours. Paraphrase the Apostle Paul's exhortation in his wrap-up on this "seizing away" (1 Thess. 4:18).

So this should be a comfort to all believers & we are to remind each other of these truths

171

We can be encouraged by Scripture even when we don't understand all it says to us.

Conclude today's lesson with ways you are encouraged personally by Paul's words in 1 Thessalonians 4:13-18.

that whether I am dead or still alive I am going to meet Christ in the air

---

1. Stephen R. Miller, *Daniel*, vol. 18 in *The New American Commentary* (Nashville: Broadman & Holman, 2001), 223.
2. Ibid., 224.
3. John E. Goldingay, *Daniel*, vol. 30 in *Word Biblical Commentary* (Nashville: Thomas Nelson, 1989), 209.
4. Miller, 224.
5. As quoted in John F. Walvoord and Roy B. Zuck, eds., *The Bible Knowledge Commentary of the Old Testament* (Wheaton, IL: SP Publications, Inc., 1985), 1359.
6. Spiros Zodhiates, ThD., gen. ed., *Lexical Aids to the New Testament, Hebrew-Greek Key Word Study Bible, New International Version* (Chattanooga, TN: AMG Publishers), #4130, #4125, 1659.
7. Walvoord and Zuck, 1358.
8. Stuart Townend and Keith Getty, "In Christ Alone." © Copyright 2001 Kingsway/Thankyou Music (ASCAP).
9. Goldingay, 209.
10. Miller, 226.
11. Ibid.
12. Achtemeier, P.J., *Harper's Bible Dictionary*, 1st ed. (San Francisco: Harper & Row and Society of Biblical Literature, 1985), 922, s.v. "Seleucids."
13. Miller, 226.
14. Achtemeier, 588, s.v. "Maccabees."
15. Ibid.
16. Ibid.
17. Ibid.
18. Walvoord and Zuck, 1358.
19. Achtemeier, 588, s.v. "Maccabees."
20. Miller, 226, footnote #26.
21. Ibid., 228.
22. Ibid., 228-29.
23. Wayne Grudem, *Systematic Theology* (Grand Rapids, MI: Zondervan, 1995), 1113.
24. Ibid.
25. Mark Hitchcock, *The Complete Book of Bible Prophecy* (Wheaton, IL: Tyndale House Publishers, 1999), 42-43.

UNEXPECTED ANSWERS TO PRAYER

9

9

UNEXPECTED ANSWERS TO PRAYER

The Hebrew is far better translated "seventy 'Sevens '" than "seventy weeks " (v. 24a).

70 X 7 = 490

Decreed: "The verb translated 'decreed' (hatak) occurs only here in the OT but is used in later

Hebrew and Aramaic to mean 'cut, cut off, decide.' … God had 'cut off' or 'cut out ' a certain

period of time (490 years) from the remainder of history for a specific purpose."[1]

This period of time had been set apart specifically for the people of Israel and

the city of Jerusalem (v. 24b).

Six critical fulfillments accomplishing "God's purpose for all history"[2] (v. 24c).

- "to finish transgression"
- "to bring in everlasting righteousness "
- "to put an end to sin"
- "to seal up vision and prophecy"
- "to atone for wickedness"
- "to anoint the most holy"

The block of time "cut out" is sliced into three sections:

1. Seven "sevens" (v. 25) 2. Sixty-two "sevens" (v. 25) 3. One "seven" (v. 27)

Sections One and Two

7 "sevens" (7 x 7)		490 YEARS		
+ 62 "sevens" (62 x 7)				
"sevens" or 483 YEARS	7 "sevens" (49 years)	62 "sevens" (434 years)	1 "seven" (7 years)	

- (The Jewish calendar is based on a 360-day lunar year.) This segment of time was set to begin with the decree to _restore_ and _rebuild_ Jerusalem. Nehemiah 2:1 sets the date "in the month of Nisan in the twentieth year of King Artaxerxes" (_March_ / _April_ 444 B.C.).

- **49 years** are intimated to completely rebuild Jerusalem "with streets and a trench."

- The consecutive **434 years** would last until "the Anointed One." Hebrew transliteration: "_Masiyah_."

- A **483-year** period equals _173,880_ days. (Jewish calendar) What occurred this many days after the first of Nisan (March 5), 444 B.C.? (Nisan 10 or March 30 A.D. 33) See Luke 19:29-40.

The Time Gap

- (v. 26): "After" is this interpretation's signal for a _gap_.

- "After the sixty-two 'sevens' the Anointed One will be _cut off_ and will have _nothing_."

- John 1:12 refers to a group of people later termed the _Church_.

- Additionally, "the _people_ of the ruler who will come will _destroy_ the city and the sanctuary" (A.D. 70).

Section Three

- The final block of seven years will begin with a _covenant_ signed between the "ruler" (the "little horn" of Daniel 7) and the people (Israel).

- This seven-year period contains a critical midpoint.

1. Stephen R. Miller, *Daniel*, vol. 18 in *The New American Commentary* (Nashville: Broadman & Holman, 1994), 258.
2. Adapted from Joyce G. Baldwin, *Daniel* (Downers Grove, IL.: InterVarsity Press, 1978), 168-169.

If you were in session 9, your head may be spinning over the seventy "sevens"! Bible study can be pretty wild, can't it? I absolutely love it and I hope you do, too. The journey is all the more wonderful because I glance to my side and see you. I'm so glad you came along. We have a good, understandable week ahead, Beloved. Days 1 through 4 have lots of room for personal application. Only day 5 highlights the seventy sevens, and perhaps our heads will have stopped spinning by then.

You and I have committed to wean ourselves from approaching the Word solely based on what it says about us. We want our culturally indoctrinated, me-centered approaches to be replaced by a God-centered approach to Bible study. At the same time, don't forget that God meant His Word to be applied! Let's not tip the scale to another unhealthy extreme by approaching Scripture strictly for the attainment of knowledge—leaving our hearts unmoved and untreated. God's Word is always to us and for us. When He additionally talks about us, let's not miss the message.

If keeping this straight seems too complicated, just ask Him daily to give you a pure, God-centered heart. That's what He's teaching me to ask. We can be confident we will get what we ask. What could please Him more?

THIS WEEK'S PRINCIPAL QUESTIONS

DAY 1 In the first year of the reign of Darius, what did Daniel realize and how did he come to this realization?

DAY 2 What did Daniel do after he realized the 70 years could be coming to an end?

DAY 3 On what basis did Daniel, a man of integrity, make his requests?

DAY 4 How does the word "while" in Daniel 9: 20-21 emphasize timing?

DAY 5 How do the events we studied in session 9 fit on the time line?

DAY ONE | UNDERSTOOD FROM THE SCRIPTURES

Today's Treasure: *In the first year of his reign, I, Daniel, understood from the Scriptures, according to the word of the Lord given to Jeremiah the prophet, that the desolation of Jerusalem would last seventy years. Daniel 9:2*

Several years ago my good friend and worship leader, Travis Cottrell, sent me a rough cut of a song he'd written with a friend to convey the ministry of the Word God had given us. I'd anticipated it but in retrospect not nearly enough. I slipped it in my CD player and pulled out of the driveway to run errands. Within seconds I had to pull over on the shoulder of the road to listen. The song was so powerful I felt as if my soul were going to jump right out of my skin. After writing this series and sensing its tone, several of us knew that no more appropriate theme song could possibly exist for Daniel than "Your Word Is Life to Me." It's the song you hear in part in every introduction and conclusion to the sessions. Today I want you to read the words because they provide the perfect introduction to our ninth week of study. See them first from the eyes of a "Daniel" who'd been chained by captivity in a foreign land and then apply them to your own life.

I am a stranger in this place;
   This world is not my home.
I want more than it can give.
   I am a desert needing rain;
I'm thirsty for your voice.
   The very reason that I live—
You are the Word, my one desire,
   An all consuming holy fire,
The very breath that I am longing for.
   My heart is desperate for Your ways.
Refine me in your holy blaze,
   If that is what it takes to know
   You more.

You are the Truth that sets me free;
   Your word is life to me.
Only the power of Your Word
   Can melt away these chains
   That have held me far too long.
So light the fire and let it burn
   These shackles and restraints,
   And I will sing this freedom song.

...

You are the Word, my one desire …
You are the Truth that sets me free.
Your word is life to me.[1]

I'm not sure the Word ever became life to Daniel more vividly than in the events of the ninth chapter. This week you'll see no few reasons why. Session 9 centered on the last segment where we concerned ourselves with the 70 sevens decreed for the nation of Israel. Today we'll back up to the very beginning of Daniel 9 and start our segment-by-segment consideration of the whole chapter. With God, timing is often as important as time; therefore, let's begin by making sure we have the timing of God's dreams and revelations to Daniel.

According to Daniel 7:1, when was the dream of the little horn, the Ancient of Days, and "one like a son of man" given to Daniel?

_____

According to Daniel 8:1, when was the vision of the ram, the goat, and the horn depicting Antiochus IV given to Daniel?

_____

Now, what is the timing of the events recorded in our present chapter

according to Daniel 9:1? _____

The timing of Daniel 9 is critical because the silver empire has defeated the golden empire and Babylon has fallen into the hands of the Medo-Persians. Daniel himself had interpreted the handwriting on the wall to Belshazzar, but he probably never dreamed the prophecy would come to pass before the night was over. The events recorded in chapter 9 probably happened not long after Daniel emerged from the lions' den but before the official decree of the Persian King Cyrus to free the captives.

A very wise Daniel, exceeding 80 years of age at this time, knew that the overthrow of the Babylonian empire was highly significant. Daniel knew the times had changed. He also knew that the best way to tell what "time" it was for the nation of Israel was to check the Scriptures.

 In the first year of the reign of Darius, what did Daniel realize, and how did he come to this realization (Dan. 9:2-3)?

_____

In week 6, we examined the primary prophecies of Jeremiah indicating a time period of 70 years for the captivity of Judah (see Jer. 25:11-12; 29:10). Daniel was a young teenager in Jerusalem around the time of Jeremiah's first predictions in 605 B.C. In *The New American Commentary,* Stephen R. Miller explains, "As Daniel studied Jeremiah's prophecy, he came to realize that the seventy-year captivity period was drawing to a close."[2]

As I looked at the passage, two things leapt off the page at me. First, Daniel clearly recognized Jeremiah's words as Scripture. For a Jewish contemporary that is amazing. The world of Daniel's day teemed with false prophets, but Daniel discerned that Jeremiah was not only a true prophet but also a writer of Scripture. You could compare Daniel's observation to 2 Peter 3:15-16.

What phrase in 2 Peter 3:16 shows that Peter recognized Paul's writings as more than just man's opinions?

☐ all his letters   ☐ hard to understand   ☐ the other Scriptures

DANIEL BELIEVED IN THE REALITY OF PREDICTIVE PROPHECY.

Daniel not only recognized Jeremiah's words as Scripture, he also believed in the reality of predictive prophecy. "Jeremiah had foretold the end of the exilic period seventy years in advance, and Daniel fully expected this prophecy to be fulfilled. ... This is the safest procedure for believers today as they study prophecies of future events."[3]

Let me put this in laymen's terms for us: Daniel believed God. And he believed the predictive words that had come through the prophet Jeremiah "were the very words of God delivered to the world through a human instrument."[4] Since the 70 years made common sense, Daniel's first approach was to take them literally. The literal approach turned out to be right.

Any serious Bible student can tell the approximate time according to the Scriptures. I'll show you how in just a moment. In the Word of God, some people may have been particularly gifted for it.

Fill in the following blanks according to 1 Chronicles 12:32 in the NIV:

"Men of Issachar, who _____

and _____

200 chiefs, with all their relatives under their command."

Issachar was one of the tribes of Israel. Scripture tells us they "understood the times." They probably did exactly what Daniel did in our present text. They read Scripture, prayed, and received insight from the Lord. The most important concept in the verse describing the men of Issachar is that they knew how to apply the information they received. They "understood the times" and "knew what Israel should do." Their example tells us that the times in which any generation lives ought to have a sizable impact on what God's people should do.

Let's practice Daniel's approach. Please read the following segments of Scripture. Then, on a scale of 1 to 10, 1 representing no apparent fulfillment and 10 representing complete fulfillment, estimate how much the times described seem to reflect our present society:

Matthew 24:12 foretells an increase in _____ and hearts

(love) that grow _____ toward the end of times (v. 14). Circle the number that you'd estimate for a present fulfillment. (There's no right or wrong answer here. We're just trying to be a Daniel.)

0   1   2   3   4   5   6   7   8   9   10

2 Timothy 3:1-5: Circle the number that you'd estimate for a present fulfillment.

0   1   2   3   4   5   6   7   8   9   10

Of course, we can't tell the exact time from these predictions, and to some degree they apply to every age. But we might estimate our general timing on the kingdom calendar. We certainly know that wickedness is vastly increasing. I also think that the overstimulation of various forms of media can cause our hearts to grow increasingly colder. We can grow tragically chilled to violence and suffering.

In my estimation our culture stunningly portrays 2 Timothy 3:1-5. No matter how much longer this era we're calling the church age will last, I believe Scripture strongly suggests that the birth pangs signaling the last days are coming closer and closer together (see Matt. 24:8). Many wonderful things will also happen toward the end, like outpourings of the Holy Spirit (see Acts 2:17) and the preaching of the gospel of Christ throughout the world (see Matt. 24:14). The men of Issachar didn't just "understand the times," they "knew what Israel should do."

Let's conclude with this question: As you come to understand a little more about our times, can you think of any way this awareness could change something you "do"? If so, share it.

It's time to check the time. Great work today, Dear One!

DAY TWO SCRIPTURE INTERACTION

Today's Treasure: *So I turned to the Lord God and pleaded with him in prayer and petition, in fasting, and in sackcloth and ashes. Daniel 9:3*

I've been giving yesterday's concluding question some thought. As the world moves increasingly closer to terrible tribulation and as the glorious return of Christ hastens, we each asked ourselves, "Should I be doing anything differently?" As we look forward to the "day of God" and also consider the destruction to come, 2 Peter 3:11 calls us to "live holy and godly lives."

As I reflect on the increasing wickedness and coldheartedness foretold in Matthew 24:12 and the descriptions of self-centered people void of self-control in 2 Timothy 3:1-5, the thought again occurs to me that holy and godly lives will not be accidental for any of us. The virus of self-gratification is far too contagious. If we don't want to catch it, we must deliberately immunize ourselves against it. Throughout the first half of our study, we discussed the huge impact any society has on its individuals, and we were challenged to fortify ourselves against the corruption of our Babylon-like culture. Let's hear the echo again.

Serious times are upon us, but we may not be paying attention. Goodness knows life offers us all manner of trivial diversions. The other day I was leaving the house with serious ministry on my mind. On the way to the car, a gnat landed right in my perfectly applied pink lip gloss. For a minute I thought I'd have to go back in the house for a spoon to dig it out. Somehow the irony of such a ridiculous distraction on my way to minister hit me humorously.

 When was the last time you felt God telling you to get a grip and see what is really important?

_____

SPIRITUAL MATURITY IS RARELY MORE OBVIOUS THAN IN OUR ABILITY TO DISCERN THE DIFFERENCE BETWEEN TRUE PERIL AND A GNAT IN OUR LIP GLOSS.

Spiritual maturity is rarely more obvious than in our ability to discern the difference between true peril and a gnat in our lip gloss. We, as a culture and as a nation, find ourselves in serious times. As I consider our "times," I don't *only* want to be fortified against the influences of wickedness. I want to be an active influence for Christ. I want to do some good! I don't just want to guard against a cold heart, I want a heart that burns with fiery passion for Christ and for a world He came to save. I want to be part of worldwide missions. I want an outpouring of the Holy Spirit on my very own head! I want to take my place in the times to which I've been entrusted. Don't you?

As you consider our times, what is the desire of your own heart?

_____

🦁 God will show each of us individual ways we can join Him in His work in our times, but He will use Daniel today to show us the first thing on our "should do" list. Reread Daniel 9:1-3. What did Daniel do after he realized the 70 years could be coming to an end? (See v. 3.)

_____

We are so culturally indoctrinated to be fast-paced, high-energy, hands-on kinds of people that we tend to think of prayer as a passive, nearly "do-nothing" reaction. We tend to pray when we don't know what else to do. Beloved, nothing shakes the heavenlies like prayer. Nothing moves the heart of God more than prayer. Furthermore, I'm not sure anything takes more energy at times than fervent prayer. As we, like Daniel and the men of Issachar, try to understand the times, we can assume without question that the time is right for prayer!

Pray when we don't know what to do! Pray when we do! Pray, pray, pray! We don't have to be formal. We don't have to be long-winded. Prayer is deliberate, open communication with God. I can sit silently in an intense awareness of His presence, waiting on Him and trying to listen and still be in a posture of prayer. I can groan and be in such pain of heart that words fail me, and God will interpret those groans as the vocabulary of prayer. We often learn the most about effective prayer, however, by listening to others pray. That's what we're going to do today.

The ninth chapter of Daniel is home to one of the most powerful prayers in the Old Testament. Please read Daniel 9:3-19 and document words or phrases that fall under these three headings:

God's faithfulness	Israel's sins	Expressions of Daniel's urgency
_____	_____	_____
_____	_____	_____
_____	_____	_____
_____	_____	_____
_____	_____	_____

We'll talk about some of our general observations tomorrow, but I'd like to draw our attentions to one important concept for the remainder of the lesson: Daniel's search of Scripture prompted interaction. Consider the practice carefully. Scripture reading was the way Daniel allowed God to speak to him in this context, _then_ prayer was the way Daniel spoke back. Oh, Beloved, if you haven't already begun to exercise an interactive approach to Scripture reading, I pray you'll start today!

When you read the Bible, the God of the universe is talking to you. So, what should you do in response? Talk back! God is looking for a two-way conversation. When we read God's Word and pause here and there to say something to Him in response, we are participating in a dialogue with the Divine! Perhaps all of this is new to you and you're wondering, "What would I say?" Consider these examples:

- While you read a difficult passage, you might open your mouth and say, "God, this is confusing to me. What in the world does this mean?" Whether He opens your eyes to a level of understanding immediately or eventually, your one-way reading has turned into a two-way conversation.
- While you read a passage that speaks of God's greatness, majesty, or power, open your mouth and worship Him for a moment and ask Him to help you see Him more readily for who He is.
- While you read a passage that you want to believe but you don't, open your mouth and ask Him to help you believe and increase your faith.
- While you read a passage describing wonderful things He's done for you, open your mouth and thank Him. Tell Him what His work in your behalf has done for you. If you feel like crying, don't just cry about Him. Cry to Him! Tell Him how deeply He touches you.
- While you read a passage that reminds you of another's need, open your mouth that very moment and intercede. You've got it.

Give an example of your own:

- _____

You see, our Scripture readings may make us think about God, but Daniel's example reminds us to turn those thoughts into dialogue. When God talks to us, Beloved, let's talk back!

DAY THREE A "WE" KIND OF ATTITUDE

Today's Treasure: *We have sinned and done wrong. Daniel 9:5*

We're focusing on the prayer of Daniel. Begin by reading Daniel 9:4-19 again. This time, however, we will search the Scriptures with a different goal. If you don't mind marking in your Bible, I'd like for you to circle every reference Daniel made to "we." If you prefer not to write in your Bible, please tally the times you see the word "we" in Daniel's prayer and record the total here: _____. Proceed when you finish your reading assignment.

Even though Daniel was only a young teen when Jeremiah first predicted the captivity of Judah, and even though he'd walked faithfully with God in Babylon, he still counted himself among the transgressors of Israel. Daniel interceded for the masses as one sharing the blame for their sins. He did not put himself above the people. Daniel knelt before God on the level ground of man's innate waywardness. "*We* have sinned. … *We* have been wicked. … *We* have not listened. … *We* are covered with shame."

Put yourself in Daniel's position. Why do you think he shared the blame for the sins of the masses even though he was innocent of many of their transgressions?

_____

Scripture records many occasions when the pleadings of one man led to the sparing or saving of an entire group—even *nation*—of people. I am not among those who think prayer for self is selfish. We must pray for ourselves as ones who will give individual account. At the same time, Scripture offers many proofs that one person's prayers can affect masses of people. Can you imagine, therefore, what we miss when we never pray fervently outside our small circle of concerns? Oh, how Satan hopes we'll think our prayers don't matter and that God's activity is limited to what we can see with human eyes.

In all honesty and in this season of your life, how convinced are you that your prayers matter?

———————————————————————

My prayers seem to go no higher than the ceiling.   God frequently answers my prayers in a mighty way.

What recent experiences—whether negative or positive—have caused you to come to this conclusion?

_____

_____

If you feel that your prayers matter little, if any, can you accept the biblical truth that God can be trusted when our human reasoning often cannot? "Trust in the LORD with all your heart and lean not on your own understanding" (Prov. 3:5)! He knows you by name, and He recognizes your voice. Whatever you do, Dear One, don't stop praying. Heaven is affected even when you don't see answers on Earth.

Daniel's example in chapter 9 suggests that the activity of intercessory prayer for the masses is not the only factor that matters. The attitude of the intercessory prayer is also greatly important. Based on Daniel's "we" attitude and God's response later in the chapter, God not only honors prayer *for* our fellowman, He especially seems to honor the intercessory prayer *of* a fellowman. He favors those who humble themselves as fellow transgressors, not those who piously place themselves above those in pitiful need of prayer. In Luke 18:11-12, Christ criticized the Pharisee who "stood up and prayed about himself." God honored the attitudes of intercessors such as Abraham, Moses, Ezra, and Nehemiah who saw themselves as the fellowmen of great transgressors and cried out for mercy along with the ones right beside them.

The concluding words of John 2 often replay in my mind. John 2:24-25 says of Christ, "He knew all men. He did not need man's testimony about man, for he knew what was in a man." I think Daniel could count himself among the transgressors of Israel because he was wise enough to know what was *in* him ... even if it hadn't always found its way *out* of him. To a great extent Daniel, too, "knew what was in a man." And he was that man.

Daniel not only knew himself. More importantly, he knew his God. He knew his was a God who kept covenant promises. A righteous God. A great and mighty God who wielded His strong arm and delivered the people out of Egypt. And in Daniel's estimation, the same God who delivered the Israelites from Egypt could deliver the Israelites from Babylon (see v. 15).

Do we pray like that, Beloved? Do we rehearse the mighty acts God has performed in the past as we request His intervention in the present? The prayer warriors of the Word often coupled their requests with remembrances like a lawyer cites a precedent before the judge hearing the case.

In this present season of your life, where are you desperate for God to wield His mighty arm?

As you make your request, start recalling in prayer God's mighty acts in the past, both in Scripture and in your life. Your faith will grow, and God will be pleased to see you exercise your humble but powerful position as His child.

Look back at Daniel 9:3 again. After Daniel searched the pertinent words of the prophet Jeremiah, he "turned to the Lord God and pleaded with him in prayer and petition." A more literal rendering of "turned to the Lord God" is "I gave my face" to the Lord God.[5] Repeatedly Daniel spoke of the shame he and the people of Israel bore because of their sin, but he knew he could lift his crimson face to God for the remedy. Sometimes Satan tries to make us feel too ashamed to pray. Beloved, you can bring anything to God! You can confess any sin and tell Him anywhere you've been.

 As we draw to a close, read Daniel 9:18 once more. On what basis did this man of integrity make his requests?

Beloved, none of us is righteous enough to earn the ear of God. He hears and He acts because of His great mercy—a mercy greater than our sin. Since the day he appeared on the pages of Scripture, Satan's specialty has been shame. Satan hopes the shame will make us hang our heads and hide. There in the dark closet of secrecy, he tries to make us feel bound and gagged. If we're in Christ, we are neither. At times of greatest shame, we need to do the exact opposite of what we feel like doing. We need to lift our faces to our God, open our mouths in confession, let Him wash us with forgiveness and bathe us with His radiance.

Chin to the sky, redemption draweth nigh.

DAY FOUR WHILE I WAS STILL IN PRAYER

Today's Treasure: *While I was still in prayer, Gabriel, the man I had seen in the earlier vision, came to me in swift flight about the time of the evening sacrifice. Daniel 9:21*

Throughout days 2 and 3 our attentions have been drawn to the passionate prayer of Daniel recorded in 9:4-19. To emphasize the timing of the event in the next segment of Scripture, please reread Daniel 9:19. Though this verse is an obvious crescendo (*Listen! Forgive! Hear! Act!*), it wasn't necessarily meant to be the conclusion. Daniel was gloriously interrupted. This divine interruption will be our focus today.

Read Daniel 9:20-23. How does the word "while" emphasize timing?

The angel Gabriel came to Daniel ...

verse 20: "while _____ "

verse 21: "while _____ "

Imagine you're in the throes of desperate pleas to God, pouring out confessions and cries of intercession, when suddenly you're interrupted by a celestial messenger who says something like, "Sorry I took so long. I got here as fast as I could. God sent me with your answer." Would you faint now or later?

Daniel recognized the angel because he'd seen him in the earlier vision recorded in Daniel 8. He also knew his name was Gabriel because he'd heard "a man's voice" calling him by name: "Gabriel, tell this man the meaning of the vision" (Dan. 8:16). If you participated in session 8, you may recall the suggestion of *The New American Commentary* that the one speaking was very likely God Himself. Whoever spoke was clearly "demonstrating his superiority over that important angel."[6] This time Daniel didn't just see Gabriel in a vision. The implication may be that the heavenly messenger appeared to him in plain sight. If we know anything about Daniel at this point in our journey, surely we know he was a man of prayer.

We have no idea how often he prayed spontaneously, but how often did he practice planned times of prayer according to Daniel 6:10?

☐ before every meal   ☐ in the morning and evening   ☐ three times

In chapter 9 our protagonist was over 80 years old. He had prayed earnestly at least three times a day for many of those years. When he lifted up the prayers recorded in Daniel 9, the furthest thing from his mind was to be interrupted by an angel with an immediate answer from God. Oh, I think Daniel had every expectation that God would hear and was merciful enough to act—but not the way He did.

Daniel knew his God, yet God never ceased surprising him. Dear One, please don't assume that God will always work in your life the way He always has. A sunset is proof that God colors outside the lines. He has no status quo. Even the laws of nature are His to interrupt. As many times as you've prayed before, today may be the day when God sends the answer so swiftly—so divinely—that you're windburned.

Let's look at several words or phrases in today's segment that speak healing to the injured parts of us that fear anonymity and silence.

1. *"While I was still in prayer."* God doesn't have voice mail. He doesn't check His messages when He gets a minute. We're not put on hold and told all calls will be answered in the order received. We don't have to wait until someone else finishes for ours to be heard. When we bring our earnest confessions and petitions before God, *while we are still in prayer, He hears.*

   How does Isaiah 65:24 echo Daniel's experience?

   _____

2. *"Gabriel … came to me … about the time of the evening sacrifice"* (v. 21). A day never passed that Daniel didn't remember the sacrifices that should have been occurring at the same time as his afternoon prayers. Captivity precluded them. In terms of meeting the requirements of the law, the conditions were unfavorable for a good hearing from God. David, the psalmist, may also have been far from Jerusalem and all the legalistic elements of acceptable worship when he wrote Psalm 141:1-2.

   As he cried out to God, what did David offer instead of incense (Psalm 141:1-2)?

   _____

   What did he offer instead of an evening sacrifice?

   _____

Generations later as Daniel sought God with all his might, confessed sin, and interceded for a captive nation, his prayers became incense and his poured-out life became the evening sacrifice.

3. *"Daniel, I have now come to give you insight and understanding"* (v. 22). I will never get over the fact that God knows us by name. When God summoned Gabriel for this terrestrial errand, He specified that he was to go to Daniel—right there in captive Babylon. Beloved, you will never pray an anonymous prayer. Your petitions never go unsigned. Gabriel came to give Daniel "insight and understanding."

Are you thinking what I'm thinking? We could certainly use an angel from God to lend some insight from time to time! Actually, we have something better. We who have received Christ as Savior have His very Spirit dwelling within us. Keep asking for understanding! Keep seeking supernatural insight! Stay in His Word so you can recognize His voice, then listen closely to what He's saying deep within you. You have the Spirit-empowered ability to hear God.

4. *"As soon as you began to pray, an answer was given"* (v. 23). This statement is stunning to me. We've already been told that "while" Daniel was praying Gabriel appeared to him, but the answer was given as soon as Daniel began. God read Daniel's heart before He heard a single word. "Before a word is on my tongue you know it completely, O LORD" (Ps. 139:4). God watched Daniel pour over His Word and knew in advance that his study would turn into prayer. Oh, let that be us! God in effect said "yes" before Daniel could get the words, "O Lord, the great and awesome God, who keeps his covenant of love" out of his mouth.

If God was this anxious to speak, why didn't He just save Daniel the trouble and send Gabriel in advance? Isn't this one of life's hardest questions: If God is sovereign and all-knowing and will do as He pleases, why should we pray at all? *Word Biblical Commentary* poses a wonderful explanation. "One person's prayer brings about the restoration of the people of God; but it is a matter of releasing that restoration which God already purposed."[7]

In your own words, what do you think this scholar means?

_____

_____

Yes, God knows what He's going to do, but He is relational to the core. He often waits to be asked and waits to be sought. And not just for answers but for the very presence of relationship.

How does Psalm 31:19 lend support to this concept?

_____

_____

Dear One, I believe with all my heart that God has great things "stored up" for those of us who esteem Him and take refuge in Him. I'm not talking about trivial things like earthly riches. I'm talking about things that matter—like a life of purpose, tremendous fruit, deep satisfaction, godly influence, open doors for ministry, restoration of relationships, and astonishing breakthroughs. Are these things dependent upon prayer? Often the answer is "yes!" They are stored up by God but released

> *"We have not received the spirit of the world but the Spirit who is from God, that we may understand what God has freely given us."*
>
> **1 CORINTHIANS 2:12**

by prayer. In the process, an incredible thing takes place. It's called relationship. Why would God care to have relationship with frail flesh and blood like us? Maybe our last insight for today from Daniel 9:23 will answer that question for us: "You are highly esteemed." The King James Version says, "thou art greatly beloved." The Hebrew "describes something or someone desired or counted precious."[8]

God sent those words through Gabriel to His servant Daniel centuries ago. He's sending them now to you, for Christ has "made us accepted in the beloved" (Eph. 1:6, KJV). Receive them, Greatly Loved One.

DAY FIVE NOW ANSWERS/DELAYED ACTIONS

Today's Treasure: *As soon as you began to pray, an answer was given. Daniel 9:23*

The Holy Spirit has really engaged me this week in our study, both spiritually and emotionally. I hope you're experiencing the same thing. Be blessed to realize that your God wants to talk to you and hear you talk back! A million other voices cannot drown out your own.

As we get started today, I'd like to focus on another point of interest in the answer God gave through Gabriel. Please reread Daniel 9:20-23; then read the rest of the chapter, verses 24-27. We drew yesterday's lesson to a conclusion with our gaze on these wonderful words: "As soon as you began to pray, an answer was given."

Daniel undoubtedly got more of an answer than he could have expected as Gabriel delivered the decree of the 70 sevens. Daniel, however, received God's answer long before the world would see God's action. The action would not be fully revealed for thousands of years. Think about it. Daniel beheld almost none of the action prophesied by the answer. Even so, he was as certain of its inevitability as he would have been had he been an eyewitness to its unfolding.

Beloved, you and I aren't likely to receive a revelation with the magnitude of Daniel 9, but we can relate conceptually, and I'll tell you how. As we seek God with all our hearts, sometimes His answer comes long before the action. Have you prayed diligently about something then believed with all your heart He gave you an affirmative answer? Have you, then, become deeply concerned as time passed and without seeing the action inferred by the answer? For instance, did God give you an assurance in your heart that your loved one would be saved? That you would be married? That you would have a child? That you were called to ministry? That a loved one would experience a great deliverance? The examples could go on and on.

If you can relate, offer your own: what request were you fully convinced God had answered affirmatively?

_____

AS WE SEEK GOD WITH ALL OUR HEARTS, SOMETIMES HIS ANSWER COMES LONG BEFORE THE ACTION.

You believe the answer came, but are you still waiting for the action? Are you doubting now what you believed with all your heart you received from God? I understand. I've done the same thing. But Daniel knew God's action was as sure as His Word. If God said it, He would do it, no matter how much time intervened. God's answer guarantees His action.

Sometimes I've wanted something so badly, I've mistaken my own wishes for what we often call "a word from God." Other times, however, I've known all the way to my marrow that God spoke to my heart on a matter and confirmed it over and over. Those are the things I don't want to give up on just because time has passed.

I try to anticipate your questions, and right about now you may be asking, "How would I know the difference?" Under the New Covenant (as New Testament believers), we have access to complete revelation through the Word of God, Genesis to Revelation; therefore, God is not nearly as likely to speak audibly from the heavens or send us angels like Gabriel. We hold in our hands what people like Daniel could only have wished for. As we seek God through the Bible, many answers are black-and-white, but others are not nearly so clear, are they? We are gloriously blessed to be led by the Spirit, but we are also challenged at times to discern that leadership.

New Testament believers walk by faith rather than sight. I wish I could give you "steps one through three" for telling the difference between something you're presuming is a word from God and something God really has told you. I can't. Sometimes only time can tell. I'll do my best, however, to describe how I try to discern the difference personally.

Every person born on planet Earth is comprised of spirit, soul, and body. The terms "spirit" and "soul" are often used interchangeably in Scripture, but when the Word of God distinguishes between the two immaterial parts of man, the soul can often be pictured as the seat of our emotions and personalities. The spirit, on the other hand, may be generalized as the part of us with the capacity to know God. First Corinthians 6:17 tells us, "He who unites himself with the Lord is one with him in spirit." In other words, when we accept Christ as Savior, His Spirit takes up residence in our spirits (see Rom. 8:9).

In my own attempts to distinguish my desires from an authentic word from God, I find that what God reveals to me in my "spirit" is deeper than what I feel or sense in my emotions or, for the sake of distinguishing the difference, my "soul." In other words, when I can put aside my feelings for a moment, what I still *consistently* sense as the leading of the Holy Spirit I assume to be a clearer word from God. Feelings come and go, but do I have a greater certainty at a deeper level that I have heard from God on a matter? If so, Dear One, I choose to believe that the action will one day come as surely as the answer. Though this approach has not been fail-safe for me, it has led me astray very few times.

Does what I've described lend any insight at all into your own challenges to discern true promises of God? If so, how?

_____

_____

GOD DOES WHAT HE SAYS. HIS ANSWER GUARANTEES HIS ACTION.

Surely one of the most pronounced lessons we can take with us from our study of the Book of Daniel is that God does what He says. His answer guarantees His action. Don't forget it!

Let's conclude week 9 with a glance back at our notes to session 9. Because the Book of Daniel has so much to say about critical events on the kingdom calendar, time lines are a very important part of our learning process. This is a great time for two reminders: (1) Many brilliant scholars through the centuries have differed dramatically on the interpretation of the 70 sevens. What I've presented to you is a possibility, not a certainty. (2) I urge you to study other notable views (of scholars) with your Bible and your mind wide open.

All that said, for consistency's sake I'd like you to recount the possible interpretation offered in session 9. Based on our session, do your best to plot the pertinent events we discussed on the following time line. Plot them as estimates only since, as we learned in our session, the exact dating of Christ's birth and death are debated. Of course, the time line isn't to scale, but its purpose is to help you picture possible interpretations of Daniel's prophecy. You can do it, Dear One! Give it a try!

How do the events we studied in session 9 fit on this time line?

7 sevens	62 sevens	Israel "on hold"	1 seven

444 B.C.		A.D. 33	A.D. 70	(…)	3 ½ years / 3½ years

The action of God's answer is coming with the clouds! And every eye shall see Him!

1. Travis Cottrell and David Moffitt, "Your Word Is Life to Me," *The Deep*, produced by Travis Cottrell. First Hand Revelation Music. 2002.
2. Stephen R. Miller, Daniel, vol. 18 in *The New American Commentary* (Nashville: Broadman & Holman, 2001), 241-42.
3. Ibid., 242.
4. Ibid., 241.
5. Ibid., 242.
6. Ibid., 231.
7. John E. Goldingay, *Daniel*, vol. 30 in *Word Biblical Commentary* (Nashville: Thomas Nelson Publishers, 1989), 266.
8. Miller, 251.

SPEECHLESS

10

SESSION TEN
SPEECHLESS

Read Daniel 10:1–11:1.

1. The ___drama___ we ___can___ ___see___ very likely ___pales___ in comparison to what ___we___ ___can't___.

"Angels are ___created___, spiritual beings with moral judgment and high ___intelligence___, but without ___physical bodies___."[1] Simply said, "___Demons___ are ___evil___ angels."[2]

2. The Bible strongly conveys a ___hierarchy___ among the ___angelic hosts___.

Who is Michael?

- An angel whose name means "who is ___like___ ___God___?"[3]
- "One of the ___chief___ ___princes___" (Dan. 10:13)
- ___Israel's___ prince and ___guardian___ (Dan. 11:1; 12:1). See Jude 9 and Rev. 12:7-12.

Look back at Daniel 10:13. "Evidently the reason that Michael became involved and not another powerful angel was that Daniel was ___interceding for Israel___ a nation especially ___entrusted___ to ___Michael's care___."

3. Read Daniel 10:13,20.

These "princes" are "rulers" and "authorities" in the "___heavenly___ realms"

(Eph. 6:12) ___assigned___ to ___earthly___ empires and the ___humans___

who govern them.

Any "princes" ___opposing___ God's ambassadors could only be ___demonic___.

• Why Persia? See Ezra 1:1-4 and 4:1-5.

• Why Greece? See Daniel 8:20-24.

4. Read Daniel 10:21,20.

As Dr. Charles R. Swindoll writes, "These verses flash a sobering warning:

___overcoming demonic___ forces is not a ___once-for-all___ matter."[5]

5. God ___purposely entrusted___ this kind of encounter and

information to ___someone like Daniel___.

1. Wayne Grudem, *Systematic Theology* (Leicester, England: InterVarsity Press, 1994), 397.
2. Ibid., 412.
3. Stephen R. Miller, *Daniel*, vol. 18 of *The New American Commentary* (Nashville: Broadman and Holman, 1994), 284.
4. Ibid.
5. Charles R. Swindoll, *Daniel: God's Pattern for the Future* (Plano, TX: Insight for Living, 1976), 127.

I hope you were as exhilarated by session 10 as I was. No one can say our God isn't a drama King. Where do we think the love of drama and mystery originates? The Word is fascinating, isn't it? I am so proud of you for persevering in this journey.

Let me give you a general idea of what is ahead. We only have two remaining weeks of daily assignments. The 12th and final chapter of Daniel is brief, so we will conclude our series together in session 12. This is the tricky part: Chapter 11 is long and historically complex; therefore, this week we will depart from our weekly routine. This week days 1 through 3 will focus on Daniel 10. Days 4 and 5 will jump ahead to Daniel 11 and have us ready for session 11.

I believe we will be helped immensely by adjusting our approach this week. Thanks for coming along! I'm praying for you!

THIS WEEK'S PRINCIPAL QUESTIONS

DAY 1 According to Leviticus 23:4-7, what was commemorated on the 14th day, and what feast was celebrated for the next seven days?

DAY 2 How is Daniel's riverbank encounter described in Daniel 10:4-6?

DAY 3 Search Daniel 10:7-19 and record every description of Daniel's posture.

DAY 4 What are God's obvious points in Isaiah 41:21-24; 44:6-8?

DAY 5 What does Daniel 11:5-9 tell you about this woman?

DAY ONE MOURNING AN ANNIVERSARY

Today's Treasure: *At that time I, Daniel, mourned for three weeks. Daniel 10:2*

Welcome to our 10th week of study! I'm so proud of you I can hardly contain myself. We have just two more weeks of homework, so let's buckle down and finish strong. I loved session 10. It was enough to motivate me to scour every remaining word of Daniel's book. I hope you feel the same way.

We'll begin our daily assignments with an important reminder of an explanation given in session 10. All remaining verses in the Book of Daniel concern the final vision. Daniel 10:1–11:1 contains the *preparation* for the vision. Daniel 11:2–12:3 relays the *contents* of the vision. Daniel 12:4-13 expresses the *final instructions* expressed in the vision. Keep in mind as we explore the last three chapters that, as a whole, they comprise Daniel's final revelation from God.

Our focus today is Daniel 10:1-4. Please read these verses and document every reference they make to time:

_____

_____

You can again see the timing clearly noted. Daniel 7:1; 8:1; 9:1; and now 10:1 all specify when Daniel received the visions or revelations from God. Whether or not the significance of each revelation's timing is blatantly clear, we can be certain they were perfectly clocked by God with divine reason. Interestingly, the first two visions came in the first and third years of Belshazzar's reign, while the second two visions came in the first and third years of the reign of Cyrus. The significance of the timing of the final revelation will become more obvious as we explore it together today.

> Daniel 10:1 tells us "a revelation was given to Daniel" in the " _____ year of Cyrus king of Persia."

The year was 536 B.C.,[1] and Daniel was about 85 years old.[2] The silver empire was thriving, and the Jewish exiles captured under the leadership of Babylon's Nebuchadnezzar had very recently been released per the decree of Cyrus. The first wave of exiles had already returned to Jerusalem and begun rebuilding the temple.

Just as Jeremiah had foretold, the captivity came to an end and new days appeared on the horizon. The trip from Babylon to Jerusalem was long and arduous. In all probability Daniel's age made the trip virtually impossible. God had a much greater purpose, of course. He retained Daniel in the best surroundings to receive revelation. Daniel didn't get to be preoccupied by the joys and daily demands of being "home" in Jerusalem.

Not coincidentally, when the Apostle John received the (final) Revelation, he was in exile on the island of Patmos, also far away from his homeland. Sometimes the complacency of "home" is not conducive to the most life-altering revelations. On an admittedly lesser level, we've experienced something similar. Have you ever noticed that some of the most life-altering moves God has made in our lives have come when we were away from our homey surroundings? Often our most defining spiritual markers happen at conferences, retreats, on mission trips, vacations, or work stints far from home rather than in the usual places. The daily-ness of home is crucial, however, because there God challenges us to believe and persevere in what He often shows us elsewhere. Sometimes "elsewhere" might have been the last place we expected to hear a dramatic word from God.

OFTEN OUR MOST DEFINING SPIRITUAL MARKERS HAPPEN FAR FROM HOME RATHER THAN IN THE USUAL PLACES.

> Can you think of a time when God chose "elsewhere" over home to reveal something life-altering to you? If so, share it.

> _____

> _____

> Imagine being Daniel. Picture watching the exiles depart while you remained behind. What kinds of things do you think Daniel felt?

> _____

> _____

The Apostle John must have felt something like you've described as he learned that the last of the remaining apostles had been martyred and he was the only one left. I don't think he was relieved to be alive. I think he wondered what on earth he was still doing here. Exile must have been particularly challenging as it seemed a waste of valuable time … until on one particular "Lord's day" John heard behind him a "loud voice like a trumpet which said, 'Write on a scroll what you see and send it to the seven churches' " (Rev. 1:10-11). And the rest was history … and prophecy.

You see, you never can tell when God will reveal Himself most powerfully to us. True God-seekers do not outlive their usefulness. If we're still here, God's still working. His greatest revelation to you and His most life-altering move in your life may be ahead. Never think for a moment you've seen the last of God.

The timing for the visit in Daniel 10:4 is significant. See Leviticus 23:4-7 …

what was commemorated on the 14th day? _Passover_

what feast was celebrated for the next seven days? _Feast of the unleavened Bread_

Turn back to Daniel 10:4. The "first month" is the Hebrew month of Nisan, corresponding to our later March and early April. It is a month of great importance to the Jews. Just as it is today, Passover was celebrated on the 14th day of Nisan with the seven-day feast of Unleavened Bread immediately following. Daniel received the visitation resulting in his final revelation on the 24th of this same month.

Throughout his time in Babylon, Daniel most assuredly commemorated the Lord's Passover and the Feast of Unleavened Bread as a Jew living abroad. The Jewish holidays (holy days) were particularly difficult for those in exile. Anniversaries of God's mighty works among the people of Israel no doubt stirred all sorts of emotions, not the least of which would have been mourning. To this day the Jews mourn even at their most festive occasions because they have no temple. The breaking of the glass at a Jewish wedding is an example of this reminder to mourn.

The Passover commemorated the great deliverance of the people of Israel from the Egyptians. Needless to say, the people of God longed for similar deliverance throughout 70 years of captivity. That this mighty act of God was often on Daniel's mind is obvious from its mention in his intercessory prayer for Israel in 9:15. The spotlight on the time of year in chapter 10 helps us imagine the kinds of things that were pressing on Daniel's heart. Anniversary dates commonly heighten emotions and, depending on the event, can stir a sense of mourning. I feel the mourning of a certain loss creep up on me every year around a particular date.

You may have experienced something similar. If so, express some of the feelings your own "anniversary" stirs:

_____

_____

"These are the LORD's appointed feasts, the sacred assemblies you are to proclaim at their appointed times: The LORD's Passover begins at twilight on the fourteenth day of the first month. On the fifteenth day of that month the LORD's Feast of Unleavened Bread begins; for seven days you must eat bread made without yeast. On the first day hold a sacred assembly and do no regular work."

LEVITICUS 23:4-7

In the midst of writing this Bible study, Houston became a temporary home to one hundred thousand people displaced by a ravenous hurricane that ate the gulf coast. I had the eye-opening, chin-dangling privilege of meeting a number of evacuees and hearing their astonishing stories. I rummaged through clothes in a homeless shelter with one mother who described her time on the roof of an apartment building with her handicapped son waiting for a helicopter to fly them to safety. Bodies swept past them in the toxic chocolate current raging through the streets. The woman was in such a state of shock that she spoke freely and almost unemotionally about sights she'll hardly be able to voice once she absorbs them. Over and over I thought, *"Jesus alone gets a soul through something like this."*

Houston's far from the prettiest city you'll ever visit, and goodness knows she sports a feverish temperature. Despite her ills, however, Houston is gracious. She threw open her doors as best she could and invited her guests to sit a spell. She offered them every job she could surface and told them to move in if they liked. Every single evacuee I met is vocally grateful, but they want to go home. Even if two feet of mud blankets the floor of what's left. On my walk this morning I noticed that the leaves are beginning to turn. I usually welcome fall, but this year something feels a little different. Autumn comes so late in Houston that fallen leaves mean Christmas trees. My heart aches with hope that every evacuee will be home for the holidays. It's what they want.

Babylon had been comparatively gracious to Daniel, but he wanted to go home. As Israel's most vital holiday came and went that year, the old man must have felt the season of his soul give way to winter. As Daniel 10 unfolds, the aging prophet surely mourned his absence among those returning to Jerusalem. But as the staggering revelations came, the rising tide of grief surely raged. Daniel realized that all hope of lasting peace awaiting the returnees in Jerusalem was gone.

Surely Proverbs 13:12a captures the state of Daniel's heart at this moment. What does it tell us hope deferred does?

_____

Hope deferred, and the old man fasted and grieved. Terrible days awaited Jerusalem—and not just under the tyranny of a Greek madman. One far worse would come. But one day her Prince will come. As will yours, Dear One. You'll recognize Him. He'll be the one on the white horse.

And he will be called Wonderful Counselor, Mighty God, Everlasting Father, Prince of Peace. Of the increase of his government and peace there will be no end. ... The zeal of the LORD Almighty will accomplish this (Isa. 9:6-7).

He will turn Israel's wailing into dancing, remove her sackcloth and clothe her with joy. Her heart will sing to Him and not be silent. (See Ps. 30:11-12.) O Lord, our God, we will join her and give You thanks forever.

DAY TWO A MAN DRESSED IN LINEN

Today's Treasure: *I looked up and there before me was a man dressed in linen, with a belt of the finest gold around his waist. Daniel 10:5*

I just returned from a conference where I had the joy of welcoming to faith in Christ a woman just a few years my senior. She attended with her young adult daughter who had prayed desperately for her for years and dragged her to every conference she would attend. Still, nothing seemed to happen. Then this weekend, suddenly the fog cleared, and the woman "saw" Jesus. She didn't see Him through a person. She saw Him through Scripture. The daughter was elated, but I could also tell she was somewhat mystified by the sudden breakthrough. Who can explain God's timing? You just never know when He's going to show up in a form a soul can't resist.

YOU JUST NEVER KNOW WHEN GOD'S GOING TO SHOW UP IN A FORM A SOUL CAN'T RESIST.

Today we will move to the next segment in the 10th chapter of Daniel where we'll find the description of the "man" he encountered "on the bank of the great river, the Tigris" (vv. 4-5). This is the lesson I promised you in session 10.

I can't wait. So without delay, please read Daniel 10:4-12 very carefully. How is Daniel's riverbank encounter described in verses 4-6?

_____

Who saw the vision? *Just Daniel*

The original Hebrew is extremely emphatic: "I saw, I, Daniel, I alone."[3] Why did the others flee and hide themselves?

They were overwhelmed w/ terror

How did Daniel react to the sight according to verses 8-9? *He had no strength left, his face turned deathly pale and he was helpless. He fell into a deep sleep — his face to the ground*

Who in heaven's name did Daniel see? Most scholars believe it was a mighty and awesome angel who hadn't been veiled in a form easier on human eyes and the human psyche. *The Bible Knowledge Commentary,* which I greatly admire, suggests the being may have been Gabriel. "Since Gabriel previously had been sent by God to reveal truth to Daniel (8:16), probably Gabriel was also the visitor on this occasion. Angels, who dwell in the presence of God who is light, are themselves clothed with light, and Daniel saw something of heaven's glory reflected in this one who visited him."[4] Lest we think the Bible doesn't paint pictures of angels that could strike an observer with this kind of awe, think again. The angelic creatures described in Ezekiel 1:4-24 could scare an onlooker under a bed.

Then again, I just can't shake the similarity of the description in Daniel 10:4-6 to several others that undoubtedly describe the Divine.

Please look up the following segments and record their descriptions:

Ezekiel 1:25-28 _____

Revelation 1:12-16 _____

The similarity might be too much for you to resist as well. Furthermore, Daniel had such a violent reaction to what he saw in the opening scene of Daniel 10 that I have trouble imagining it being an angel—particularly one he'd encountered earlier.

Before we wrap up our conclusion and put a bow on it, we better consider the serious problems Daniel 10 presents with the interpretation. The being we studied in session 10 spoke of being "resisted" for "twenty-one days" by the (angelic) prince of the Persian kingdom. He also testified to Daniel that the angel, Michael, came to help him. Could this be Christ? Could a demon actually detain Him? Would He need an angel's help? Hardly! How do we reconcile these unfitting pieces?

I lean heavily toward the interpretation of scholars who believe the being described in Daniel 10:4-9 differs from the being described throughout the remainder of the chapter. I'll show you how this could be.

Glance back at Daniel 8:15-16 and recall the excerpt I've referenced several times from *The New American Commentary*. This commentary interprets the mighty "man" who wielded superiority over Gabriel as "best understood to be God Himself."[5] We discussed that a literal rendering of the phrase "from the Ulai" in 8:16 "is literally 'between the Ulai' River (i.e., between its banks) and depicts this being as 'hovering in the air' above the middle of the river."[6] The being undoubtedly commanded authority over the mighty Gabriel.

Fast-forward to our present scene in Daniel 10 and reconsider verses 9-11. Couldn't Daniel have first seen a vision of the Divine, collapsed into a deep sleep, and then been stirred by the touch of a second and lesser being—an angel—in verse 10? Just as God introduced the interpretation in chapter 8 and then turned the explanation over to the angel, couldn't He do the same in chapter 10? I believe it's quite possible He did.

I'll show you another hint that could support this interpretation. Look at the being's words in Daniel 10:11 that I'm suggesting as a second figure in the scene. "Daniel, you who are highly esteemed, consider carefully the words I am about to speak to you, and stand up, for *I have now* been sent to you." The emphasis is mine, and I added it for your serious consideration.

Couldn't the angel have been introducing himself to the scene at this point? Offer your thoughts and certainly feel welcome to take a different view:

_____

_____

Does a second being suddenly arriving on the scene in Daniel 10 seem awkward? The interjection of various heavenly beings to a scene is not at all uncommon in Daniel. Hear *The New American Commentary* on the matter:

> At least four holy angels [in Daniel 10–12] appear in this vision and the "man dressed in linen" is unquestionably in charge (cf. 12:6-7). Therefore the personage described in 10:5-6 is a theophany, but the contents of the vision are related by the interpreting angel, who is introduced at v. 10. In the Book of Revelation there is a similar pattern. On occasions John encountered Christ himself (e.g., 1:12-20), whereas at other times he was instructed by an angel.[7]

In the *Geneva Series of Commentaries,* Dr. Edward J. Young agrees: "the description seems to indicate that the majestic Person here presented is none other than the Lord Himself. The revelation therefore is a theophany, a preincarnate appearance of the eternal Son."[8]

I'm certainly in no position to be dogmatic, but the thought of Daniel encountering Christ is pretty exciting, isn't it? He'd seen Him earlier in the courtroom vision with the Ancient of Days, but in Daniel 10 He is revealed in the glorious array of Revelation 1—a sight, by the way, that dropped the Apostle John to the ground like a dead man. No one knew Jesus better in His earthly ministry than the Apostle John, yet when he saw the immortal, glorified Lord, he nearly died of overexposure.

Have you ever thought about how you'd react if Jesus suddenly appeared to you while you were praying? I have! How do you picture your reaction?

_____

_____

Daniel's personal encounter with Christ in Daniel 10 would have a far deeper impact than his vision of Him in Daniel 7. The sight Daniel beheld in our present chapter was so stunning that he didn't regain his composure until the angel touched him and gave him strength in 10:18. Daniel seemed far more shaken by the presence of the angel in our present chapter than he did the eighth chapter. Seeing the angel in relationship to the "man dressed in linen" may have greatly escalated Daniel's response. If the President of the United States suddenly walked in my office and told me to listen carefully to every word his agent was going to tell me, I'd not only be awestruck by a visit from our head of state, but I'd also have a new respect for his agent. I might even be afraid of him because of his access to such power.

No matter whose interpretation is accurate, we can know beyond a shadow of a doubt that the glory of Christ Jesus, our immortal King, exceeds anything that can be depicted on a page or explained in human vocabulary. As you conclude today, worship His Majesty. And next time you pray, envision your Great High Priest, arrayed in white linen "with a belt of the finest gold around his waist," ever living to make intercession for you (Heb. 7:25).

DAY THREE SET YOUR MIND

Today's Treasure: *Do not be afraid, Daniel. Since the first day that you set your mind to gain understanding and to humble yourself before your God, your words were heard, and I have come in response to them. Daniel 10:12*

I've loved Daniel 10! We have no idea what unseen activity surrounds us! I can hardly wait until we sit at Christ's feet in heaven and hear the behind-the-scene stories of historical events. No doubt about it. We will sit bug-eyed. God's ways are unfathomable, His creativity untamable. Just when we think we've heard it all, God will tell His side of the story.

> **GOD'S WAYS ARE UNFATH- OMABLE, HIS CREATIVITY UNTAMABLE.**

Beloved, if you and I could see the whole picture surrounding our own histori-cal events, we'd go face to the ground in startling amazement. Imagine Christ saying to you one day in glory, "Take a look at this scene with me, Child. I want you to see what was going on in the heavens when you were going through that crisis. Look at all that happened in your behalf. Gaze at that great cloud of witnesses cheering you on to victory. Now aren't you glad you chose to walk by faith and believe Me?"

Looking back on your life journey, which season or moment do you most hope God will show you "behind the scenes"?

_____

I hope God one day shows me what was happening behind the scenes after the worst time of despair in my adult life when I was absolutely certain I did not have the wherewithal to persevere in ministry. I know a war was going on in the heavens and that the devil was hitting me so hard that Christ alone could have gotten him off of me. I dearly love a good drama, so I hope I get to grab a bag of popcorn and see your behind-the-scenes shot, too.

Today is our final look at Daniel 10. I warned you that we'd take a little differ-ent approach this week. Daniel 11 is so long and involved that we're going to steal days 4 and 5 from this week to get a jump on it. For now, let's zero in on the final participant in the scene recorded in Daniel 10: Daniel himself.

In your own words what did the angel say to Daniel in 10:12?

_____

Search Daniel 10:7-19 and record every description of Daniel's posture:

Face down, trembling on hands & Knees, helpless

As we seek to draw personal application from Daniel's 10th chapter, we have great difficulty relating on a human level to the one whose "body was like chrysolite, his face like lightning" (v. 6). Furthermore, we have never been—nor will we ever be—angels. Daniel presents our only opportunity to relate in this chapter. Daniel 10 also offers our final invitation to dig treasures from the mine of his personal life. We must be very careful not to allow Daniel to seem so high above us in character that becoming a Daniel in our Babylonian atmosphere seems increasingly out of reach.

GOD WANTS US TO HAVE INTEGRITY SO WE CAN BE TRUSTED WITH RESPONSIBILITY.

We made the commitment to become people of integrity in overwhelmingly enticing surroundings. But let's not stop there. God doesn't mean for us to have integrity just for integrity's sake. He wants us to have integrity so we can be trusted with responsibility. Christ didn't set us free just for freedom's sake. He sets us free so we can get out there and do what He's called us to do. Daniel represents more than character. He represents a life God can use wildly in the worst of circumstances. Daniel's intense relationship with God fills me with holy jealousy. I want what Daniel had. I want to be a person God can use to show Himself mighty.

I want to be a person to whom God reveals Himself. I want to be a person of vision. I think you do, too, and I think you have your own ideas of who you want to be when this study is over. Use this space to express it.

_____

_____

God's use of Daniel wasn't accidental. Yes, God is sovereign, and He can work through whomever He wishes, but the pages of Daniel convey a mysterious and wonderful balance between God's will and man's choice. God will do *what* He's planned, but by God's sovereign allowance, man can greatly impact …
- *whom* He'll use,
- *when* He'll move, and
- *how* He'll act.

Stunningly so. Let's take a good look at Daniel 10:12 and shape some possible concepts from it. Daniel had obviously known the God of Abraham since childhood, but today's verse implies that big things began to happen (heaven heard and responded) from the time Daniel started doing certain things.

Fill in the following blanks from Daniel 10:12. "Do not be _____ ,

Daniel. Since the first day that you _____ to …

gain _____ and to _____
before your God, your words were heard, and I have come in response to them."

Consider the following exhortations I have drawn from the well of this descriptive verse. You'll note I've listed Daniel's admonitions followed by my comments:

- *Do not be afraid.* Daniel didn't let overwhelming fear stop Him from responding to God or daring to approach Him again. Baldwin writes, "to be named as the recipient of a special divine message was a costly privilege."[9]

Meditate on the lives of those who drew near to God and heard His voice. Nothing was easy about encountering His glory. They lived way out on the edge. I'm reminded of the children of Israel in Exodus 20. "When the people saw the thunder and lightning and heard the trumpet and saw the mountain in smoke, they trembled with fear. They stayed at a distance and said to Moses, 'Speak to us yourself and we will listen. But do not have God speak to us or we will die' " (Ex. 20:18-19). They let fear keep them in the distance.

Beloved, a Daniel life—out there and exposed to God's glory—quickens every nerve ending. It's not the pain-free life. It's not the safe-at-a-distance life. But, Beloved, it is life most alive. Life most abundant. Dear One, what role does fear play in your life? At times fear has played the starring role in mine, and you can be sure Satan was sitting in the director's chair.

How about you? Describe the role fear has played in your life.

In the past, it immobilized me. But now I try to go immediately to prayer.

Fear God and nothing else. You will experience things other people only read about.

- *Set your mind.* Our minds are the battlefield on which this fight is won or lost. Satan will tangle with us as long as we let him. A wavering mind writes an invitation in the sky. It tells him we'll let him.

Will we truly make up our minds? Will we "set [our] minds on things above, not on earthly things" (Col. 3:2)? Or, will we remain double-minded and half-hearted and spend our God-given tenure on planet Earth making no discernable difference?

To "set our minds" is to make up our minds, once and for all. To cease wavering back and forth and blending into our environments. When doubts arise and troubles come, we don't fall back because we've made up our minds. " 'You do not want to leave too, do you?' Jesus asked the Twelve. Simon Peter answered him, 'Lord, to whom shall we go? You have the words of eternal life' " (John 6:67-68). Say to Him out loud today: I've made up my mind, Lord. I'm in and in I'll stay.

- *Gain understanding.* Daniel never stopped learning because he never stopped seeking understanding. We are impressed with Abraham and Moses because they were old when God called them, and yet they were used mightily. Daniel's example is even more impressive. His faithfulness stretched from 15 to 85. He became a product of his own prayer: "Praise be to the name of God for ever and ever; wisdom and power are his. ... He gives wisdom to the wise and knowledge to the discerning" (Dan. 2:20-21).

Daniel didn't sit back and wait for understanding. He sought it with all his might. Read Proverbs 2:3-5 aloud if possible. What do these verses tell you about pursuit?

"If you call out for insight and cry aloud for understanding, and if you look for it as for silver and search for it as for hidden treasure, then you will understand the fear of the LORD and find the knowledge of God."

PROVERBS 2:3-5

• *Humble yourself before your God.* We often talk about whether we can trust God, but our concluding question is, Can God trust us? Can He trust us with power, insight, and influence as He did Daniel? Or will our pride get in the way?

C.S. Lewis wrote, "There is one vice of which no man in the world is free; which every one in the world loathes when he sees it in someone else; and of which hardly any people, except Christians, ever imagine they are guilty of themselves … it was through Pride that the devil became the devil: Pride leads to every other vice: it is the complete anti-God state of mind."[10]

We can't ignore it; we have to deal with it. Our minds are pre-set on pride. Daniel "set [his] mind … to humble [himself] before [his] God" (Dan. 10:12). Every day, Beloved, we've got to wake up, drop to our knees, and push the reset button on our pride-prone minds and program them for humility. God wants to trust us. Can He?

DAY FOUR JUMPING AHEAD

Today's Treasure: *After he has appeared, his empire will be broken up and parceled out toward the four winds of heaven. Daniel 11:4*

Today we jump ahead to Daniel 11 so we'll have plenty of time to study each historical segment. Daniel 10 involved the encounter introducing the revelation. Daniel 11 records the actual revelation. The contents of this meaty chapter are key events that play out in history and will ultimately usher in the end. I will pepper our history lessons with prophecy lessons to offer added incentive. Once again, keep in mind that Daniel received the revelation as prophecy, but we will have the vantage point of viewing most of it as history. The prophecy Daniel received in this chapter contains such astonishing detail that skeptics have tried to date the book after the events. Foretelling and fulfilling prophecy, however, is God's specialty. See for yourself.

Please read the following segments and record God's obvious point in each one:

Isaiah 41:21-24 _____

Isaiah 44:6-8 _____

Describe each thing Isaiah 46:10 says God does. *He made known the end from the beginning.*

_____

_____

We cannot overestimate the biblical importance of fulfilled prophecy. "Twenty-seven percent of the Bible is prophecy, and 20 percent of the books of the Bible are prophetic."[11] God's ability to foretell and fulfill sets the Bible in a class completely by itself. No other text of the world's religions can begin to compete.

In Josh McDowell's masterful book *The New Evidence That Demands a Verdict,* he describes Professor Peter Stoner's findings in *Science Speaks.* By using the modern science of probability, he refers to 48 Old Testament prophecies fulfilled in the life of Christ. "Stoner considers forty-eight prophecies and reports, 'We find the chance that any one man fulfilled all 48 prophecies to be 1 in 10^{157}'" (1 in 10 with 157 zeroes).[12] Keep in mind this is only a small slice of hundreds of general prophecies that have already been fulfilled.

Beloved, I don't just take God at His word because people told me to. God didn't give us a brain so we'd be ridiculously gullible. God said, "Come now, let us *reason* together" (Isa. 1:18, emphasis mine). Reasonable people can believe God and take Him at His Word because God has proved believable.

Yes, we walk by faith, but we stand on fact. The disciples didn't just hope Jesus was the Son of God when they refused to recant to save themselves from martyrdom. They knew He was. They'd seen His miracles. They'd heard Him foretell what would happen. Then they saw Him fulfill it. "That which was from the beginning, which we have heard, which we have seen with our eyes, which we have looked at and our hands have touched—this we proclaim concerning the Word of life" (1 John 1:1).

We believe because God has proved Himself believable. He has also undoubtedly proved Himself believable to you and me personally. Really give the following question some thought:

GOD HAS PROVED BELIEVABLE.

What would you consider to be the key to your own personal trust in God?

His Faithfulness

OK, let's turn to today's text in Daniel 11. You may recall that the first verse is connected to the previous chapter as the angel continues to introduce the revelation and convey some of the battle that has taken place in the heavenlies.

Read Daniel 11:2-4 and circle names of two recognizable kingdoms it describes.

Greece   Rome   Babylon   Persia   Macadamia

See! You already have a familiar foundation this segment will build on. Persia and Greece are not strangers to us at this point. The angel begins chapter 11's prophetic history of key events with the Persian period. Keep in mind, Daniel was living in it.

In verse 2 the angel told Daniel that _____ more kings would appear

in Persia, then a _____ who would exceed the others in wealth.

" 'Three more kings' would refer to those after Cyrus, who was then reigning (cf. 10:1). Xerxes I (486-465 B.C.) is clearly identified as the fourth king by the description of his great wealth and expedition against Greece. It is a matter of historical record that the three kings who ruled between Cyrus and Xerxes I were Cambyses (530-522), Smerdis (pseudo-Smerdis or Guatama 522), and Darius I Hystaspes (522-486). Kings after Xerxes are not mentioned, apparently because the later Persian rulers were not germane to the writer's purpose."[13] No, Beloved, I won't be quizzing you on the names of the three kings between Cyrus and Xerxes. You'll be glad to know that "pseudo-Smerdis" is neither a Smurf nor pertinent to our study.

Who was king at the time of Esther (Esth. 1:1-3)? _____

This is the ruler mentioned above as the fourth who exceeded all others in wealth. Xerxes is also known as Ahasuerus in the Book of Esther. He "attacked Greece with a massive army and captured Athens in 480 B.C."[14]

Look back at Daniel 11:3. You are very familiar with this mighty king. He was depicted in Daniel 8:8 as the horn broken off "at the height of his power."

Who was he? _____

If you participated in session 8, you are not only familiar with Alexander the Great; you already know the interpretation of Daniel 11:4. "After he has appeared, his empire will be broken up and parceled out toward the four winds of heaven. It will not go to his descendants."

Look back at your notes in session 8. To whom was the Greek Empire "parceled out" after Alexander the Great died and his legitimate heir was murdered? Please also list the lands parceled out between them:

Names	Lands
Cassander	Macedonia & Greece
Lysimacus	Thrace and parts of Asia Minor
Ptolemy	Egypt & parts of Asia Minor
Seleucus	Syria, Israel, & Mesopotamia

Excellent. See how knowledgeable you are? Before we started this Bible study, you didn't even know you cared about figures like Cassander and Seleucus, did you? Though Daniel 11 is lengthy and complex, every bit of it builds on familiar ground that you and I will walk together. It will make more sense as we go; and ultimately, we'll behold its great significance.

OK, we need a break. How about a knock-knock joke?

Knock knock. Who's there?
Dwayne. Dwayne who?
Dwayne the bathtub, I'm dwowning!

In case you're drowning in Daniel 11, we'll call it a day, Sweet One. I hope so much your soul is experiencing a satisfaction that God gives to a child who has studied to show herself approved and then actually grasps what she's studying. You and I aren't nibbling on spiritual milk and cookies. We don't have to feel the least chastisement from the writer of Hebrews who chided, "Though by this time you ought to be teachers, you need someone to teach you the elementary truths of God's Word all over again. You need milk, not solid food!" (Heb. 5:12). Nope. Not guilty. We've been cutting into a thick slab of spiritual T-bone.

As for me, in the words of the psalmist, my soul has been "satisfied as with the richest of foods" (Ps. 63:5). I hope yours has, too.

I am so crazy about you. So glad we got to take this trip together.

DAY FIVE ALLIES AND ENEMIES

Today's Treasure: *The daughter of the king of the South will go to the king of the North to make an alliance. Daniel 11:6*

I'm so glad you tuned back in! I thought I might have lost you on the knock-knock joke. Better to say you dropped out over my bad jokes than over the challenges of God's Word. Remember, God gladly gives knowledge and understanding to all who ask. Keep asking! We're getting smarter by the day.

We will conclude our present unit with considerations of the next segment in Daniel 11. Promise you'll hang in here with me because this chapter gets complex. I just can't let you drop out this late in the game because the end is so worth the means. I beg you to strengthen your commitment to run this race to the finish line. Also, ask God to make the material fascinating to you. He'll do it! He did it for me.

As we get started, I hope you've had your coffee because these verses may go over the head of anyone not quite awake. If you're morally opposed to caffeine, please disregard my last statement and try not to get the string on your herbal tea bag in a knot. I'm a work in progress. My dilemma is that I tend to make better progress when I've had a cup of dark roast. I'm just fooling with you, Sweet Thing. A grin can be refreshing before we get down to business.

Now, please read Daniel 11:5-9 and quit trying to distract me.

See what I mean? Now, don't you wish you'd had that second cup? Somebody may have just sworn off her chamomile. At least this segment has a woman in it! For crying

GOD GLADLY GIVES KNOWLEDGE AND UNDERSTANDING TO ALL WHO ASK.

out loud, the only women we've seen so far were Belshazzar's wives and concubines, and they contributed little to the character of our gender.

 What does Daniel 11:5-9 tell you about this woman?

_____

If you participated in session 8, you are more familiar with the king of the South and the king of the North than you realize. Daniel 11:5-9 and the verses that follow (vv. 10-20) "comprise a history of the ongoing conflicts between two divisions of the Greek Empire, the Ptolemaic (Egyptian) and the Seleucid (Syrian), from the death of Alexander (323 B.C.) until the reign of Antiochus IV Epiphanes (175-163 B.C.)."[15] The segment we're studying today was fulfilled more than a century before the reign of the evil Antiochus, but I want you to see the whole picture in order to grasp our present snapshot.

Let's have a quick review and make sure we're grasping it: What two Greek dynasties (out of the four) had ongoing conflicts according to the information in this paragraph? Give the original generals' names:

_____   _____

THE CENTER OF THE EARTH IN OLD TESTAMENT PROPHECY IS ISRAEL, THE "BEAUTIFUL LAND."

This piece of information is very important: "The revelation [in Daniel 11:5-20] was limited to these two divisions because Palestine, the home of God's people, lay between them and was continually involved in their later history."[16] Your answer should be Ptolemy and Seleucus. Please recall with me that the common denominator of all the Gentile empires in the "times of the Gentiles" is their authority over the Holy Land. The perimeters of the Babylonian Empire, the Medo-Persian Empire, the Grecian Empire, and the Roman Empire were very different. But they each in turn ruled Israel. Hear this well: Their connection to the Holy Land is the very reason why prophecies concerning these empires and their divisions find their place in Scripture and not just secular history books. The center of the earth in Old Testament prophecy is none other than Israel, the "Beautiful Land." Read this paragraph as many times as necessary to absorb the information. It is the key to understanding the entire 11th chapter.

I hope you caught a quick fact I threw into the mix in session 8 as I explained how Israel became such an important land during the reign of Antiochus. He wanted Egypt and fought vehemently with the Ptolemaic ruler. Israel lay in between and took the brunt of the Madman's madness. Today's segment (vv. 5-9) foretold the infancy of this struggle through the lines of the kings of the South and the kings of the North. The very references of "North" and "South" are themselves in relationship to Israel. South of Israel was Egypt (Ptolemy's land). North of Israel were Syria and Babylon (Seleucus's land).

The "king of the South" referenced in verse 5 is Ptolemy I Soter (323-285 B.C.), the ruler of Egypt. (See the reference in verse 8 to Egypt as the land of the king of the South.) He had been one of Alexander's extremely capable generals.[17] In verse 6, the "king of the South" is Ptolemy II (285-246 B.C.) and in verses 7-8 Ptolemy III (246-221 B.C.) is the "king of the South."[18] Whew! Stay with me here, and you'll see how it all comes together over the next few days.

During the power struggle described in Daniel 11:5-9, "the Ptolemies controlled Palestine. Their attempt to make peace is foretold in v. 6."[19] This is the reference to the "daughter of the king of the South" who "will go to the king of the North to make an alliance" (Dan. 11:6). According to my best commentaries, the historical events foretold in this segment are quite complex. Dr. Charles Swindoll has a remarkable gift for simplifying very complicated facts into terms regular people can understand. Therefore, I've called on his help for the following synopsis. As you read his explanation, keep checking the Scriptures that relate.

> Through marriage to his daughter, Berenice, Ptolemy II offered an alliance to Seleucid's grandson Antiochus II ("the king of the North"). To marry Berenice, Antiochus II had to divorce his wife, Laodice. Later, the scorned Laodice had Berenice, her son, and Antiochus II murdered; then she put her son, Seleucus II, on the throne.
>
> Verses 7-9 foresee the rest of the story. Berenice's brother ("one of the descendants of her line" [AKA: Ptolemy III]) avenged her death by attacking Seleucus II ('the king of the North'). He killed Laodice and took back to Egypt "their metal images and their precious vessels of silver and gold." Later, Seleucus II tried to retaliate, but he failed. He "enter[ed] the realm of the king of the South," but "return[ed] to his own land."[20]

Let's nail some of this down. Be relieved to know that you won't need to memorize this segment of history and know all these names by heart to grasp the Book of Daniel. However, I certainly want you to have studied them. According to the previous four paragraphs, identify the following:

The original king of the South: ___*Ptolemy*___
(Hint: one of the four generals of Alexander the Great.)

What land is referenced as "South"? ___*Egypt*___

The original king of the North: ___*Seleucus*___
(Same hint.)

What land is referenced as "North"? ___*Syria Babylon*___

The daughter of the king of the South: ___*Berenice*___

What happened to her? ___*Murdered*___

Once again, let me say loudly that every bit of this information was given to Daniel as prophecy! Every detail came to pass just as the angel assured Daniel it would. And now we call these events history.

OUR GOD KNOWS WHAT WILL BE ... JUST AS INTRICATELY AS HE KNOWS WHAT HAS BEEN.

Beloved, God knows the details. Far in advance, I might add. What does any of this history have to do with you and me? Well, it's biblical history; therefore, it is pertinent to us. As the spiritual seed of Abraham (see Gal. 3:29), these events are part of our spiritual history. Furthermore, the Scriptures we've studied today are prophecies fulfilled, a fact which builds our faith by reminding us that God is good for His Word. Lastly, today's segment reminds us that God knows the events that have not yet occurred in our lives so intimately that they are like history to Him. Our God knows what will be ... just as intricately as He knows what has been.

What is your response to such a realization? Share it in the form of a prayer in the space below as you conclude today's lesson.

_____

_____

_____

_____

1. John F. Walvoord and Roy B. Zuck, eds., *The Bible Knowledge Commentary of the Old Testament* (Wheaton, IL: SP Publications, Inc., 1985), 1365.
2. Stephen R. Miller, *Daniel*, vol. 18 in *The New American Commentary* (Nashville: Broadman & Holman, 2001), 277.
3. Ibid., 282.
4. Walvoord and Zuck, 1365.
5. Miller, 231.
6. Ibid.
7. Ibid., 282.
8. Edward J. Young, *Daniel* (Melksham, Wiltshire: Wm. B. Eerdmans Publishing Co., 1949), 225.
9. Joyce G. Baldwin, *Daniel* (Downers Grove, IL: InterVarsity Press, 1978), 180.
10. Patricia S. Klein, ed., *A Year with C.S. Lewis*, (San Francisco: Zondervan, 2003) by C. S. Lewis Pte. Ltd., 87. Excerpt from *Mere Christianity*.
11. Mark Hitchcock, *The Complete Book of Bible Prophecy* (Wheaton, IL: Tyndale House Publishers, 1999), 16.
12. Josh McDowell, *The New Evidence That Demands a Verdict* (Nashville: Thomas Nelson Publishers, 1999), 194. A substantial portion of this material was originally published by Here's Life Publishers, Inc. © 1972, 1975, 1979, 1981 Campus Crusade for Christ.
13. Miller, 291.
14. Charles R. Swindoll and Bryce Klabunde, *God's Pattern for the Future,* Insight for Living Bible Study Guide, From the Bible teaching of Charles R. Swindoll (Plano, TX: Insight for Living, 1996), 130.
15. Ibid., 292-93.
16. Ibid., 293.
17. Ibid.
18. Walvoord and Zuck, 1367.
19. Swindoll, 131.
20. Ibid.

KINGS IN
SUCCESSION

11

11

KINGS IN SUCCESSION

1. The ceasing of daily _Sacrifice_ (v. 31).

   Selfishness versus _Sacrifice_

2. The corruption of _flattery_ (v. 32).

   The Hebrew word for "corruption" means "to profane, defile, pollute, corrupt; to be wicked,

   hypocritica. Essentially denotes straying away from the right path. Manifested in

   the completely _twisted_ _values_ of godless people."[1]

   "First Maccabees 1 implies that they found themselves drawn into _Cooperation_

   with a policy that had gone _beyond_ their _original_

   expectations."[2]

3. The people who _know_ _their_ _God_ (v. 32b).

   Consider the meanings of the following words:

   • "firmly—to be strong, be _Courageous_; to make firm ... to _harden_."[3]

   • "resist"—The *New King James* offers a wonderful translation of the term:

     "but the people who know their God shall be strong, and carry out _great_

     exploits."

4. The _wise_ who will _instruct_ many (v. 33).

   Word Biblical Commentary translates _the wise_ as "the _discerning_."[4]

   The Old Testament Lexical Aids add these synonyms for the Hebrew word _sakal_:

   "To be _circumspect_... to pay attention to."[5]

5. The _insincere_ who will join them (v. 34) Compare Ezra 4:1-5.

6. Some of the wise who will _stumble_ (v. 35).

   The same Hebrew word is employed in both instances of "fall"

   in verses 33 and 34 and in "stumble" in verse 35.

   The Hebrew word means "to _totter_, stumble, stagger, fall, be overthrown;

   to _faint_, become _weak_."[6]

1. Spiros Zodhiates, _Hebrew Greek Key Word Study Bible, New International Version, Old Testament Lexical Aids,_ (Chattanooga: AMG Publishers, 1996), #2866, 1516.
2. John E. Goldingay, _Daniel,_ vol. 30 of _Word Biblical Commentary_ (Dallas: Word Books, 1989), 302.
3. Zodhiates, #2616, 1514.
4. Goldingay, 303.
5. Zodhiates, #8505, 1553.
6. Ibid., #4173, 1524.

LET'S DRAW ENOUGH LIVING WATER TO SPLASH ON EVERYONE AROUND US.

You made it all the way to the last week of study! I wish I could take you out to eat and celebrate with you. At the very least, consider yourself tightly hugged. I have never been more proud of a group of participants. This journey has demanded something of us—and just when we thought it would let up, it pushed us further. Hopefully our venture has also significantly increased our faith and circumcised our hearts. Those of you who have persevered to this point in your daily assignments and weekly sessions have undoubtedly matured in your working knowledge of Scripture. If you've paid attention, you honestly couldn't have helped it. Rest assured, your sweet brain has not atrophied an iota for lack of exercise for the last 10 weeks.

THIS WEEK'S PRINCIPAL QUESTIONS

DAY 1 What facts were foretold about Antiochus III the Great in Daniel 11:15-19?

DAY 2 What did the angel forecast about the heart of the king of the North (v. 28)?

DAY 3 According to verse 36, what will this self-exalting king say?

DAY 4 What part of our study of Daniel has been most instructive to you personally?

DAY 5 According to Revelation 21:1-6, what things will no longer exist in the new heaven and new earth?

DAY ONE ANTIOCHUS III THE GREAT

Today's Treasure: *The invader will do as he pleases; no one will be able to stand against him. He will establish himself in the Beautiful Land and will have the power to destroy it. Daniel 11:16*

A few weeks ago a young man walked up to me in an airport and said, "I know you'll think this is the strangest thing you've ever heard, but you are one of my wife's best friends, and you've never even met her." I grinned from ear to ear and replied, "You want to hear something stranger? She's one of mine."

To the sheer puzzlement of the men in our lives, you and I—so different in age, background, gifting, and personality—are good friends. Girlfriends. Not so unlike the women who served Jesus in His earthly tenure. We head to the well together with pitchers on our heads, chattering incessantly, filled with anticipation to draw deeply from the Living Water. And if we've drawn enough, it will splash on everyone around us through the course of the day. I do love being a woman, and you, Dear Woman, are one serious Bible student. My heart nearly bursts as I boast in your God. You have made the trip to Babylon, and the road has been rough at times. No doubt in my mind, it's given you some headaches.

Every now and then on my way home after an intense day of research, I'll tell Keith on the phone that my brain feels like it's about to crack. Sometimes he tells me to come home and he'll do his best to keep me from having one profound thought for the rest of the evening. I always laugh. I don't doubt you've felt like your brain was going to crack a few times in this journey. If I could, I'd spend a celebratory evening with you laughing our heads off and doing our best not to think a single profound thought. You are wonderful, Dear Sister. You bring me such joy.

We are studying Daniel 11. I hope you got to be part of session 11 and our study of Daniel 11:32-36. We viewed the scriptural bridge between the historical reign of Antiochus IV Epiphanes (the foreshadowing one) and the prophetic reign of the Antichrist (the forthcoming one), known as the "little horn" in the Book of Daniel. Thus far in our daily assignments we've studied the first nine verses of Daniel 11. On week 10, day 5 we overviewed this chapter as a composite history of the conflict between the Ptolemaic (Egyptian) dynasty and the Seleucid (Syrian) dynasty stretching from the death of Alexander the Great to the rise of Antiochus IV Epiphanes.

> Remember, their conflict is biblically significant because a very important piece of land was between Syria and Egypt. What was it?

☐ Italy   ☐ Israel   ☐ Iowa   ☐ India

You'll recall Daniel 8 refers to this part of the world as the "Beautiful Land." Reflect on session 8 for a moment and recall the demonstration I made with some of our sisters on the platform representing each dynasty. We learned that the evil Antiochus IV was the eighth ruler in the Seleucid dynasty. To give you an idea of the history recorded in Daniel 11, try to grasp that seven Ptolemaic rulers (kings of the South) and seven out of eight Seleucid rulers (kings of the North) are represented in Daniel 11:5-35.

The following chart of the kings in the Seleucid Dynasty (kings of the North) will help you organize your thoughts as we study this challenging chapter. It may mean little to you now, but it will help tremendously as we continue.

Daniel 11:5 . . . . Seleucus I Nicator (312-281 B.C.)
not referenced . . . . Antiochus I Soter (281-262 B.C.)
Daniel 11:6 . . . . Antiochus II Theos (262-246 B.C.)
Daniel 11:7-9 . . . . Seleucus II Callinicus (246-227 B.C.)
Daniel 11:10 . . . . Seleucus III Soter (227-223 B.C.)
Daniel 11:10-11,13,15-19 . . . . . . Antiochus III the Great (223-187 B.C.)
Daniel 11:20 . . . . Seleucus IV Philopater (187-176 B.C.)
Daniel 11:21-32 . . . . Antiochus IV Epiphanes (175-163 B.C.)[1]

Quick review: Whose dynasty is reflected by the kings of the:

North _____   South _____

Now let's read Daniel 11:10-19. According to the chart, what two Seleucid kings (of the North) are reflected in this segment of Scripture? (I'm only asking for their names.)

_____   _____

As you study the chart, you can see that Antiochus III the Great is obviously the Seleucid ruler emphasized most in this segment of Scripture. His brother, Seleucus III, is only inferred in the reference to the sons (see v. 10) of the king of the North (see v. 9) who "will prepare for war" (see v. 10). Please don't confuse Antiochus III the Great with Antiochus IV Epiphanes. Antiochus III was the Madman's father and a very powerful ruler in his own right.

 List several facts that were foretold about Antiochus III the Great in verses 15-19. Be particularly careful not to overlook anything concerning Israel.

_____

Antiochus III made one primary contribution to the biblical narrative. He amassed a huge army and shoved the Ptolemies out of Israel. "He was joined by many Jews— 'violent men among [their] people' (v. 14)—who viewed him as their champion. However, Antiochus III the Great wasn't the savior Israel had hoped for."[2]

Beloved, allow these words to echo in the empty places of your soul: any alternative "savior" will either disappoint us or totally devastate us. Have you learned this lesson personally? ☐ yes ☐ no If so, in the margin tell how.

Years ago I heard an acronym for the word "Easter" that I've never forgotten: **E**very **A**lternative **S**avior **T**akes **E**arly **R**etirement. My personal experiences have certainly cast affirmative votes in favor of the principle. You may recall that the prophet Isaiah was on the scene about a century before the prophet Jeremiah. He gave words of warning that the people of God should have heeded. By the time Jeremiah delivered his prophecies, their fulfillment was imminent.

What do each of the following passages tell us about substitute saviors:

Isaiah 17:10-11 _____

Isaiah 43:11 _____

As much as the Jews who endured the conflicts between Egypt and Syria wanted Antiochus III to be their champion, he could not. Apart from the LORD, there simply is no savior. Daniel 11:17-19 "predict(s) Antiochus III's failed attempts to conquer the world."[3] One of his attempts involved a daughter.

What did verse 17 foretell his doing?

_____

History recorded the fulfillment. "Backed by Antiochus's army, the Syrians forced terms of peace ('an alliance') upon the Egyptian king. To seal the agreement, Antiochus gave his 'daughter,' Cleopatra, to Ptolemy V as a wife. Antiochus hoped that

**EVERY
ALTERNATIVE
SAVIOR
TAKES
EARLY
RETIREMENT.**

through Cleopatra he could gain further control over Egypt. Yet the plan did 'not succeed,' for Cleopatra loved her husband and supported the Ptolemaic cause completely."[4]

Thank goodness, love is still stronger than politics and manipulation. Cleopatra's story sounds like the makings of a great movie, doesn't it? Before we think the movie's already been made, I'm afraid this Cleopatra is not the one who wrapped Julius Caesar and Mark Antony around her little finger. The woman in Daniel 11 is Cleopatra I while history's most famous Cleopatra was IV.[5]

Antiochus III's final attempt to conquer was an invasion he launched into Asia Minor and Greece. He was "pushed back by Rome's iron legions and forced to pay a heavy tribute. His epitaph in verse 19 sums up his life's disappointing end."[6]

Fill in the blank (v. 19): "After this, he will turn back toward the fortresses of

his own country but will _____ ."

When you first read today's segment, you probably wondered what on earth the terminology described and why on earth you cared. As we conclude today's lesson, surely you found something about Antiochus III the Great's story interesting or intriguing. What was it?

_____

_____

Thanks for your attention to detail today. Persevere, Dear One! We're almost finished! And I have a feeling that when we turn the last page, we're going to miss the mental workout. When we return to business as usual, we may be bored for a while.

This is a great time to suggest you start thinking about what Bible study you're going to do next. Study under many teachers, and stay in God's Word! He's an adventure like no other.

DAY TWO A VILE KING'S SUCCESSION

Today's Treasure: *The king of the North will return to his own country with great wealth, but his heart will be set against the holy covenant. He will take action against it and then return to his own country. Daniel 11:28*

Let's begin by taking a good look at the title of today's lesson. Sound familiar? Are chapter rhymes running rampant in your head? What a great time for a pop quiz! (Will you ever study with me again?)

One of our chief goals in this study of Daniel is to become familiar with the basic themes of each chapter. Recall as many of our chapter rhymes as you can. I've given you some hints to help. You can check page 232, but give yourself a little time to remember first!

Daniel One: Carried _____

Daniel Two: _____ Statue

Daniel Three: From a _____ Furnace _____

Daniel Four: I'll _____ Some More

Daniel Five: Says the Handwriting, "_____!"

Daniel Six: The _____ Fixed

Daniel Seven: There's a _____ in Heaven

Daniel Eight: _____ Spreads Hate

Daniel Nine: _____ in Time

Daniel Ten: Where's the _____ Been?

Daniel Eleven: A _____ Succession

Daniel Twelve: Shine Bright _____

Excellent! Even if you only knew a handful by heart, you know more about God's Word than you did before you started. You're certainly not backing up.

Let's read our text for today: Daniel 11:20-32. Look back at your chart of Seleucid kings on day 1 and identify each of the rulers depicted in the following segments:

Daniel 11:20_____ Daniel 11:21-32_____

These two names are far more familiar to you if you participated in session 8. Both of these rulers were sons of Antiochus III. Seleucus IV Philopater was his first son, and he inherited more than his throne. He "inherited an empty treasury and a heavy debt to Rome."[7] This debt is inferred in the reference to the "tax collector" he would send out. "To raise money, [Seleucus IV Philopater] sent his prime minister, Heliodorus, to Jerusalem … to seize the temple funds." According to 2 Maccabees 3:7-40, "a frightful vision of mighty angels prevented"[8] Heliodorus's plunder of the temple.

As conveyed in Daniel 11:20, Seleucus IV Philopater's rule lasted only a few years, but he "was not killed by an angry mob ('in anger') like his father or 'in battle.' "[9] In session 8 I told you that he was murdered by his evil younger brother (per *The Bible Knowledge Commentary,* 1358), Antiochus IV Epiphanes. He was the one we've come to know as the "Madman." Some of the commentaries and history books I've read since that time attribute Seleucus IV Philopater's murder to Heliodorus, his tax collector and prime minister, who reportedly "poisoned the king."[10] The association of both Antiochus IV Epiphanes and Heliodorus with the death of Seleucus IV Philopater could possibly mean they conspired to kill the king.[11]

Daniel 11:21 certainly infers foul play in the "contemptible person who has not been given the honor of royalty." The throne should have gone to Seleucus IV Philopater's son and rightful heir, Demetrius Soter.[12] It was stolen instead by "the harbinger of the Antichrist: Antiochus IV Epiphanes."[13]

Several of my commentaries identify the "prince of the covenant" in verse 22 as the revered Jewish high priest, Onias III.[14] If this is accurate, his removal by Antiochus IV Epiphanes was the beginning of Israel's worst nightmare. Elsewhere he was regarded somewhat highly for a time. He was a very shrewd politician who "redistributed the wealth and won widespread support among the lower classes. (See v. 24.) When he became strong, he invaded Egypt and defeated Ptolemy VI (See v. 25)."[15]

Swindoll continues, "After the battle, the two kings feasted together, toasting and making bargains." How is this meeting described in verse 27?

The two liars seemed perfect for one another, didn't they? Antiochus IV, the game player, had met his match. As a result, he failed to take control of Egypt.

"Frustrated at only a partial victory, Antiochus IV returned to his land but, on the way, took out his aggression on the Jews."[16] This was the horrifying turning point for the Jews under this Seleucid ruler. Verse 28 reflects the changing tide.

🦁 What does verse 28 forecast regarding the heart of the king of the North (Antiochus IV)?

We've talked several times about "setting" or "resolving" our hearts and minds to honor God as Daniel did. We've talked about the clear-headed determination involved and the necessity of making up our minds. The same kind of resolve is reflected in Antiochus IV as he set his heart "against the holy covenant." He purposed in his heart and made up his mind to be against anything related to the covenant relationship between the Jews and their God. Look at telling phrases in verse 28 side by side: "His heart will be set against the holy covenant. He will take action against it."

You see, set hearts and minds will always turn to action. When you and I deliberately, determinately set our hearts and minds on God, the new setting converts into new actions. The same is true in the negative sense. Once we set our hearts and

SET HEARTS AND MINDS WILL ALWAYS TURN TO ACTION.

minds on carnality or perversity, the new setting will convert into new action. Antiochus IV Epiphanes made up his mind to hate the Jews, and his hatred turned into action. Such thoughts don't stay in the mind. They inflate in the mind until, like a bursting balloon, they explode into life.

"Setting his heart 'against the holy covenant' (v. 28), [Antiochus IV] wreaked havoc in temple affairs, set up his pawn as high priest, and cruelly crushed a minor rebellion. Two years later, in 168 B.C., he tried to conquer Egypt again."[17]

What would oppose Antiochus IV according to Daniel 11:30?

_____

_____

In history's fulfillment of these prophecies, these ships were "the Roman fleet that had come to Alexandria at the request of the Ptolemies. Thus the fourth empire, which would eventually defeat the third (Greece), is introduced."[18] Four miles outside Alexandria, the Roman commander Gaius Popilius Laenas met Antiochus IV. The Roman handed him a letter ordering his immediate withdrawal from Egypt or war with Rome. "Then the Roman commander drew a circle in the sand around Antiochus and told him that he must respond before stepping from the circle."[19]

The Seleucid ruler well remembered his father's defeat at the hands of the Romans. Antiochus, therefore, "stood in humiliated silence for a brief interval and then acquiesced to the demand," withdrawing in "utter humiliation."[20] This event is undoubtedly what is referenced in verse 30 with the words "he will lose heart."

What is the next thing we read this ruler would do after losing heart (v. 30)?

_____

_____

Praise God, we who are redeemed have very little in common with someone as evil as Antiochus IV. We have, however, very likely had a strong reaction to embarrassment or a feeling of humiliation.

 Reflect for a moment and then name a few ways Satan can take advantage of someone (namely you or me) who feels humiliated or embarrassed.

_____

_____

WE ARE WISE WHEN WE LEARN TO VENT OUR FEELINGS TO OUR APPROACHABLE GOD.

Embarrassment involves a sudden flush of feelings looking for a way to vent. We are wise when we learn to vent to our approachable God. After his humiliation, Antiochus turned back and vented his fury against the Jews and rewarded those who would forsake the covenant. "He vented his rage on the Jews once more, this time slaughtering thousands, outlawing Judaism, and converting the temple to a pagan shrine (vv. 30b-31)."[21] This was the tidal wave of persecution that led to the "abomination that causes desolation" (v. 31).

Good heavens! That was a history lesson, wasn't it? But never lose sight of the fact that it was given to Daniel—not as history—but as _____. (If you didn't write the word *prophecy,* we might need a private tutoring session. I still have the 70 'sevens' of Daniel on my hardwood den floor in case you need a refresher.) Are you grasping the magnitude of the details of fulfilled prophecy in Daniel? What kind of God can do this kind of thing? The One and Only.

DAY THREE THE ARROGANT ENEMY OF GOD

Today's Treasure: *The king will do as he pleases. He will exalt and magnify himself above every god and will say unheard-of things against the God of gods. Daniel 11:36*

Is your head still spinning from yesterday's lesson? Be encouraged that our remaining days of study will seem more personally relevant. Beloved, God is proud of us for hanging in there through studies of His Word that aren't only us-oriented. Yesterday's segment of Scripture ended where our session 11 began. Today, therefore, we will hopscotch over the session portion (11:31-36) and look to the final segment of 11. Please read Daniel 11:36-45. We will consider some of the details in a few minutes, but how we identify the figure will greatly influence how we view the descriptions.

In session 11 we referred to the transition that takes place in verse 36. Virtually across the board, Bible scholars identify the king of the North portrayed in verses 21-35 as Antiochus IV Epiphanes. On the other hand, generous disagreement centers on the identity of the one referenced in verses 36-45. I definitely believe verses 36-45 give us a glimpse of the future Antichrist. Please follow along as I explain why.

First we can rule out the possibility that these final verses in Daniel 11 are continued references to Antiochus IV. Many phrases in this section don't fit Antiochus, but I believe one will prove most sufficient.

What two kings will rise up against this figure "at the time of the end" (v. 40)?

_____

Obviously, the figure depicted is neither the king of the North nor the king of the South. So Antiochus IV could not be the king in this portion of Scripture. However, Antiochus IV does immediately precede him for good reason if what "may be called the traditional interpretation in the Christian Church"[22] is accurate. "Interpreting this passage to foretell Antichrist has been a widely accepted view since ancient times (e.g., Chrysostom, Jerome, Theodoret)."[23] Jerome held tightly to this view "almost sixteen hundred years ago."[24] "Today the majority of both amillennial (e.g., Young) and premillennial (e.g., Archer) scholars interpret this king to be Antichrist."[25]

Baldwin, one of my favorite scholars, is careful not to automatically hold a traditional point of view, yet she sees hints of an intermingling of eschatological events with descriptions of Antiochus in the final segment.[26] *The New American Commentary* adds, "The clearest indication that this 'king' will live in the latter days is that the resurrection of the saints will take place immediately after God delivers his people from this evil individual's power (cf. 12:2)."[27]

"In reality a description of Antichrist should not be considered surprising in a context with Antiochus IV, for both of these oppressors of God's people have previously been given a prominent place in Daniel's prophecies (cf. chaps. 7-9). Thus Gabriel had now ceased to speak of Antiochus and had begun to describe the one he closely resembled (or typified), the eschatological Antichrist."[28] In verse 36, "the most notorious tyrant who will ever live is introduced into the narrative."[29]

With an increased level of confidence about his identity, let's look at several descriptions of this king to come, particularly in the introductory verse. First, we are told that he will "exalt and magnify himself above every god" (v. 36). We don't have to stretch to make the application that all self-exaltation originates with Satan. It is as deeply rooted as the trees of the garden of Eden and as tall as the tower of Babel. Self-exaltation is too high on Satan's agenda for any of us to avoid the temptation. The Book of Daniel shows us how to deal with our poisonous pride. Let's learn the lessons from Scripture so God won't have to send us on our own field trip.

 How do you specifically guard against self-exaltation? In other words, when you come under this exact temptation, what keeps you from falling for it?

I've pressed the question because this temptation will come too often and too insidiously for us not to have a predetermined plan of action. If we aren't armed in advance with a mind-set, a past experience, or a battery of Scriptures, we're probably going to fall to the temptation to exalt ourselves. We won't pass this pop quiz accidentally. As we've established before, God is "for us" even in His insistence that we exalt Him alone. We weren't fashioned to be worshiped.

According to verse 36, what will this self-exalting king say?

When was the last time you said, "I thought I'd heard it all"? This verse clearly conveys the Antichrist's vile mouth will surpass anything we've imagined. " 'Unheard-of things' is a translation of the Hebrew ... which denotes 'astonishing, shocking, or unbelievable things.' "[30] Verse 37 tells us "he will show no regard for the gods of his fathers or for the one desired by women." "This verse states that Antichrist will reject whatever religion is practiced by his ancestors. If this individual arises from the peoples of ancient Rome (which chapters 7 and 9 indicate), his family religion would probably be some form of Christianity."[31] You can imagine how many ways his lack of regard for "the one desired by women" has been interpreted.

THE BOOK OF DANIEL SHOWS US HOW TO DEAL WITH OUR POISONOUS PRIDE. LET'S LEARN THE LESSONS FROM SCRIPTURE SO GOD WON'T HAVE TO SEND US ON OUR OWN FIELD TRIP.

Some people have taken this verse to mean that the Antichrist will have no desire for women and will practice homosexuality. *The Amplified Bible* implies a much higher likelihood: "He shall not regard the gods of his fathers or Him [to Whom] women desire [to give birth—the Messiah]." A Jewish woman's ultimate desire was to be chosen to bear the Messiah. That's one reason why a greater premium was placed on sons than daughters. Jewish parents believed any Jewish son could perhaps be the Messiah, but obviously a daughter held no such hope.

Look back at verse 36. If our present interpretation is accurate, how long will

the Antichrist be "successful"?_____

This vile king's rule will not last a millisecond past God's predetermined time. Satan will not almost win. He will be unleashed only as far as the leash God gives him. At no time will God be out of control. The Antichrist will wreak terrible and increasing havoc as long as he can. Satan's fury will explode to its fullest measure because he knows his time is short. (See Rev. 12:12.) Take another look at Daniel 11:40 and the reference to the predicted time when the "king of the South will engage him in battle, and the king of the North will storm out against him." Israel will be the hot spot of horrific war at this time (see v. 41) and "many Jews will flee, seeking refuge among the Gentile nations."[32] *The Bible Knowledge Commentary* views Revelation 12:14-16 in reference to this time.[33]

Please read Revelation 12:14-16. What does the passage describe?

_____

I want you to conclude today by reading a very familiar segment of Scripture with eschatological ties you may not have recognized. Matthew 24–25 records a lengthy discourse straight from the mouth of our Savior concerning the end of times. Consider specifically Jesus' words in Matthew 25:31-46. Certainly this segment of Scripture is rightly applied as a divine entreaty to care for the needy, but today's lesson calls for a look from its eschatological perspective.

Look at Matthew 25:32. Who will be gathered before the throne of Christ?

"All the _____."

When will this gathering of nations before Christ's throne take place (v. 31)?

_____

In your own words, what will be the basis of this judgment of nations? (What will they have done or failed to do?)

_____

Many of us believe that the reference Christ made to "these brothers of mine" was specifically to the Jews. The word translated *nations* means *Gentiles*.[34] "These are all people, other than Jews, who have lived through the Tribulation period. They will be judged individually, not as national groups. They are described as a mingling of sheep and goats, which the Lord will separate."[35] This judgment is not the one portrayed at the great white throne (see Rev. 20:11) following the millennium and only involving the lost. This is a judgment of Gentiles that will occur after Christ's return "to determine who will and will not enter the kingdom."[36]

The Antichrist will do everything he can to completely exterminate the Jews during the time of great tribulation (see Rev. 12:17). *The Bible Knowledge Commentary* gives one explanation of this interpretation: "A Gentile going out of his way to assist a Jew in the Tribulation will mean that Gentile has become a believer in Jesus Christ during the Tribulation. By such a stand and action, a believing Gentile will put his life in jeopardy. His works will not save him; but his works will reveal that he is redeemed."[37]

Christ's words in Matthew 25:31-46 tell us not only what's to come but also how to live. Surely God esteems little more than our care for the hungry, thirsty, naked, and imprisoned. Nothing could be more biblical (see Isa. 58). From the right hand of His Father, Christ will gaze upon every action and every detail during the coming days of tribulation. He will have great decisive interest in every life regarding this question: "How did you treat My suffering people?"

And some people think God has forgotten the Jews.

DAY FOUR THE EVERLASTING KINGDOM

Today's Treasure: *Of the increase of his government and peace there will be no end. He will reign on David's throne and over his kingdom, establishing and upholding it with justice and righteousness from that time on and forever. Isaiah 9:7*

We only have two daily assignments and one session remaining in our journey together. Our task for the last 11 weeks has been to study the Book of Daniel, and I pray with my whole heart that our approach has delivered at least a decent overview.

 What part of our study of Daniel has been most instructive to you personally? In other words, if a friend asked you what you've learned and you could only answer in a few phrases or sentences, what would you say?

_____

Had our task been to study eschatology comprehensively and thoroughly, we would have fallen significantly short of the goal. If you've particularly enjoyed the study of prophecy introduced in our series, allow me to encourage you once again to continue your study on your own. Explore various views and interpretations, but protect your mind against fly-by-night writings predicting exact dates regarding a rapture or Christ's second coming. Christ Himself told us no one knows the day or hour. Be equally wary of writings identifying present world leaders as the Antichrist. He will not be clearly revealed until the midpoint of the seven-year tribulation, and our current world condition is not grave enough to strongly suggest we've entered such a time.

Ask your pastor to recommend a variety of books by reputable scholars. More than anything else, keep your Bible open! You have a good head on your shoulders. As you compare what you read with Scripture, if the material seems bizarre or far-fetched, it probably is—even if its author is sincere. We are flesh-and-blood teachers, and God alone can be taken wholly at His Word.

Knowing that we have only two daily assignments remaining, I'd like to round out our time line just a bit today and tomorrow. Ending well will necessitate more expansive lessons and readings on our two final days, but I pray you'll find the material captivating.

The end of Daniel 11 depicts the Antichrist in "his royal tents between the seas [the Mediterranean Sea and the Dead Sea] at the beautiful holy mountain" then assures us "he will come to his end, and no one will help him" (v. 45). We're not left to wonder when his end will come. Revelation 19:20 clearly teaches that soon after Christ's second coming, He will cast the Antichrist (the Beast) and his false prophet alive into "the fiery lake of burning sulfur." Daniel 12, our text for our final session, opens with the promise of ultimate deliverance for the faithful and resurrection for the dead. The book has a wonderful ending ordained perfectly by God, but I find myself wishing it had a few more chapters describing what happens next.

The Book of Daniel greatly prioritizes the promise of the coming kingdom, yet it gives us few details about life during its existence. God knew He'd store those riches in other books of the Bible. I am convinced that if we knew more about life on earth during the millennial reign of Jesus Christ, we'd anticipate it with a near jump-up-and-down kind of joy. Today we'll get a sampling of what planet Earth—and those dwelling on it—can anticipate. Maybe it will put a little jump in your joy. Tomorrow we will look at the final event on the kingdom calendar and draw our series to a close in session 12.

The Word of God has many references to the coming kingdom. In a moment you'll look up several of those in the Book of Isaiah. Remember, we can freely study God's Word together while we disagree on the details of end-time events. I believe strongly that the Bible teaches a thousand-year earthly reign of Christ before the final judgment. So I see these Scriptures describing that millennial kingdom. Others believe the reign of Christ follows the final judgment. They apply these Scriptures to the new heavens and new earth. Whoever is correct, I can absolutely promise you one thing. Whatever God has for us exceeds our wildest imagination. It is outrageously impossible for the coming kingdom of the living Christ to turn out to be a disappointment.

KEEP YOUR BIBLE OPEN AND COMPARE WHAT YOU READ WITH SCRIPTURE.

OUR PLANET WAS MADE SIGNIFICANT BY THE FOOTPRINTS OF GOD.

"In the beginning God created the heavens *and the earth*" (Gen 1:1, emphasis mine). One little insignificant planet. He formed man from its dust and told him to rule over it. Instead, it ruled over him. "God so loved that world that he gave his one and only Son" (John 3:16). The millennium is the grand finale of a planet made significant by the footprints of God.

Please read Isaiah 9:1-7; Isaiah 11:6-10; Isaiah 35:1-10 and record distinctive descriptions regarding the coming kingdom in the appropriate box:

The King	The People
The Earth	The Earth's Creatures

No wonder "the whole creation has been groaning as in the pains of childbirth right up to the present time" (Rom. 8:22)! With every quake of a mountain and heave of a sea, earth groans for the healing presence of King Jesus. When He returns, Scripture infers that much of the physical earth will be restored to an Eden-like state. That's not all. When the One by whom "all things were created" and through whom "all things hold together" (Col. 1:16-17) sits enthroned on planet Earth, His peace will permeate every facet of existence. We will get to see life on earth as Christ would have it.

 Come on! Have a little jump in your joy! What excites you most as you consider this view of the coming kingdom?

_____

_____

Until that glorious day, Earth groans and God hears. When the time is right, "then the LORD my God will come, and all the holy ones with him. On that day there will be no light, no cold or frost. It will be a unique day, without daytime or nighttime—a day known to the LORD. When evening comes, there will be light. On that day living water will flow out from Jerusalem, half to the eastern sea and half to the western sea, in summer and in winter. The LORD will be king over the whole earth. On that day there will be one LORD, and his name the only name. … Then the survivors from all the nations that have attacked Jerusalem will go up year after year to worship the King, the LORD Almighty, and to celebrate the Feast of Tabernacles" (Zech. 14:5-9, 16-18).

"Our Father which art in heaven, Hallowed be thy name. Thy kingdom come. Thy will be done in earth, as it is in heaven" (Matt. 6:9-10, KJV).

DAY FIVE TIME GIVES WAY TO ETERNITY

Today's Treasure *As for you, go your way till the end. You will rest, and then at the end of the days you will rise to receive your allotted inheritance. Daniel 12:13*

I can hardly believe we've arrived at our final destination in our daily assignments. In the last 24 hours, God has caused me to laugh over three separate reminders of how consumed I've been with this project. I found notes I wrote on the back of an airplane boarding pass, more notes on a pad of paper from a hotel room, then this morning Keith found copious notes that had slipped under his car seat when we had to take a road trip and I couldn't spare the writing time. My dear man set me up for success in the backseat of his SUV with a pair of soundproof headphones and a laundry basket full of commentaries at my side.

I have never had to let a study spill into my personal time like this one, but Keith knew it was temporary insanity and supported me throughout. The shorter length of writing time coupled with the demanding depth of the Book of Daniel caused me to discover all sorts of unexpected writing environments. I wish you could have seen the manicurist's face when I typed on my laptop with one hand while she worked on the other. My best discovery was the hair dryer at the beauty salon where I had to sit while my color "baked." The steady drone of the dryer provided the best white noise I've had in years.

Though stressful at the time, each of these memories will cause me to shake my head and laugh for years to come as I reflect on the wild ride we've taken together. I wouldn't have missed it for the world, Beloved. Thank you so, so much.

I believe nothing could be more appropriate as an ending for our Daniel study than viewing the biblical ending of the prophetic time line. As our study ends, we'll see how everything ends. In our previous lesson we focused on life on planet Earth during the thousand-year reign of Christ. Today we will consider the Book of Revelation's account of the events that follow. Our final lesson will be long, but I can assure you it will be thrilling. It will include four segments of Scripture stretching from Revelation 20:1–21:6. Revelation 20 unfolds immediately after the record of the expulsion of the beast and false prophet into the "fiery lake of burning sulfur" (Rev. 19:20). Let's get started with the first segment.

Please read Revelation 20:1-6 and answer the following questions:

Where will Satan be during the thousand-year reign of Christ?_____

Many people of God will be martyred during the terrible time of tribulation. List everything this segment of Scripture tells you about them.

_____

_____

Quick question: When all is said and done, do you think those who give up their lives for the sake of Christ will be sorry they paid such a price?

☐ Yes ☐ No Why or why not?

_____

As you can see, resurrections for different groups of people take place at different times, as do their subsequent judgments. Keep in mind that everyone will appear before God's throne, believers and unbelievers alike, but not at the same time and certainly not with the same results.

We do not have the time to explore each judgment, but here are some basics: Christians will stand before the judgment seat of Christ to receive reward or loss of reward based on our deeds (see 2 Cor. 5:10; 1 Cor. 3:10-15). Each person's "work will be shown for what it is, because the Day will bring it to light. It will be revealed with fire, and the fire will test the quality of each man's work" (1 Cor. 3:13). Loss of reward will primarily reflect things such as overlooked opportunities and impure motives.

Though I believe we will have a momentary awareness of any loss of reward at our judgment Paul assures us that "there is now no condemnation for those who are in Christ Jesus" (Rom. 8:1). By no stretch of the imagination do I believe that our most sinful moments will be publicly exposed when we are judged.

What does 1 John 4:16-18 tell us about our judgment?

_____

The following is my understanding of the judgment sequences: Unbelieving Jews who are alive at the end of the tribulation will be judged after the second coming of Christ (see Matt. 25:1-30). Believing Jews will enter the kingdom as the redeemed to join others who will reign with Christ under His supreme authority. Unbelieving Gentiles who are alive at the end of the tribulation will be judged after these Jews (see Joel 3:1-2; Matt. 25:31-46). Believing Gentiles will be judged as well and enter the kingdom among the redeemed and reigning.[38]

In a few moments we will read the segment reflecting the final judgment of unbelievers. First, let's read the segment describing Satan's final act and his subsequent judgment: Revelation 20:7-10. Is anything recorded in this segment a surprise to you? If so, what?

_____

_____

As you can see, one final war will take place at the end of the thousand-year reign of Christ. Follow me carefully here: according to the interpretive view I share, the millennium will begin with an entirely saved population. Those people, however, will have children who will also have children. A thousand years leaves ample time for many generations. Christ will not force them to believe any more than He has forced us to believe. Christ will rule over all nations "with an iron scepter" (see Rev. 19:15) so none will openly rebel. An undisclosed segment of the population, however, will refuse to allow Him to reign over their hearts. They will stand as proof that all man's rebellion and waywardness cannot be blamed on the enemy. He will be bound, and yet numbers will still be too proud to give Jesus their hearts.

What does this say to you about man?

_____

Satan will be loosed for a short season at the end of the millennium and be allowed one last stand. His deceptions will resonate with the minds of proud men who want to believe him, and they will foolishly gather with him against the King of kings.

The finale of man's sin will be much like its beginning. Rebellious humanity will want to believe the supreme lie of Satan who proposes, "Why worship God when you can be your own god?"

How shocked they'll be to awaken to the lie. In reality, man never could be a god. Those who chose themselves unknowingly made Satan their god. That's how Christ could say to Peter when he suggested Christ not surrender His life, " 'Get behind me, Satan! You are a stumbling block to me; you do not have in mind the things of God, but the things of men' " (Matt. 16:23). Bottom line? In the end, the things of independent men will turn out to be the things of Satan. Fire will devour the rebellious (see v. 9), and judgment will fall on the devil, "for, lo his doom is sure."[39]

Hear this clearly: Satan will not get away with one single scheme he waged against you. There will be a reckoning.

Scripture records a final judgment in our next segment. Please read Revelation 20:11-15.

IN THE END, THE THINGS OF INDEPENDENT MEN WILL TURN OUT TO BE THE THINGS OF SATAN.

Some scholars believe this resurrection and impending judgment at the "great white throne" is reserved only for the lost. "From other scriptures it seems that all the righteous dead have been raised, including Old Testament saints, the dead of the Great Tribulation, and the church saints, the body of Christ. Thus it may be assumed that verses 11-15 refer to the judgment of the wicked dead, who according to verse 5 would not be resurrected until after the thousand years and will have no part in what is called 'the first resurrection.' "[40] If this interpretation is accurate, the judgment rendered in this harrowing courtroom involves how these will spend eternity as much as where. The judgment rendered at the great white throne involves punishment.

Verse 12 records a very important piece of information. Complete this

sentence: "The dead were judged _____ as recorded in the books."

This verse quite possibly infers degrees of punishment. Though hell will be a place of inescapable and terrible misery, it will not be uniform. The punishment of some will be much worse than others. God's punishments always fit the crime.

> If the interpretation of degrees of reward in heaven and of punishment in hell is accurate, does it make sense to you? Share your point of view.

_____

_____

Other scholars interpret this judgment as involving both the lost and the saved. "These are part of the 'rest of the dead' who were resurrected at the close of the thousand-year period (v. 5). ... Reference to the book of life as part of the final testimony suggests a general judgment of the entire human race (excluding the martyrs who had already entered into their reward)."[41]

Whatever the case, we can rely on the words of Romans 2:2: "Now we know that God's judgment against those who do such things is based on truth." God is just, and we can rest assured that all timing and all punishment will be appropriate.

> To the extent that our last scene was horrible, our next scene is wonderful. I can hardly wait for you to read 1 Corinthians 15:24-26 to see what happens next. List every event described:

_____

_____

OUR FATHER'S KINGDOM WILL COME.

Behold the glorious summation in verse 24! At this point, God's kingdom will have come and Christ will have done His Father's will on earth as it was in heaven. He will have reigned victoriously for a thousand years over the earth He created according to their plan. At the fullness of time, Christ will "[hand] over the kingdom" to His Father. It will then merge with the eternal kingdom, and all creation's purpose will be accomplished. Christ will then face and destroy His ultimate enemy.

> According to 1 Corinthians 15:26, what is Christ's ultimate enemy?

☐ Satan   ☐ death   ☐ sin   ☐ wrinkles

Chills rush down my arms, and my soul leaps within me! No more caskets. No more funerals. No more heart-ripping good-byes.

> Fill in a blank of your own: No more _____!

All praise to King Jesus, our Victor and Lord!

I can hardly proceed, but we must. Let's look at our final segment together. Of course, we will officially conclude our series with session 12 in Daniel 12, but our next reading will provide an appropriate benediction to our overview of eschatology.

Please bask in the words of Revelation 21:1-6. These verses describe the final event on the kingdom calendar. The clock will tick its final tock, and God will usher in the eternal state. According to these verses, what things will no longer exist in the new heaven and new earth?

_____

God is about to wrap it up and put a bow on it for us. Look carefully at the profound words in verse 6. What is done? After all we've studied regarding the time line of God's kingdom calendar, what do you think God means?

_____

To me, nothing could be more appropriate after all our time lines than to take a look at a concept of God's calendar for planet Earth from beginning to end. Needless to say, the time line I'm placing before you is my interpretation and intended to be a general overview just to give us an idea. I have provided it for you below.

Fill in the following final events (in abbreviated small print!) based on today's Scripture readings:

- Satan's release, the final war, and his judgment
- The great white throne and man's final judgment
- Christ hands the kingdom over (or presents it) to His Father
- Christ destroys death
- The new heaven and new earth, representing the eternal state

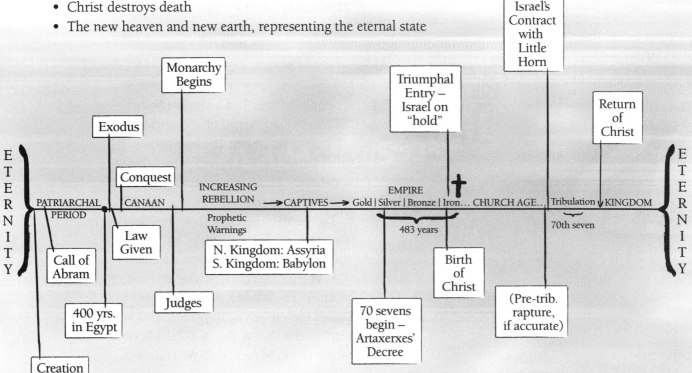

231

Scripture's final chapter begins with the words, "Then the angel showed me the river of the water of life, as clear as crystal, flowing from the throne of God" (Rev. 22:1). I wonder which angel it will be. Will it be the one who interpreted the court-scene vision to Daniel where the Ancient of Days occupied a throne with a "river of fire" flowing from it (see Dan. 7:9-10)? And was this the same angel God called Gabriel in the very next chapter (see Dan. 8:16)?

God alone knows, but I would not be at all surprised. After all, Gabriel seemed to work for God in His calendar department. The calendars I hang on the wall in my kitchen each year have scenes on them for every month. I'm a people-person, so I especially like the ones with priceless pictures of people on them.

Revelation 22:4 leaves us with man's most priceless picture hanging right there on the last page of God's Scripture calendar. Ah, man at his best. You just have to read it for yourself and record it here.

_____

_____

HIS NAME WILL BE ON THEIR FOREHEADS.

No, Scripture doesn't let us see God described in this final scene. No words can depict Him. Instead, Revelation 22:4 pictures man finally looking at God. Yes, right at His face. What's that on their faces? Look up with your mind's eye at their foreheads and picture His Name. No wonder those in Revelation 20:4 "hadn't received [the beast's] mark on their foreheads." There was no room for any other name.

Salvation is found in no one else,
for there is no other name under heaven
given to men by which we must be saved.
Acts 4:12

CHAPTER RHYMES FOR THE STUDY OF DANIEL

Daniel's Book: Just a Quick Look
Daniel One: Carried off to Babylon
Daniel Two: Neb's Dream Statue
Daniel Three: From a Fiery Furnace Freed
Daniel Four: I'll Humble Neb Some More
Daniel Five: Says the Handwriting, "You die!"
Daniel Six: The Lions' Jaws Fixed
Daniel Seven: There's a Judge in Heaven
Daniel Eight: Antiochus Spreads Hate
Daniel Nine: Seventy 'Sevens' in Time
Daniel Ten: Where's the Angel Been?
Daniel Eleven: A Vile King's Succession
Daniel Twelve: Shine Bright Till All Is Well
Daniel's Done: Now, Didn't We Have Fun?

1. John F. Walvoord and Roy B. Zuck, eds., *The Bible Knowledge Commentary of the Old Testament* (Wheaton, IL: SP Publications, Inc., 1985), 1367.

2. Charles R. Swindoll and Bryce Klabunde, *God's Pattern for the Future,* Insight for Living Bible Study Guide, from the Bible teaching of Charles R. Swindoll (Plano, TX: Insight for Living, 1996), 131.

3. Ibid., 132.

4. Stephen R. Miller, *Daniel*, vol. 18 in *The New American Commentary* (Nashville: Broadman & Holman, 2001), 296.

5. Swindoll, 132.

6. Ibid.

7. Ibid.

8. Miller, 297.

9. Ibid.

10. Ibid.

11. Ibid.

12. Swindoll, 132.

13. Ibid.

14. Swindoll, 132. Walvoord and Zuck, 1369.

15. Swindoll, 132.

16. Ibid.

17. Ibid.

18. Miller, 301.

19. Ibid.

20. Ibid.

21. Swindoll, 132-33.

22. Edward J. Young, *Daniel* (Melksham, Wiltshire: Wm. B. Eerdmans Publishing Co., 1949), 247.

23. Miller, 306.

24. Ibid.

25. Ibid.

26. Joyce G. Baldwin, *Daniel* (Downers Grove, IL.: InterVarsity Press, 1978), 199-203.

27. Miller, 305.

28. Ibid., 306.

29. Ibid.

30. Ibid.

31. Ibid., 307.

32. Walvoord and Zuck, 1372.

33. Ibid.

34. Walvoord and Zuck, 80.

35. Ibid.

36. Ibid.

37. Ibid., 81.

38. Swindoll, *God's Pattern for Future,* 154-55.

39. Martin Luther, "A Mighty Fortress is Our God," 1529. Translation by Frederick Henry Hodge, 1852.

40. Walvoord and Zuck, 982.

41. Robert H. Mounce, *New International Commentary on the New Testament* (Grand Rapids, MI: William B. Eerdmans Publishing Company, 1998), 376.

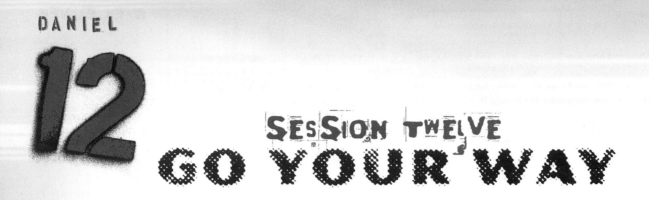

SESSION TWELVE
GO YOUR WAY

Today we conclude our journey in the last chapter of the Book of Daniel. God's final assurances to Daniel are fitting assurances to us as well as we draw our corporate study of this fascinating book to a close.

1. We have the assurance of _Israel's deliverance_. Compare verse 1 with verses 5-7.

   • In God's drama, unparalleled _distress_ can _set_ the perfect _stage_ for unparalleled _deliverance_. See Ezekiel 20:5-6,39-40

   • See Revelation 7:9-10,13-14. Such distress will not lead to _Israel's_ deliverance _alone_.

2. We have the assurance of _bodily_ _resurrection_ (v. 2).

3. We have the assurance that lights willing to _shine in the darkness_ will _shine_ _forever_. Compare Philippians 2:14-16.

4. We have the assurance that the willing will be _purified_ and the

   wicked will _continue to be wicked_ (v. 10).

5. We have the assurance that God's _plan_ will _unfold_

   to the _finest detail_ .

   See Daniel 12:11-12. Reflect on Revelation 21:22-26.

May God's send-off to us reflect His send-off to Daniel:

- May the words and _concepts_ He's taught us be _sealed_ in us.

- May we _go our ways_ like Daniels.

DANIEL
FINAL EXAM

FROM SESSION 1 AND DANIEL 1

1. What empire took Israel captive in the opening chapters of the Book of Daniel?
    - A. Babylon
    - B. Assyria
    - C. Egypt
    - D. Judah

2. Who was the king that besieged Jerusalem and ordered the captivity?
    - A. Jehoiakim
    - B. Belshazzar
    - C. Nebuchadnezzar
    - D. Darius

3. Who delivered Judah's king into this pagan king's hands?
    - A. Cyrus
    - B. The Devil
    - C. Jehoiakim
    - D. The Lord

4. The Book of Daniel opens with Jerusalem besieged and children of God taken captive in the summer of what year?
    - A. 505 B.C.
    - B. 605 B.C.
    - C. 705 B.C.
    - D. 805 B.C.

5. What was Daniel's Babylonian name?
    - A. Belshazzar
    - B. Belteshazzar
    - C. Belshalom
    - D. Betholator

6. Which of the following is *not* one of the Hebrew names of Shadrach, Meshach, and Abednego?
    - A. Adonijah
    - B. Hananiah
    - C. Mishael
    - D. Azariah

7. Which of the following was *not* stated as a characteristic of the kind of people Nebuchadnezzar ordered Ashpenaz to "bring in"?
    - A. Aptitude for learning
    - B. Without physical defect
    - C. Strong work ethic
    - D. From the royal family

8. What was Nebuchadnezzar's primary goal for the Hebrew young men?
    - A. Completely indoctrinating them in Babylonian culture
    - B. Making them a mockery to their people
    - C. Making them prefer Babylon
    - D. Wooing them to renounce their God

9. What kept Daniel and the other three from losing their identity and integrity?
    - A. Fasting
    - B. Interceding
    - C. Seeking favor
    - D. Resolving

10. What did we name the "Babylon Motto" based on Isaiah 47:8,11?
    - A. "I will be like the Most High."
    - B. "I am, and there is none besides me."
    - C. "I am, and there is none except me."
    - D. "I am, and it's all about me."

FROM SESSION 2 AND DANIEL 2

11. Daniel 2:20-23 were our only memory verses. What prompted Daniel to say and pray these things?
    - A. Fear that he and his friends would be executed with the other wise men
    - B. Urgency for his three friends who were facing the fiery furnace
    - C. Gratefulness for being given the interpretation of Neb's dream
    - D. Desire for Neb to know his God

12. Which of the following phrases is *not* included in our memory segment (2:20-23)?
    - A. He gives mercy to the merciful.
    - B. He sets up kings and deposes them.
    - C. He changes times and seasons.
    - D. He gives wisdom to the wise.

13. We learned the statue in Nebuchadnezzar's dream represented four Gentile empires and the order of their fulfillment. Which of the following is correct?
    - A. Babylon, Medo-Persia, Greece, Rome
    - B. Babylon, Greece, Medo-Persia, Rome
    - C. Babylon, Rome, Medo-Persia, Greece
    - D. Babylon, Medo-Persia, Rome, Greece

14. Which of the following representations of the dream statue is *not* correct?
    - A. Greece: belly and thighs of bronze
    - B. Babylon: head of gold
    - C. Rome: legs of iron
    - D. Medo-Persia: chest and arms of bronze

FROM SESSION 3 AND DANIEL 3

15. How tall was the image of gold King Nebuchadnezzar set up?
    - A. 75 feet
    - B. 80 feet
    - C. 90 feet
    - D. 100 feet

16. What was everyone commanded to do when the music began to play?
    - A. Fall down and worship Nebuchadnezzar.
    - B. Rise up and hail Nebuchadnezzar, "King forever!"
    - C. Give the God of Daniel praise.
    - D. Fall down and worship the image of gold.
17. Who was conspicuously missing in the scene surrounding the fiery furnace?
    - A. Daniel
    - B. Shadrach
    - C. Meshach
    - D. Nebuchadnezzar
18. How many "men" did Nebuchadnezzar see "walking around in the fire"?
    - A. Three
    - B. Four
    - C. Two
    - D. Five
19. According to our session and based on Daniel 3:25, what was the only thing that burned when the three were thrown into the fiery furnace?
    - A. Their robes
    - B. Their turbans
    - C. Their sashes
    - D. The ropes that bound them
20. Who did we interpret the fourth man in the fire to be?
    - A. Christ
    - B. Gabriel
    - C. Michael
    - D. God the Father

FROM SESSION 4 AND DANIEL 4

21. What is Daniel 4 about?
    - A. Nebuchadnezzar's health
    - B. Nebuchadnezzar's palace
    - C. Daniel's dream
    - D. Nebuchadnezzar's humbling
22. In Daniel 4, Nebuchadnezzar had a dream that began with the image of an enormous tree. A heavenly messenger ordered the tree to be cut down but left with a stump and roots. What did this represent according to Daniel's interpretation?
    - A. It was a reminder of what happens to the proud.
    - B. Neb's kingdom would be restored under certain conditions.
    - C. Babylon would be rooted in the next empire.
    - D. Jerusalem would be restored.
23. Which of the following was *not* part of the advice Daniel gave Nebuchadnezzar to help him avoid such chastisement?
    - A. Renounce your sins.
    - B. Do what is right.
    - C. Be kind to the oppressed.
    - D. Fast from everything but water.

24. How did Nebuchadnezzar live "until seven times" passed by for him?
    - A. Like a wild animal
    - B. Like a tree
    - C. Like a madman
    - D. Like a pauper
25. When would Nebuchadnezzar be restored?
    - A. When he fell on his face
    - B. When he released the captives
    - C. When he acknowledged that heaven rules
    - D. When he cried out to God for mercy

FROM SESSION 5 AND DANIEL 5

26. Who gave the banquet in Daniel 5?
    - A. Belteshazzar
    - B. Nebuchadnezzar
    - C. Belshazzar
    - D. Daniel
27. How was something holy treated as unholy that night?
    - A. They toasted their false gods with goblets taken from the temple.
    - B. They humiliated the Jews and renounced their God.
    - C. They brought women to the feast.
    - D. They ate from silver platters taken from the temple.
28. What were the words "mene, mene, tekel, parsin"?
    - A. A warning to Nebuchadnezzar
    - B. The inscription on the base of the image
    - C. Words given to Daniel
    - D. Handwriting on the wall
29. What very important change took place the night of the banquet?
    - A. The Medo-Persians killed Belshazzar and took Babylon.
    - B. The Persians killed Darius the Mede.
    - C. Cyrus released the Hebrew captives.
    - D. Daniel dreamed of the Ancient of Days.

FROM SESSION 6 AND DANIEL 6

30. What ruler was trapped into issuing a decree that led Daniel to the lions' den?
    - A. Cyrus
    - B. Darius
    - C. Nebuchadnezzar
    - D. Belshazzar
31. What was Daniel guilty of doing?
    - A. Praying
    - B. Worshiping
    - C. Fasting
    - D. Refusing to bow
32. How did the king react to Daniel being spared?
    - A. He was furious.
    - B. He was relieved.
    - C. He was overjoyed.
    - D. He was terrified.

FROM SESSION 7 AND DANIEL 7

33. In the second half of the book, Daniel is no longer the interpreter of dreams and visions. He is the recipient. In his first dream he saw animated representations of the four empires. (These corresponded to the metallic representations of Neb's dream statue.) Which of the following represented the Medo-Persian Empire?
    - A. A lion with wings of an eagle
    - B. A leopard with four wings
    - C. A beast with large iron teeth
    - D. A bear up on one of its sides

34. Whom did Daniel see with "eyes of a man and a mouth that spoke boastfully"?
    - A. Antiochus IV Epiphanes   C. The Devil
    - B. The "little horn"   D. Alexander the Great

35. Which of the following terms is not synonymous with the others?
    - A. The false prophet   C. The beast
    - B. The Little Horn   D. The Antichrist

36. What position of God is depicted most clearly by the title, "Ancient of Days"?
    - A. Universal Judge
    - B. Universal Creator
    - C. Lord of Heaven and Earth
    - D. Sovereign Ruler

37. Which of the following does not happen to Christ in this scene?
    - A. He enters Jerusalem.
    - B. He approaches the Ancient of Days.
    - C. He is given authority, glory and sovereign power.
    - D. All peoples and nations worship Him.

38. If the interpretation we discussed is accurate, what reference is made to the future time of great tribulation in this chapter of Daniel?
    - A. "Times of greatest wrath"
    - B. "Times of woe"
    - C. "A time, times and half a time"
    - D. "The worst of times"

39. Scriptures tell us the Little Horn will "oppress" the saints of God. What does this mean according to the definition we learned for "oppress"?
    - A. He will imprison them.
    - B. He will try to wear them out.
    - C. He will deceive them.
    - D. He will persecute them.

FROM SESSION 8 AND DANIEL 8

40. According to our study, which of the following is not an interpretation of an image in Daniel's vision?
    - A. Ram: Medo-Persian Empire
    - B. Goat: Grecian Empire
    - C. One large horn on the goat: Alexander the Great
    - D. Head of bronze: Nebuchadnezzar

41. After the prominent horn was "broken off" at the "height of his power," "four prominent horns grew up." Who were these "four prominent horns"?
    - A. The sons of Alexander the Great
    - B. Generals who served under Alexander the Great
    - C. The illegitimate heirs of Alexander the Great
    - D. The Seleucids

42. Which of the following gives the correct names of these four men?
    - A. Cassander, Lysimachus, Ptolemy, Seleucus
    - B. Cassander, Antiochus the Great, Cyrus, Seleucus
    - C. Cassander, Lysimachus, Petra, Selime
    - D. Cassandra, Lysimachus, Ptolemy, Selectra

43. What is distinct about the mention of Gabriel in Daniel 8?
    - A. He looks like Christ.
    - B. He didn't have wings.
    - C. Only Daniel could hear his voice.
    - D. His name is the first given to an angel in Scripture.

44. Who is the wicked "stern-faced king" and "master of intrigue" in Daniel 8?
    - A. Antiochus IV Epiphanes
    - B. Antiochus the Great
    - C. The Antichrist
    - D. Belshazzar

FROM SESSION 9 AND DANIEL 9

45. What prompted Daniel's lengthy intercession recorded in Daniel 9? What he understood …
    - A. from the inspired writings of Isaiah
    - B. as he studied the Torah
    - C. from his vision
    - D. from the inspired writings of Jeremiah

46. How long was their present captivity and the desolation of Jerusalem predicted to last according to the writings Daniel studied?
    - A. 100 years   C. 49 years
    - B. Times and half a time   D. 70 years

47. When was Daniel's answer given according to Gabriel?
    A. At the time of the evening sacrifice
    B. As soon as he began to pray
    C. At the time of the morning sacrifice
    D. At the time of his repentance

48. What did Gabriel tell Daniel was decreed for his people and his holy city?
    A. 70 years   C. 70 Sabbath years
    B. 70 'sevens'   D. 77 seasons

49. Who is the "Anointed One," according to our interpretation?
    A. Christ, the Messiah   C. The counterfeit son
    B. Cyrus the King   D. The Ancient of Days

50. Scripture predicted the "Anointed One" would be "cut off and will have nothing." We learned that He was "cut off" when He was crucified. According to our session, in what way did Christ "have nothing"?
    A. He had no descendants.
    B. He was forsaken momentarily by all His disciples.
    C. He was not acknowledged as Messiah by the nation of Israel.
    D. He was forsaken momentarily by His Father.

FROM SESSION 10 AND DANIEL 10

51. According to our study, which of the following is *not* among the reasons why the "man dressed in linen" in Daniel's final vision might very well have been Christ?
    A. The similarity of the description to the one who is undoubtedly Christ in Revelation 1.
    B. Daniel's exceedingly strong reaction to the sight.
    C. Gabriel called him the "Son of Man."
    D. The detained angel could have been a separate individual from the "man dressed in linen."

52. Why was the speaking angel detained?
    A. The prince of the Persian kingdom resisted him twenty-one days.
    B. The prince of the Grecian kingdom resisted him twenty-one days.
    C. The prince of the power of the air resisted him twenty-one days.
    D. He couldn't finish his homework for Daniel.

53. According to our study, who were these princes of Persia and Greece?
    A. Cyrus and Alexander the Great
    B. Angels God had assigned to the kingdoms
    C. Future kings of the empires
    D. Demons presumably assigned to influence the kingdoms

54. Who is "Michael"?
    A. Israel's God-assigned angelic "prince"
    B. The demon assigned to influence Israel
    C. Gabriel's assistant
    D. Satan's arch enemy

55. What does the name "Michael" mean?
    A. Strong man of God   C. Prince of God
    B. Archangel of God   D. Who is like God?

FROM SESSION 11 AND DANIEL 11

56. The histories of what two Greek dynasties are recorded in Daniel 11?
    A. The Seleucids and the Ptolemies
    B. The Cassanders and the Lysimachusians
    C. The Alexanders and the Egyptians
    D. Antiochus and Antichrist

57. Why are the conflicts of these two dynasties important scripturally? (B)
    A. They emerge into the Roman Empire.
    B. The Beautiful Land (the land of Israel) was positioned between them.
    C. They were both completely annihilated by God.
    D. The Messiah emerged from one of them.

58. According to our study, which of the following does not apply to Antiochus IV Epiphanes in Daniel 11?
    A. A king of the North
    B. A king who corrupts with flattery
    C. A king who temporarily abolishes the daily sacrifice
    D. The king who "will exalt and magnify himself above every god"

FROM SESSION 12 AND DANIEL 12

59. What is one of the primary themes in this chapter?
    A. The new heavens and the new earth
    B. Resurrection
    C. Final rewards
    D. Daniel's death

60. Who are "like stars forever and ever"?
    A. Those who don't experience the "second death"
    B. Those who are resurrected from the dead
    C. Those who lead many to righteousness
    D. Those who become Daniels in their generation.

CHRISTIAN GROWTH STUDY PLAN

In the Christian Growth Study Plan *Daniel: Lives of Integrity, Words of Prophecy* is a resource for course credit in the subject area Bible Study in the Christian Growth category of diploma plans. To receive credit, read the book; complete the learning activities; attend group sessions; show your work to your pastor, a staff member, or a church leader; then complete the form. This page may be duplicated. Send the completed form to:

Christian Growth Study Plan; One LifeWay Plaza Nashville, TN 37234-0117; Fax (615) 251-5067; e-mail cgspnet@lifeway.com

For information about the Christian Growth Study Plan, refer to the current Christian Growth Study Plan Catalog, located online at *www.lifeway.com/cgsp* or contact the Christian Growth Study Plan office, (800) 968-5519, for the specific plan you need for your ministry.

Daniel: Lives of Integrity, Words of Prophecy
COURSE NUMBER: CG-1191

PARTICIPANT INFORMATION

Social Security Number (USA ONLY-optional) | Personal CGSP Number* | Date of Birth (MONTH, DAY, YEAR)

Name (First, Middle, Last) | Home Phone

Address (Street, Route, or P.O. Box) | City, State, or Province | Zip/Postal Code

Email Address for CGSP use

Please check appropriate box: ☐ Resource purchased by church ☐ Resource purchased by self ☐ Other

CHURCH INFORMATION

Church Name

Address (Street, Route, or P.O. Box) | City, State, or Province | Zip/Postal Code

CHANGE REQUEST ONLY

☐ Former Name

☐ Former Address | City, State, or Province | Zip/Postal Code

☐ Former Church | City, State, or Province | Zip/Postal Code

Signature of Pastor, Conference Leader, or Other Church Leader | Date

*New participants are requested but not required to give SS# and date of birth. Existing participants, please give CGSP# when using SS# for the first time. Thereafter, only one ID# is required. **Mail to:** Christian Growth Study Plan, One LifeWay Plaza, Nashville, TN 37234-0117. Fax: (615)251-5067.

Revised 4-05